MY PALS ARE HERE!

Science Tests

Primary 3&4

Dr Kwa Siew Hwa

Marshall Cavendish Education

Published by Marshall Cavendish Education
An imprint of Marshall Cavendish International (Singapore) Private Limited
A member of Times Publishing Limited
Times Centre, 1 New Industrial Road, Singapore 536196
Customer Service Hotline: (65) 6411 0820
E-mail: tmesales@sg.marshallcavendish.com
Website: www.marshallcavendish.com/education/sg

First published 2008
Reprinted 2009, 2010

ISBN 978-981-01-1386-5

Edited by: Joyce Koh, Linda Lee and Ting Szu Kiong
Cover design by: Cephas Chew

Printed in Singapore by Times Graphics Pte Ltd

Preface

My Pals are Here! Science Tests Primary 3&4 aims to provide pupils with the practice they need to excel in Science. The tests, which cover the Primary 3&4 Science syllabus comprehensively, assess pupils on their understanding of scientific concepts. They consist of multiple choice questions across a range of difficulty levels and structured questions that encourage pupils to employ the various process skills.

The tests are organised thematically according to the textbooks. Topical tests for each theme are followed by a thematic assessment, which can be used for the continual assessment of pupils.

The cross-thematic assessments at the end of the book each covers several themes and can be used as final revisions before the examinations. Cross-thematic Assessment 1 covers the themes Diversity and Cycles, Cross-thematic Assessment 2, Systems, Interactions and Energy, and Cross-thematic Assessments 3 and 4, all five themes.

The tests are designed to be completed within 30 minutes, and the thematic and cross-thematic assessments, in an hour.

Answers to the questions come with a marking scheme.

Contents

BLANK

Test 1 Diversity

Marks: /50

Topics:
- Classifying Things
- Living and Non-living Things
- Plants

Name: ____________________ Class: ________ Date: ____________

Section A (15 x 2 = 30 marks)

For each question, four options are given. Choose the correct answer and write down your choice, 1, 2, 3 or 4, in the brackets provided.

1. Which of the following is a characteristic of all living things?

   (1) They eat plants for food.
   (2) They make their own food.
   (3) They move from place to place to find food.
   (4) They need food to live. ( )

2. The diagram below shows the classification of X and Y.

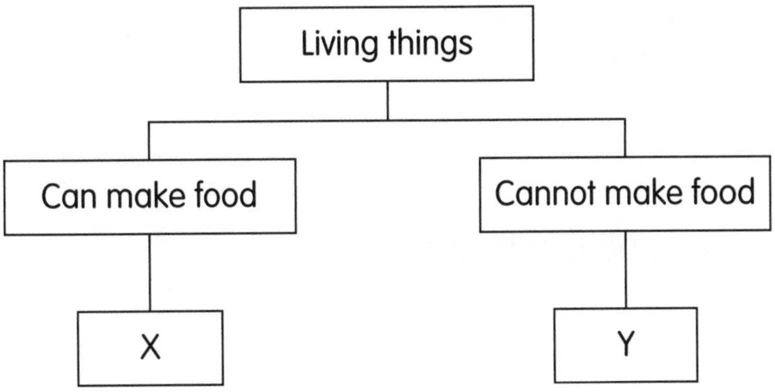

   Which of the following is always correct about X and Y?

   (1) X is a plant and Y is an animal.
   (2) X is a living thing and Y is a non-living thing.
   (3) X is a plant and Y depends on other living things for food.
   (4) X needs food to survive. Y does not need food to survive. ( )

3. A fire engine can move about and sound the siren. But the fire engine cannot ____________.

(A) grow
(B) reproduce
(C) respond to changes

(1) A and B only
(2) B and C only
(3) A and C only
(4) A, B and C ( )

4. Study the classification chart below.

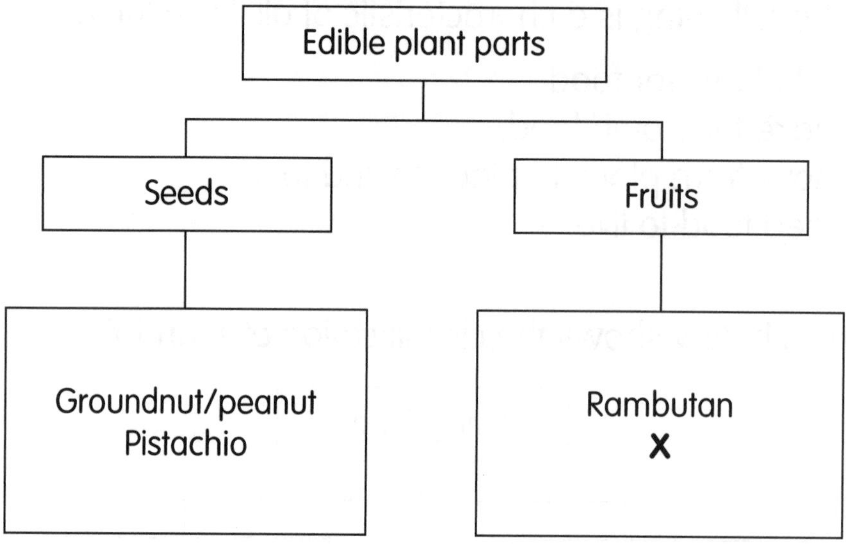

Which of the following can be **X**?

(1) Broccoli
(2) Carrot
(3) Cucumber
(4) Sweet potato ( )

5. Study the classification table below.

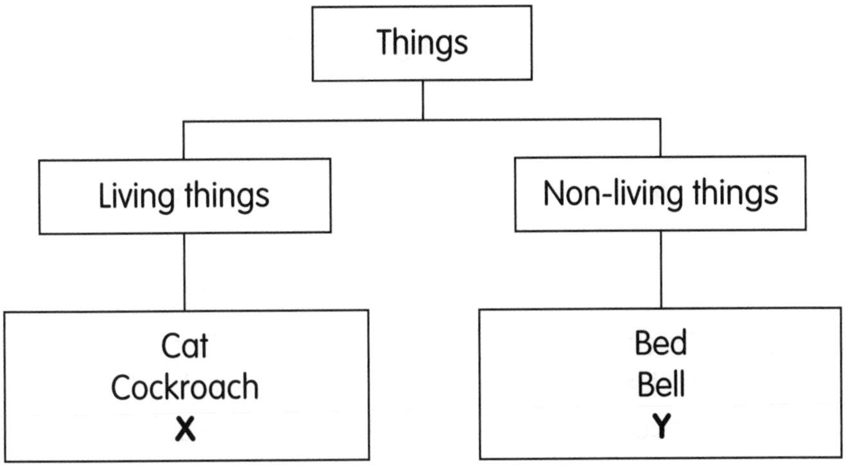

Which of the following correctly represents **X** and **Y**?

	X	Y
(1)	Rat	Carpet
(2)	Bag	Bird
(3)	Fish	Fruit fly
(4)	Shoe	Stone

( )

6. Which of the following statements is true about plants?

(1) Plants depend on other plants for food.
(2) Plants can move but not from place to place.
(3) Plants respond quickly to changes around them.
(4) Plants can only reproduce from seeds. ( )

7. Which of the following statements is true about non-living things?

(1) They can move by themselves.
(2) They need air.
(3) They cannot grow.
(4) They can have young. ( )

8. Which one of the following will die if there is no air?

(1) A balloon
(2) An ant
(3) A basket ball
(4) A car tyre ( )

9. Study the classification chart below.

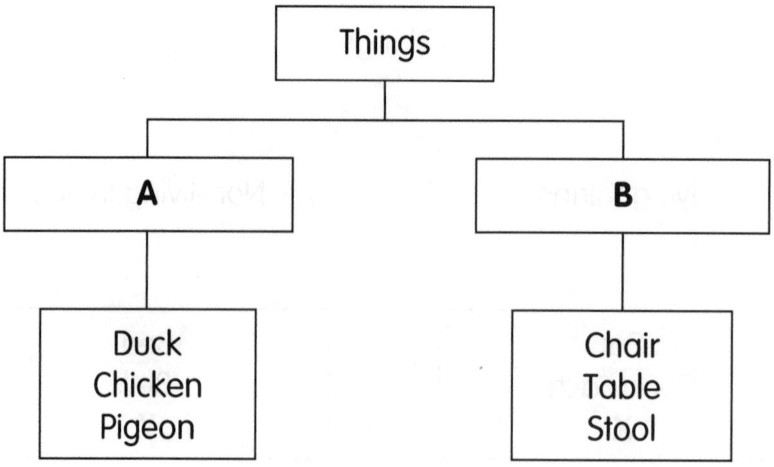

Which of the following can be used to describe A and B?

	A	B
(1)	Cannot reproduce	Can reproduce
(2)	Cannot move	Can move
(3)	Have four legs	Have two legs
(4)	Living things	Non-living things

( )

10. Which one of the following statements about a seed is correct?
   (1) A seed is alive because it can grow into a new plant given the right conditions.
   (2) A seed is dead when it is removed from the fruit.
   (3) A seed is not alive because it cannot move.
   (4) A seed is not alive because it does not respond to changes. ( )

11. What should **A** and **B** be in the classification chart below?

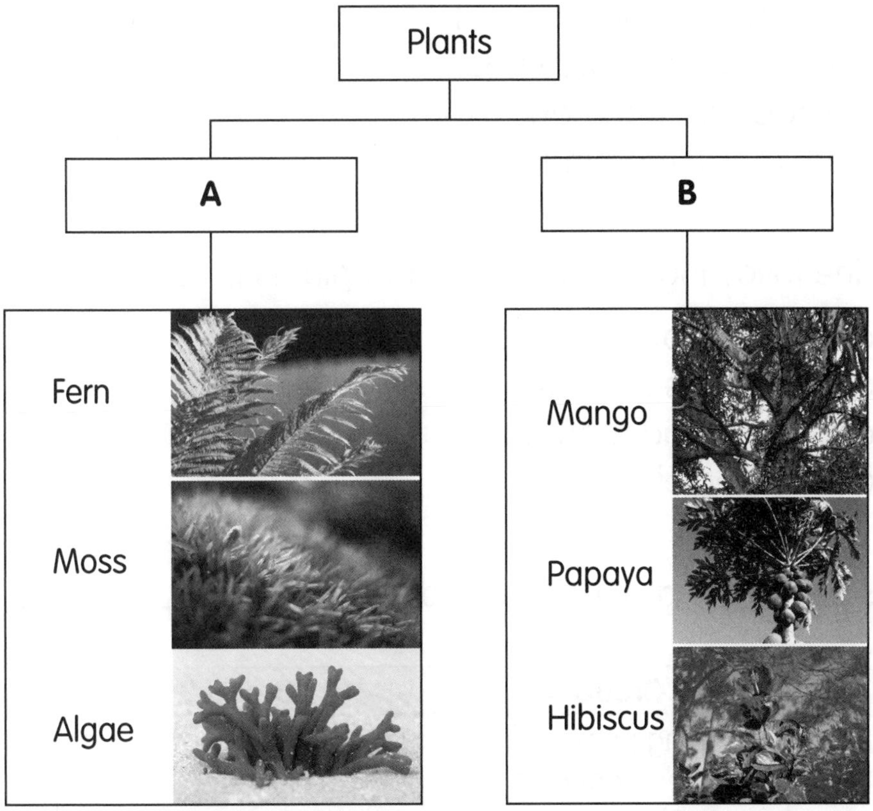

	A	B
(1)	Tiny	Big
(2)	Non-flowering	Flowering
(3)	Not edible	Edible
(4)	Live in water	Live on land

( )

12. Which one of the following is true about a fern?

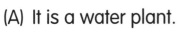

(A) It is a water plant.
(B) It does not produce flowers.
(C) It can make its own food.

(1) A and B only
(2) B and C only
(3) A and C only
(4) A, B and C

( )

13. Which of the following groups consists of living things that live on land?

(1) Water melon, banana, coconut
(2) Lotus, seahorse, sea cucumber
(3) Green algae, sea anemone, ixora
(4) Seaweed, moss, morning glory ( )

14. Which of the following statements about plants is correct?

(1) All plants grow from seeds.
(2) All plants produce flowers.
(3) All plants grow and reproduce.
(4) All plants are edible. ( )

15. The items below are grouped according to their ____________.

Group A	Group B
Ping pong ball Ten-cent coin Shirt button	Party balloon Hula hoop Car tyre

(1) shape
(2) size
(3) colour
(4) weight ( )

Section B (20 marks)

Write your answers for each question in the blank spaces provided.

16. Circle TRUE or FALSE for each statement. [3]

(a) All living things can move. TRUE / FALSE

(b) All plants have flowers. TRUE / FALSE

(c) Classification always puts things together based on their uses. TRUE / FALSE

17. Mum asks Jack to tidy up his study table. Use the graphic organiser below to help Jack decide where to put his things. [3]

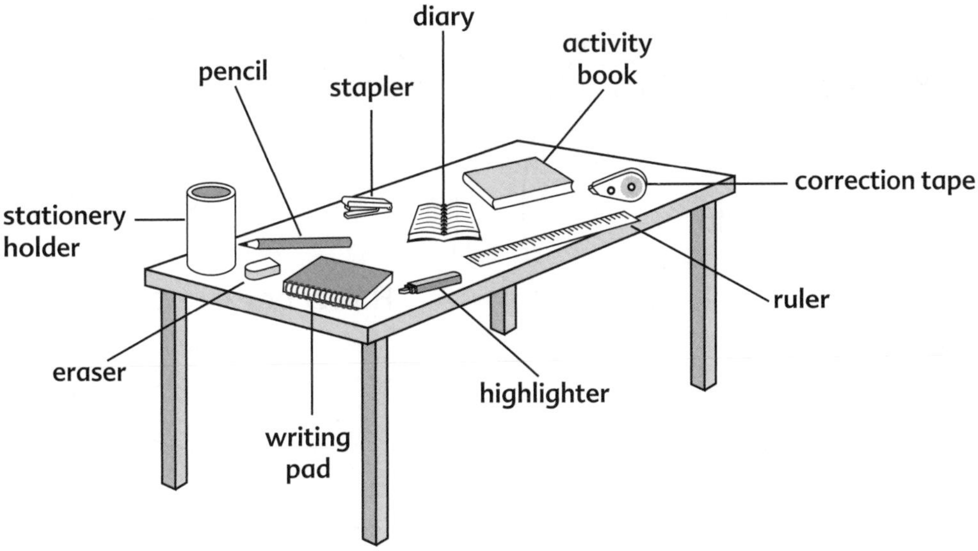

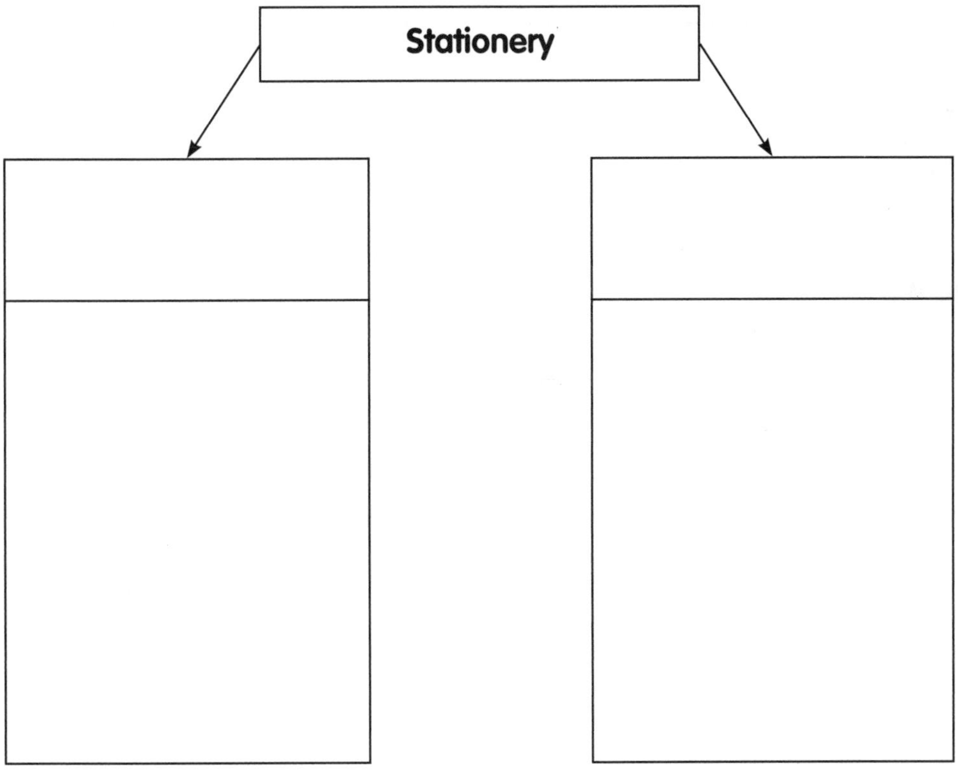

18. Study the two groups of things below.

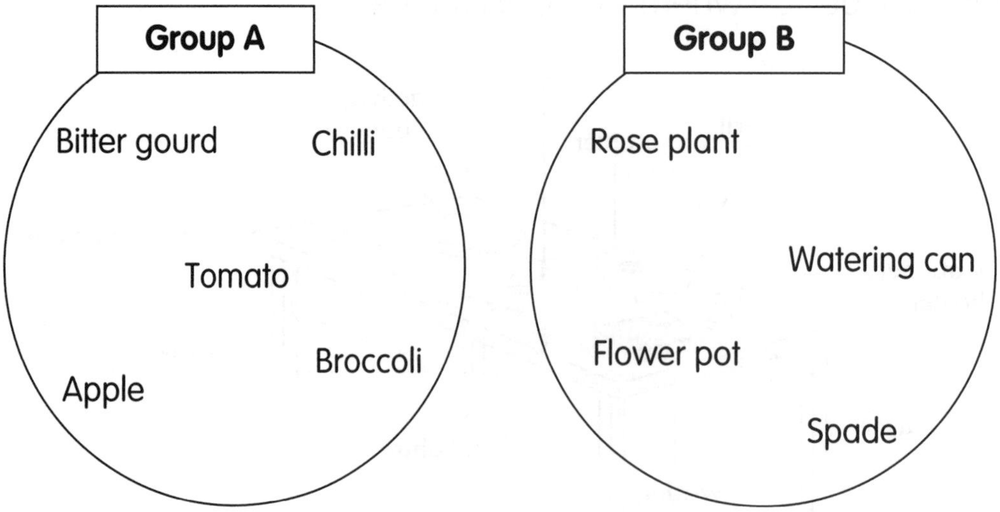

	Which item does not belong with the group?	Why?
Group A		
Group B		

[4]

19. James was given a hamster for a pet. However, he could not afford to buy a hamster cage. He could only use the transparent box (shown in the picture below), which his uncle had given to him.

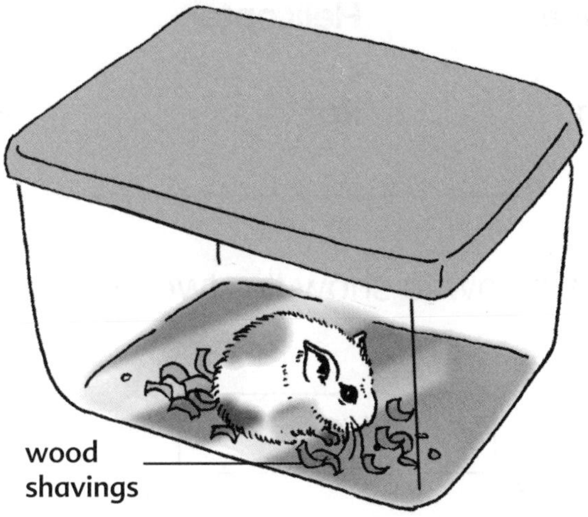

(a) What must James provide the hamster with, in order for it to stay alive? [3]

____

____

____

(b) If James does not make any changes to the box, his hamster will die very soon. State one change James could make to the box to keep his hamster alive. [1]

____

____

20. The list of objects below can be classified in two groups. Each group will have the same number of objects.

Water bottle	**Helicopter**	**Mosquito**
Paper bag	**Rat**	**Bird**

Complete the charts below to show the two ways of classifying the above objects. [6]

(a)

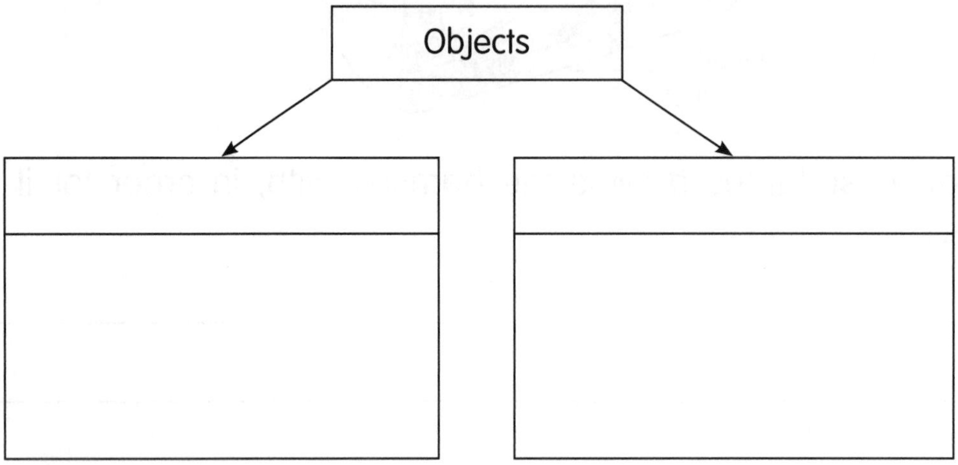

(b)

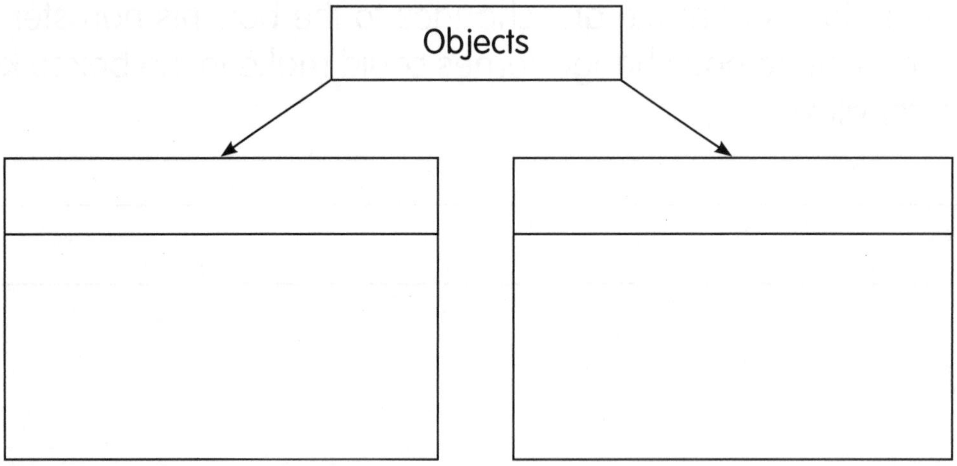

End of Paper

Marks:

/50

Test 2 Diversity

Topics:
- Animals
- Classifying Animals

Name: ______________________ Class: ________ Date: ____________

Section A (15 x 2 = 30 marks)

For each question, four options are given. Choose the correct answer and write down your choice, 1, 2, 3 or 4, in the brackets provided.

1. Which of the following statements about the life cycles of animals is true?

   (A) The butterfly has a four-stage life cycle.
   (B) The cockroach has a three-stage life cycle.
   (C) Animals reproduce to ensure that their own kind continues to be found on Earth.

   (1) B only
   (2) B and C only
   (3) A and C only
   (4) A, B and C ( )

2. What do a snail and a caterpillar have in common?

   (1) They eat plants for food.
   (2) They have the same shape.
   (3) They have the same kind of outer covering.
   (4) They look like their parents. ( )

3. Study the classification chart below.

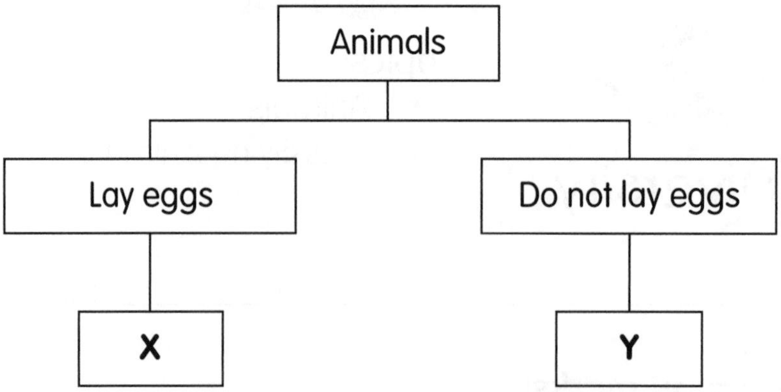

Which of the following are likely to be X and Y?

	X	Y
(1)	Housefly	Bat
(2)	Dog	Mouse
(3)	Fish	Mosquito
(4)	Snail	Turtle

( )

4. What can a duck do that a hen cannot?

(1) It can lay eggs.
(2) It can move from place to place.
(3) It can swim.
(4) It can grow. ( )

5. The animals in the table are grouped according to ____________.

Group A	Group B
Lion	Whale
Tiger	Seal
Leopard	Dolphin

(1) where they live
(2) their outer covering
(3) the way they reproduce
(4) their size ( )

6. A fish, a bird and a crocodile have one thing in common. What is it?

(1) They live in water.
(2) They lay eggs.
(3) They eat animals only.
(4) They have scales as their outer covering. ( )

7. Which of the following statements is true about a goat?

(A) It has hair on its body.
(B) It needs air, water and food to survive.
(C) It produces milk for its young.

(1) A and B only
(2) B and C only
(3) A and C only
(4) A, B and C ( )

8. Which of the following statements is true about animals?

(A) Animals depend on plants or other animals for food.
(B) Animals can move from place to place.
(C) Animals respond to changes around them.

(1) A and B only
(2) B and C only
(3) A and C only
(4) A, B and C ( )

9. The riddle below best decribes ____________.

"I am a small animal.
My body, which has a hard outer covering, is divided into three parts.
My babies grow from the eggs I lay.
What am I?"

(1) an insect
(2) a bird
(3) a mammal
(4) a fish ( )

10. The following animals are grouped according to where they live.

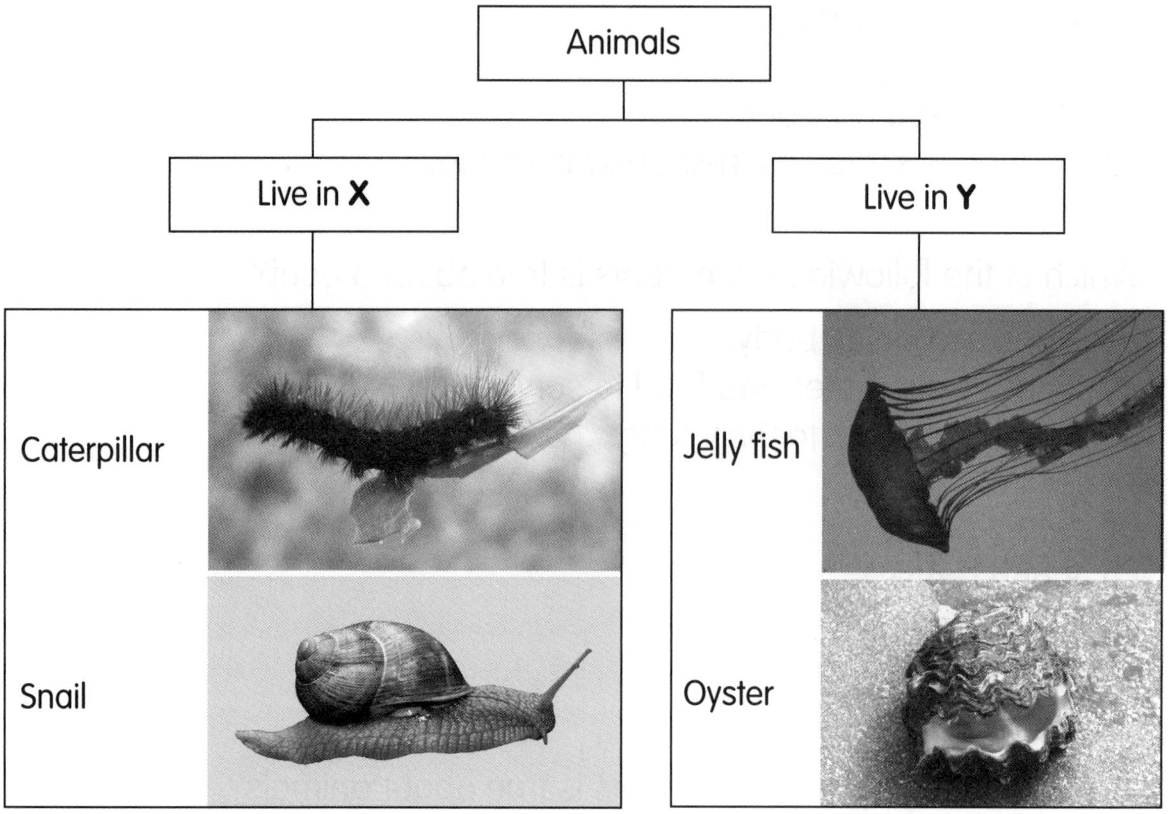

Which of the following correctly represents **X** and **Y**?

	X	Y
(1)	Tree	Burrow
(2)	Burrow	Garden
(3)	Garden	Sea
(4)	Sea	Tree

( )

11. What should A and B be, in the classification chart below?

Which of the following can be used to describe **A** and **B**?

	A	B
(1)	No body covering	Has body covering
(2)	Young	Adult
(3)	Useful	Harmful
(4)	Live in water	Live on land

(   )

12. Look at the animals in the diagrams below.

Which of the following statements about these two animals is correct?

(1) They reproduce in the same way.
(2) They have similar outer coverings.
(3) Their young look different from the adult.
(4) They move about in the same way. ( )

13. Which of the following outer coverings belong to a cobra?

(1) Shells
(2) Scales
(3) Hair
(4) Feathers ( )

14. Which one of the following statements about a caterpillar is correct?

(1) It is part of a three-stage life cycle.
(2) It's young lives in water.
(3) The young looks like the adult.
(4) It sheds its old skin as it grows bigger. ( )

15. Which one of the following is true about a monkey?

(A) It can move in more than one way.
(B) It reproduces in the same way as a leopard.
(C) It can live both on land and in water.

(1) A and B only
(2) B and C only
(3) A and C only
(4) A, B and C ( )

Section B (20 marks)

Write your answers for each question in the blank spaces provided.

16. Circle TRUE or FALSE for each statement. [3]

    (a) Animals come in different sizes and shapes. TRUE / FALSE

    (b) All animals have outer coverings over their skin. TRUE / FALSE

    (c) All birds have a beak, two wings and a pair of legs. TRUE / FALSE

17. Classify these eight animals according to the way they reproduce. [4]

Frog	**Pigeon**	**Elephant**	**Lizard**
Cheetah	**Giraffe**	**Python**	**Whale**

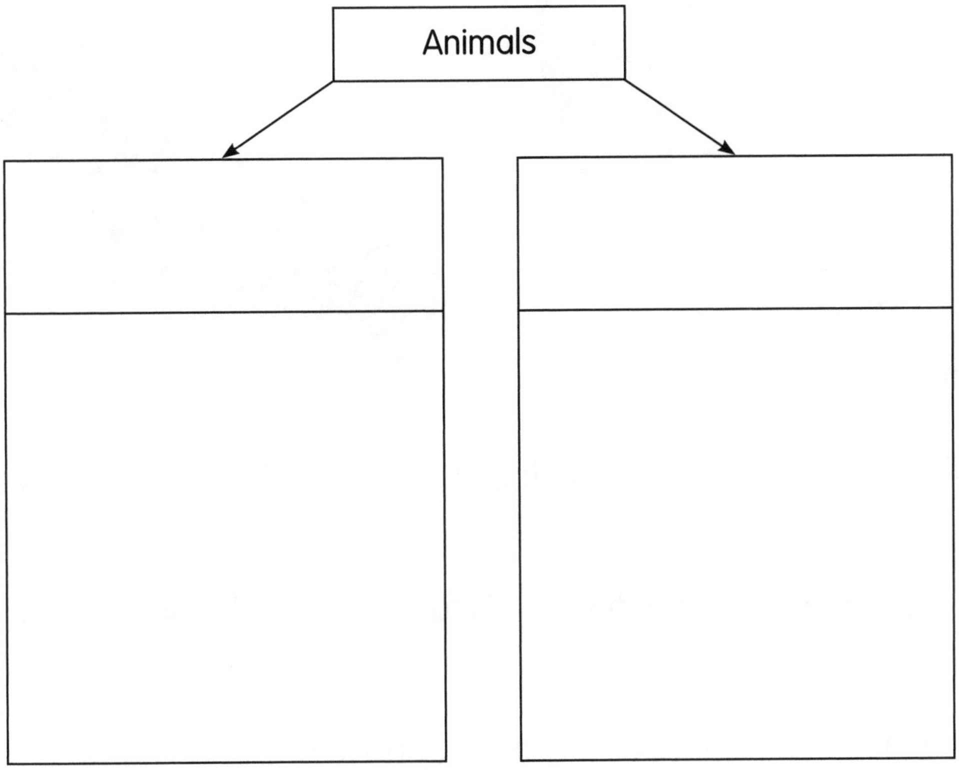

18. (a) Animals may be classified into mammals, birds, fish and insects. Draw lines to match the characteristics to the animal group. [4]

Characteristic			**Animal group**
Live in water	•	•	Mammals
Give birth to young	•	•	Birds
Can fly	•	•	Fish
Have six legs	•	•	Insects

(b) How are the spiny anteater and platypus different from other mammals? [1]

____

19. Look at the animals below.

(a) Which group of animals do they belong to? Circle your answer. [1]

Mammals	**Reptiles**	**Birds**	**Amphibians**	**Insect**

(b) What kind of outer covering do they have? [1]

____

(c) State two uses of the outer covering of these animals. [2]

Use 1 ____

Use 2 ____

20. Draw lines to match the animals with the same type of body covering. [4]

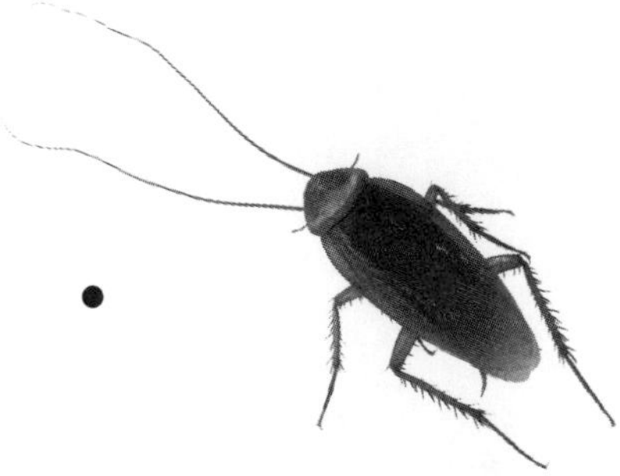

End of Paper

BLANK

Test 3

Diversity

Marks: /50

Topics:
- Fungi and Bacteria
- Exploring Materials

Name: ______________________ Class: __________ Date: ______________

Section A (15 x 2 = 30 marks)

For each question, four options are given. Choose the correct answer and write down your choice, 1, 2, 3 or 4, in the brackets provided.

1. Bread mould and bacteria are examples of ____________.

   (1) fungi
   (2) micro-organisms
   (3) harmful organisms
   (4) spores ( )

2. Which of the following statements is true about fungi?

   (A) Fungi come in different shapes and sizes.
   (B) All fungi are harmful.
   (C) All fungi reproduce by spores.

   (1) A and B only
   (2) B and C only
   (3) A and C only
   (4) A, B and C ( )

3. Which of the following is true about bacteria?

   (1) All bacteria are harmful to man.
   (2) Bacteria need water to survive and grow.
   (3) Yeast is a type of bacteria.
   (4) Bacteria reproduce in the same way as bread mould. ( )

4. Which of the following is true about bread mould?

(A) It reproduces by spores.
(B) It needs moisture to grow.
(C) It grows on bread and makes its own food.

(1) A and B
(2) B and C
(3) A and C
(4) A, B and C ( )

5. Which one of the following statements is true about microorganisms?

(A) Micro-organisms are living things.
(B) Micro-organisms can only be seen under the microscope.
(C) Micro-organisms can make their own food.

(1) A and B only
(2) B and C only
(3) A and C only
(4) A, B and C ( )

6. Mrs. Tan bought some apples from the market. She left them in the refrigerator and forgot all about them. Two weeks later, she found that some of the apples were covered with a layer of grey powder. What is this powder?

(1) Algae
(2) Bacteria
(3) Yeast
(4) Mould ( )

7. Which of the following is true for bacteria and fungi?

	Bacteria	Fungi
(1)	Harmful	Useful
(2)	Need food and water to grow.	Need water only to grow.
(3)	Reproduce by dividing.	Reproduce from spores.
(4)	Come in various shapes and sizes.	Come in various shapes and sizes.

( )

8. Which of the following correctly describes the similarities between plants and fungi?

(A) They need water to stay alive.
(B) They may be useful or harmful to man.
(C) They can make their own food.
(D) They reproduce to ensure continuity of their kind.

(1) A and B only
(2) A and D only
(3) B and D only
(4) A, B and D only ( )

9. Study the classification chart below.

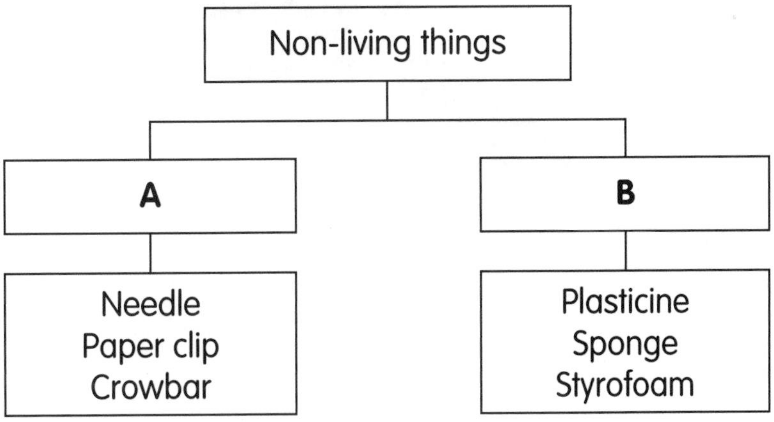

Which of the following should A and B be?

	A	B
(1)	Hard	Soft
(2)	Heavy	Light
(3)	Small	Big
(4)	Flexible	Stiff

10. The objects below are classified in the same group.

Which one of the following can be placed in the group?

(1) Sieve 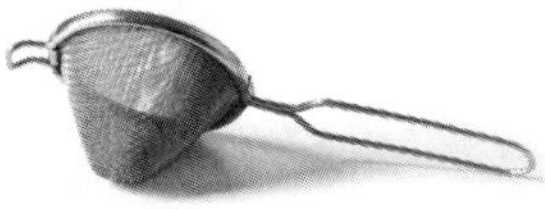

(2) Mug 

(3) Ladle 

(4) Coaster  ( )

11. Which of the following is the best material for making the handle of a frying pan?

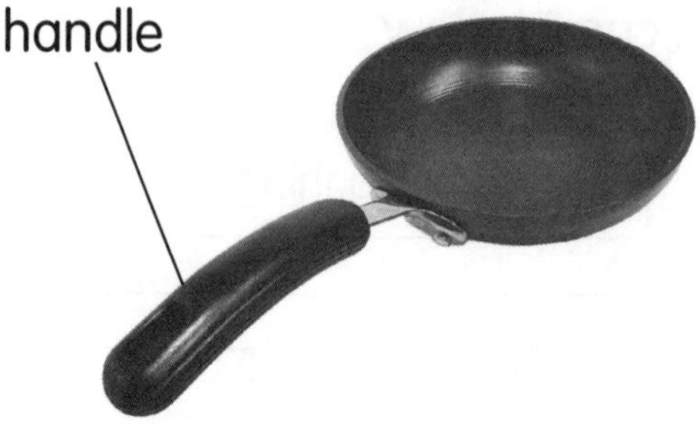

(1) Brass
(2) Ceramic
(3) Plastic
(4) Rubber ( )

12. The diagram below shows the classification of objects according to the materials they are made of.

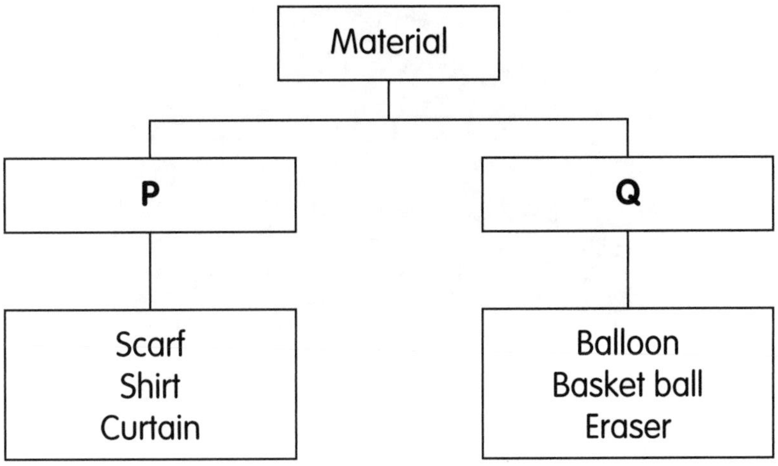

Which of the following is the best answer for P and Q?

	P	Q
(1)	Rubber	Plastic
(2)	Fabric	Rubber
(3)	Plastic	Rubber
(4)	Rubber	Fabric

( )

13. Which of the following may be grouped together with an ice cream stick?

(A) Wooden crate
(B) Bamboo pole
(C) Key
(D) Paper

(1) A and B only
(2) B and D only
(3) A, B and D only
(4) A, B, C and D ( )

14. If you need to choose a material to make a paper weight, it is most important that the material is __________?

(1) heavy
(2) flexible
(3) big
(4) transparent (it can be seen through) ( )

15. For a garden hose to be useful, it should be __________.

(A) hard
(B) flexible
(C) light
(D) transparent (it can be seen through)

(1) A and B only
(2) B and C only
(3) A, C and D only
(4) B, C and D only ( )

Section B (20 marks)

Write your answers for each question in the blank spaces provided.

16. Circle TRUE or FALSE for each statement. [3]

(a) Bacteria and mushrooms reproduce in the same way. TRUE / FALSE

(b) Fungi feed only on dead plants and animals. TRUE / FALSE

(c) Bacteria can be seen only under the microscope. TRUE / FALSE

17. The diagram below shows bacterial cells seen under a microscope at three different times.

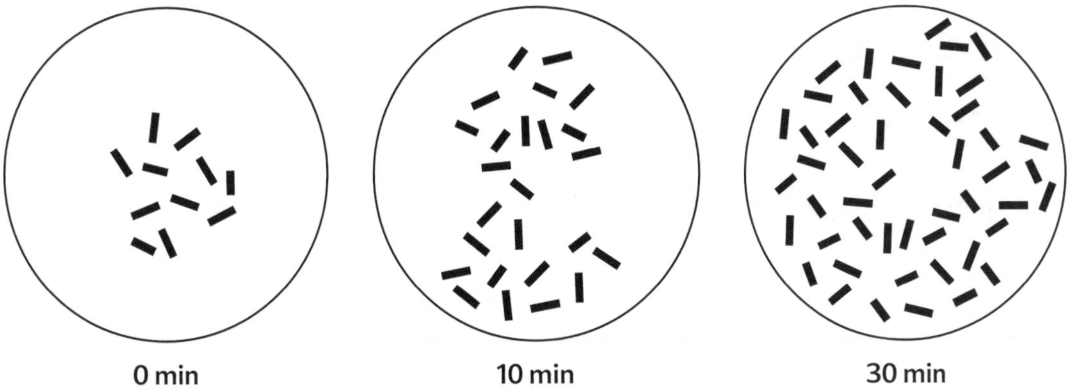

(a) Complete the table below to show the growth of bacterial cells over time. [3]

Time (min)	0	10	20	30	40	50
Number of bacterial cells			32		80	100

(b) What must be present for the bacterial cells to increase in number? Circle your answer. [1]

Fire **Food** **Soil** **Electricity**

18. The diagram below shows a group of living things.

(a) Which group of organisms do they belong to? Tick your answer. [1]

☐ Flowering plants ☐ Fungi

☐ Ferns ☐ Non-flowering plants

(b) How do they reproduce? Tick your answer. [1]

☐ Seeds

☐ Cell division

☐ Spores

(c) Where do they get their food? [1]

____

____

(d) Some of the organisms in this group are useful to humans. In what way are they useful? [1]

____

19. Study the following table carefully and answer the questions that follow.

Group X	Group Y
Plastic fork	Radio
Toothpick	Kettle
Rag	Pencil

(a) What would be a suitable heading for each group? [2]

Group **X**: ________________

Group **Y**: ________________

(b) In which group, **X** or **Y**, should each of the following objects be placed? [3]

(i) Rubber band ________________

(ii) Clothes peg ________________

(iii) Thermos flask ________________

20. Match the objects to their properties. [4]

Properties			Object
Soft and absorbs water	•	•	Pin
Flexible and elastic	•	•	Towel
Stiff and hard	•	•	Mirror
Shiny and breaks when dropped	•	•	Rubber band

End of Paper

BLANK

Marks:

/100

Thematic Assessment 1

Diversity

Name: ______________________ Class: __________ Date: ______________

Section A (30 x 2 = 60 marks)

For each question, four options are given. Choose the correct answer and write down your choice, 1, 2, 3 or 4, in the brackets provided.

1. Which one of the following is grouped wrongly?

	Living thing	Non-living thing
(1)	Caterpillar	Kettle
(2)	Goldfish	Glass
(3)	Monkey	Marble statue
(4)	Moon	Milk

( )

2. Which of the following statements is correct?

(1) Clouds are living things because they can move.
(2) A radio is alive because it can produce sound.
(3) A mosquito larva is a living thing because it needs air, water and food.
(4) A coconut tree is a non-living thing because it cannot move from place to place. ( )

3. Which of the following will not change as you grow?

(1) Length of fingers
(2) Colour of eyes
(3) Size of feet
(4) Facial appearance ( )

4. Which of the following is the function of a stem?

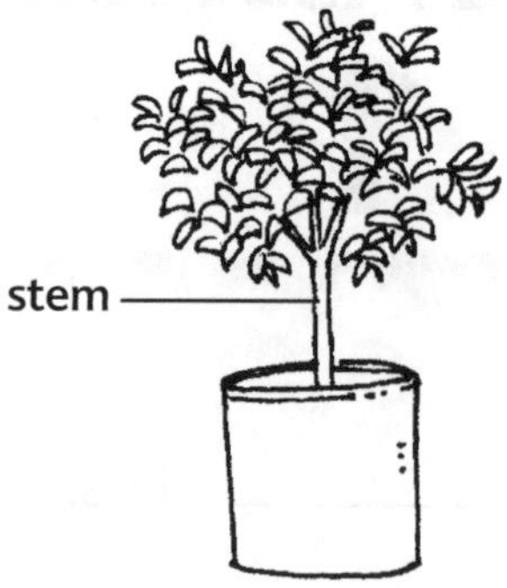

(A) To hold the plant upright.
(B) To carry food and water to different parts of the plant.
(C) To take up water.

(1) A and B only
(2) C and D only
(3) A and C only
(4) A, B and C ( )

5. Which of the following states the similarity between a plant and an animal?

(1) They usually respond quickly to changes around them.
(2) They depend on other living things for food.
(3) They need air, water and food to survive.
(4) They reproduce by giving birth to their young. ( )

6. Three identical plants were placed in containers as shown below.

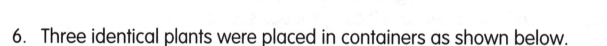

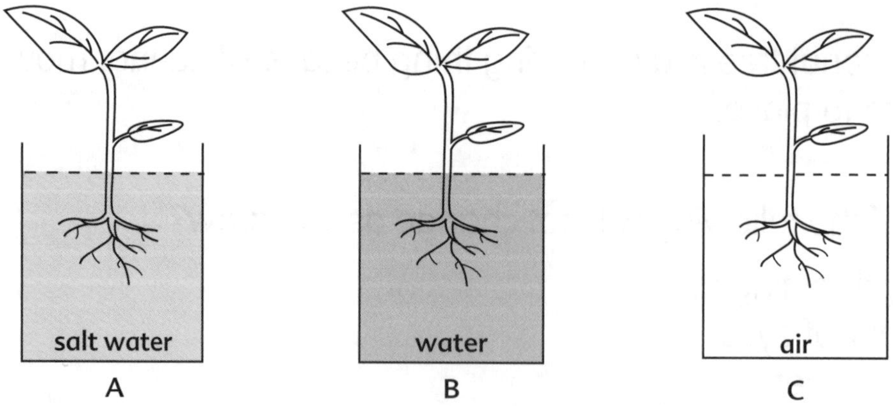

Which of the following results is expected after one week?

(1) Plant A will grow taller than Plants B and C.
(2) Plant B and C will wilt.
(3) Plant B will grow healthily while Plants A and C will wilt.
(4) All the plants will grow healthily. ( )

7. The animals in the table are grouped according to ____________.

Group A	Group B
Snake	Squirrel
Goldfish	Bat
Lizard	Hamster

(1) where they live
(2) their outer covering
(3) the shape of their bodies
(4) how they move about ( )

8. What are **X** and **Y** likely to be?

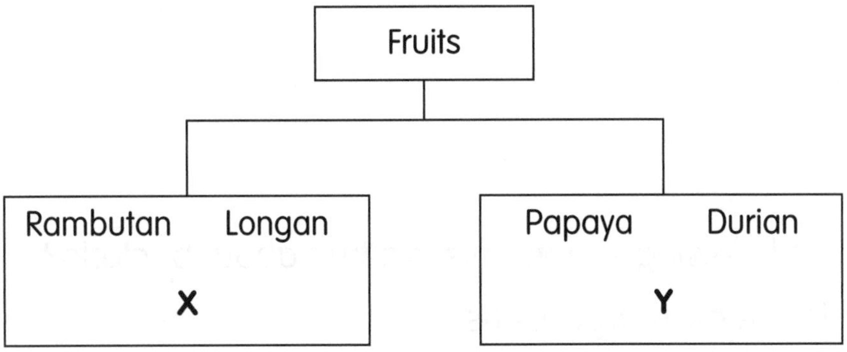

	X	Y
(1)	Strawberry	Water melon
(2)	Mango	Apple
(3)	Banana	Pear
(4)	Cherry	Lychee

( )

9. Annie planted a pot of string bean seedlings. She recorded the heights of the seedlings every two days for six days.

	Average height of seedlings (cm)			
Ruler	**Day 0**	**Day 2**	**Day 4**	**Day 6**
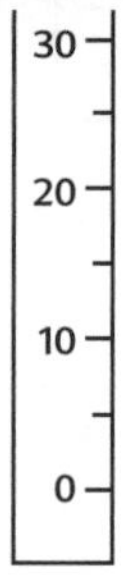				

The experiment shows that plants can ____________.

(1) grow
(2) move
(3) stretch
(4) bend ( )

10. Which of the following statements are true about bacteria?

(A) Bacteria are microorganisms.
(B) Bacteria do not need water to survive.
(C) Bacteria can cause food to decay.

(1) A and B only
(2) B and C only
(3) A and C only
(4) A, B and C ( )

11. Plants are living things because they ____________.

(1) make food
(2) absorb water
(3) grow
(4) do not move from place to place ( )

12. How are the following fruits alike?

papaya

watermelon

star melon

(A) They have smooth skin.
(B) They are edible.
(C) They have many seeds.

(1) A and B only
(2) B and C only
(3) A and C only
(4) A, B and C ( )

13. What can an adult plant do, that a young seedling cannot?

(1) Make its own food.
(2) Take in water with its roots.
(3) Stand upright.
(4) Produce seeds. ( )

14. Study the diagrams below carefully.

The animals are grouped according to ____________.

(1) their outer covering
(2) their size
(3) their shape
(4) the place they live in ( )

15. Mary wants to conduct an experiment to find out which place in her house is best for growing a bird's nest fern. Which of the following variables should Mary keep constant?

(A) Size and shape of the pots.
(B) Amount of water used to water the plants each day.
(C) Amount of soil in each pot.

(1) A and B only
(2) B and C only
(3) A and C only
(4) A, B, and C ( )

16. Study the diagrams below carefully.

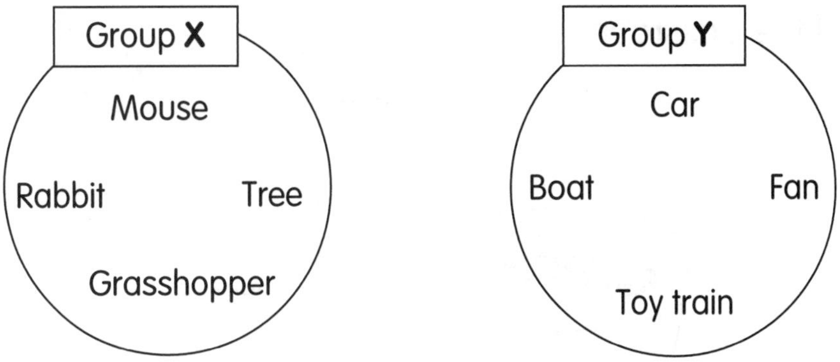

Which of the following correctly represents **X** and **Y**?

	X	Y
(A)	Can move by itself	Cannot move by itself
(B)	Can grow	Cannot grow
(C)	Can make its own food	Cannot make its own food

(1) A and B only
(2) B and C only
(3) A and C only
(4) A, B, and C ( )

17. Zafira wanted to observe the growth of string beans from seeds. She set up the experiment as shown in the diagram below. The pot was placed in a corner of the classroom.

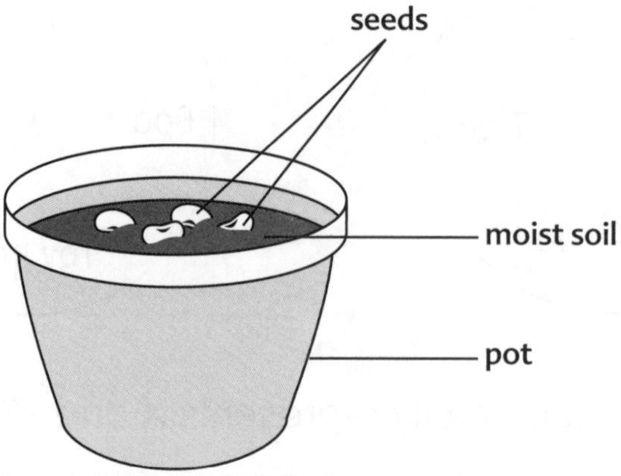

After one week, Zafira noticed that none of the seeds germinated to become young plants. What could be the reason?

(1) There were not enough nutrients in the soil for the seeds to germinate.
(2) There was not enough water for the seeds to germinate.
(3) The seeds were not alive.
(4) There was not enough air in the classroom. ( )

18. The diagram below shows some plants. In what way are they similar?

(1) They can produce flowers.
(2) They make their own food.
(3) They reproduce from seeds.
(4) They grow on land. ( )

19. Which of the following statements correctly describes the animals below?

(1) They feed on plants only.
(2) They feed on other animals.
(3) They feed on other living things.
(4) They make their own food. ( )

20. The following animals are grouped together based on one characteristic. What is it?

(1) They move in the same way.
(2) They eat the same kind of food.
(3) They have the same shape.
(4) They have different outer coverings. ( )

21. Which of the following statements is true about the leaves of plants?

(A) They are always green in colour.
(B) They come in different shapes and sizes.
(C) They make food for the plant.
(D) They are not always green in colour.

(1) A, B and C
(2) B and D only
(3) A, C and D
(4) B, C and D ( )

22. The animals below are classified into two different groups, **P** and **Q**.

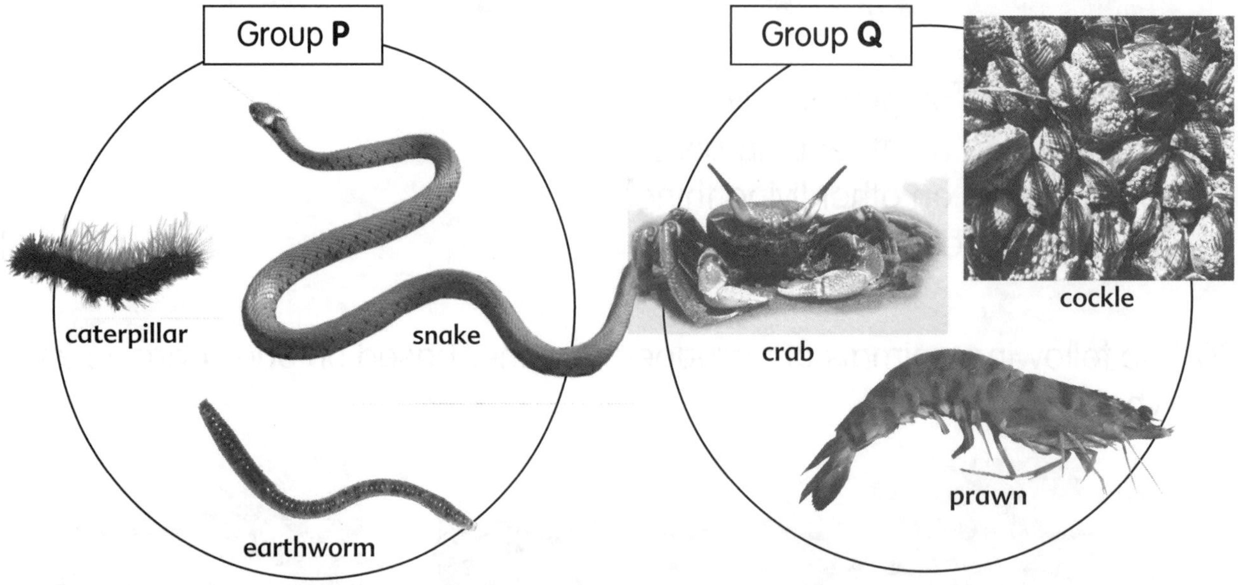

Which of the following is correctly grouped?

	P	Q
(1)	Guppy	Snail
(2)	Millipede	Lobster
(3)	Centipede	Beetle
(4)	Lizard	Starfish

( )

23. The objects below are classified into two different groups **X** and **Y**. The objects are classified according to __________.

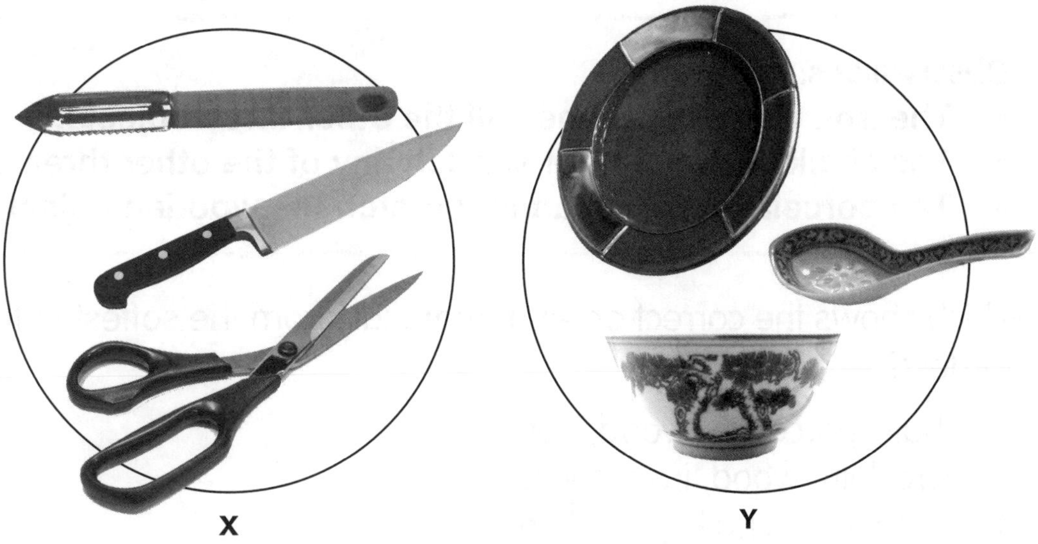

(A) the materials they are made of
(B) their use
(C) their shape
(D) their size

(1) A and B only
(2) C and D only
(3) A, B and C only
(4) A, B, C and D ( )

24. Which of the following objects is made of a material that allows us to see through it?

(1) Porcelain mug
(2) Glass cup
(3) Metal plate
(4) Aluminium foil ( )

25. Four objects made of iron, wood, porcelain and chalk are used to scratch each other.

Observations:

- **The iron object scratches all the other three objects.**
- **The chalk object cannot scratch any of the other three objects.**
- **The porcelain object cannot scratch the wooden object.**

Which shows the correct order of materials from the softest to the hardest?

(1) Chalk, porcelain, wood, iron
(2) Porcelain, wood, iron, chalk
(3) Wood, iron, chalk, porcelain
(4) Iron, wood, porcelain, chalk ( )

26. An object X is made up of three types of materials — plastic, cloth and metal. Which of the following is likely to be object X?

(1) Shirt with buttons
(2) School bag
(3) Bed sheet
(4) Curtain ( )

27. How many types of materials are used to make a simple candle?

(1) 1
(2) 2
(3) 3
(4) 4 ( )

28. Some of the materials we use today come from plants and animals. Which of the following correctly represents where the materials are from?

	From plants	From animals
(1)	Wood	Plastic
(2)	Clay	Fur
(3)	Cotton	Leather
(4)	Silk	Feather

( )

29. Plastic is a versatile material. It can be used to make many things. Which of the following may be made from plastic?

(A) Fish tank
(B) Shoe rack
(C) Comb
(D) Cup

(1) A and C only
(2) B and D only
(3) A, C and D only
(4) A, B, C and D ( )

30. Look at the objects below carefully.

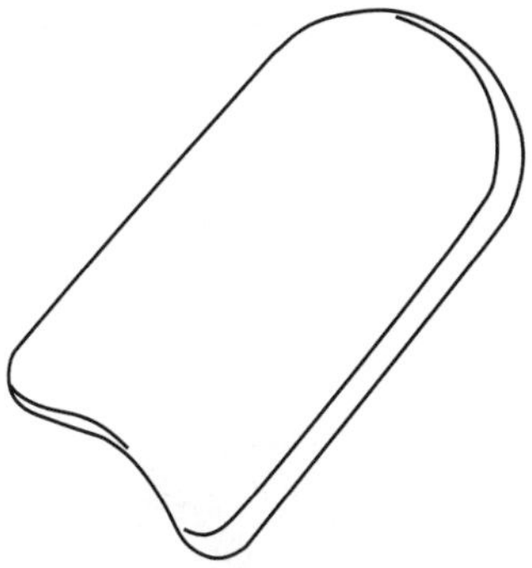

styrofoam float

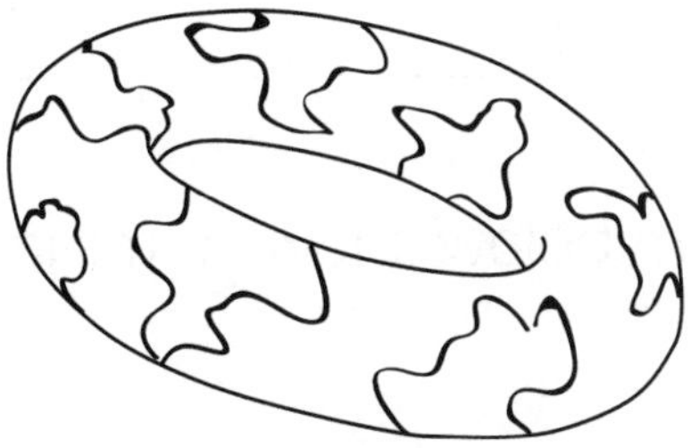

inflatable float

What characteristics do the objects have in common?

(1) They are made of the same materials.
(2) They have the same shape.
(3) They have the same use.
(4) They have the same size. ( )

Section B (40 marks)

Write your answers for each question in the blank spaces provided.

31. Use the given words to fill in the blanks in the organiser below. [6]

Reproduce	**Air**	**Respond to stimuli**
Water	**Food**	**Move**

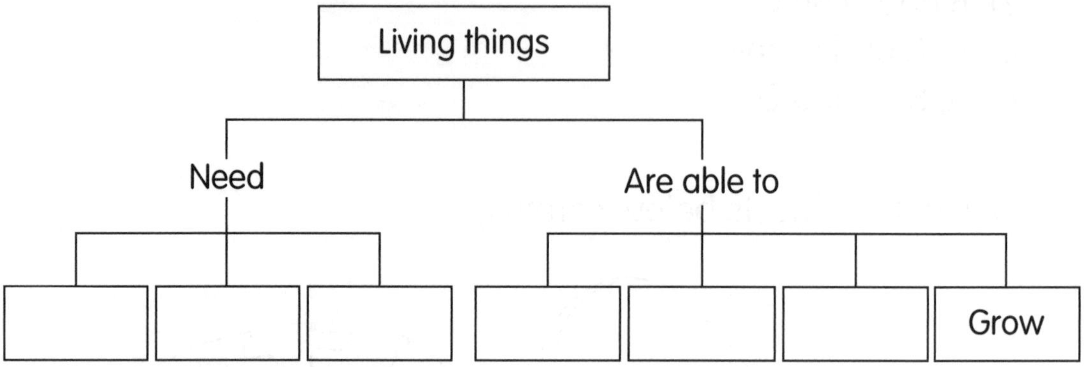

32. The diagram below shows a millipede.

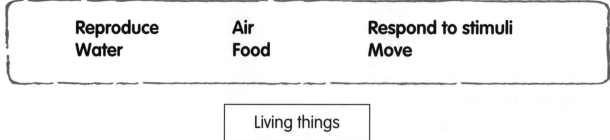

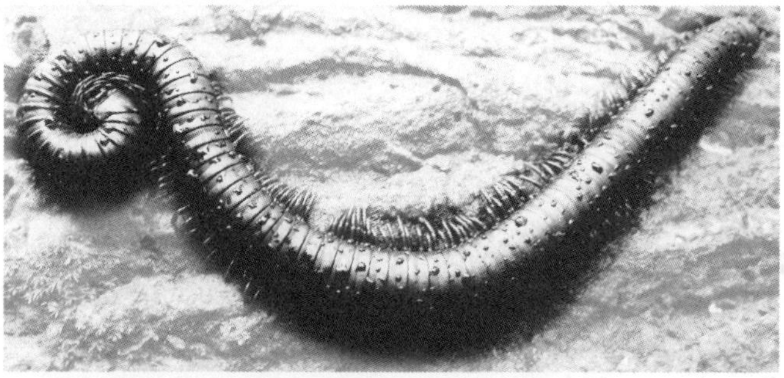

(a) How will the millipede respond when it is disturbed? [1]

____

(b) Why do you think the millipede behaves in this way? [1]

____

(c) The above is an example of how living things respond to their surroundings. Give another example of a living thing responding to its environment. [1]

____

33. Moulds and ferns are both living things. Compare their characteristics using the graphic organiser below. [4]

Two similarities
(a) ______________________________
(b) ______________________________

Mould — Ferns

Two differences	
(a) ____________________	____________________
(b) ____________________	____________________

34. Compare the following animals. [5]

Two similarities
(a) ______________________________
(b) ______________________________

Two differences	
(a) ____________________	____________________
(b) ____________________	____________________

35. Use the given words to complete the classification chart below. [7]

Animals **Heavy** **Non-flowering** **Plants**
Living things **Flowering** **Non-living things**

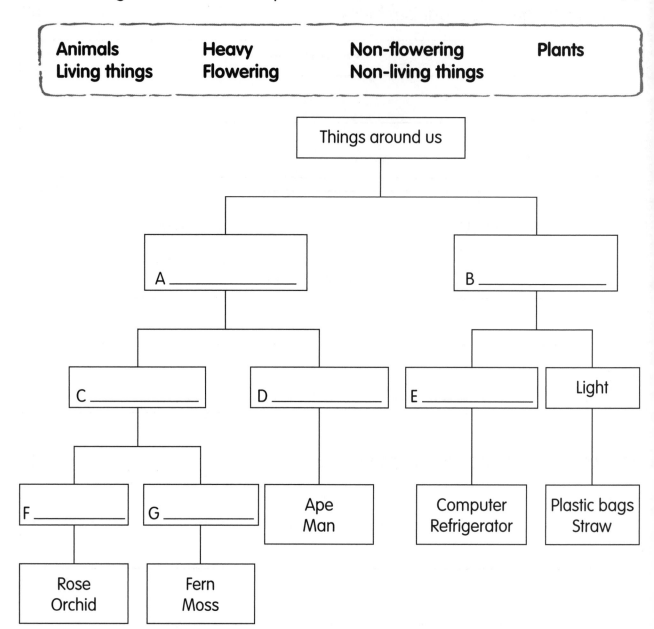

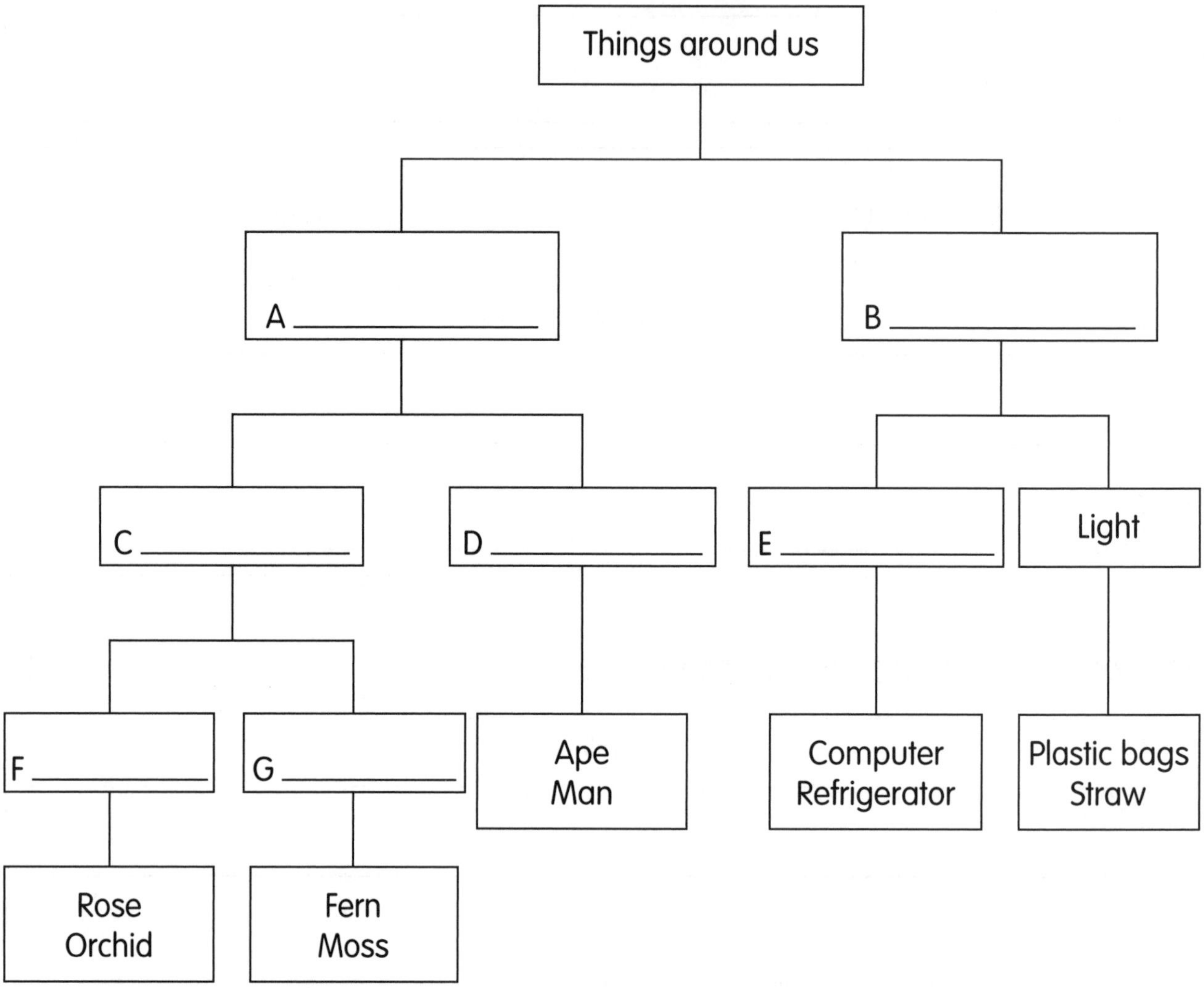

36. Give two reasons for each statement. [8]

Statement	Two reasons
(a) A spider is not an insect. 	Reason 1: ______________________ ______________________ Reason 2: ______________________ ______________________
(b) A bat is not a bird. 	Reason 1: ______________________ ______________________ Reason 2: ______________________ ______________________
(c) A whale is not a fish. 	Reason 1: ______________________ ______________________ Reason 2: ______________________ ______________________
(d) A mushroom is not a plant. 	Reason 1: ______________________ ______________________ Reason 2: ______________________ ______________________

37. Use the given words to complete the classification chart below. [7]

Plastic **Can be seen through** **Cork**
Cannot be seen through **Copper coin** **Iron nail**
Clay pot

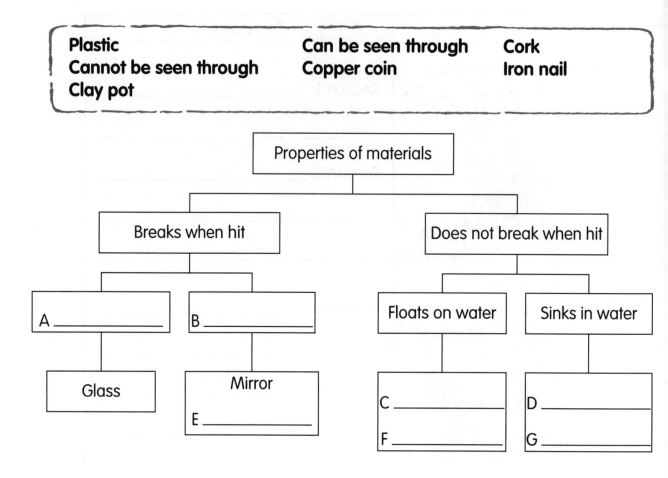

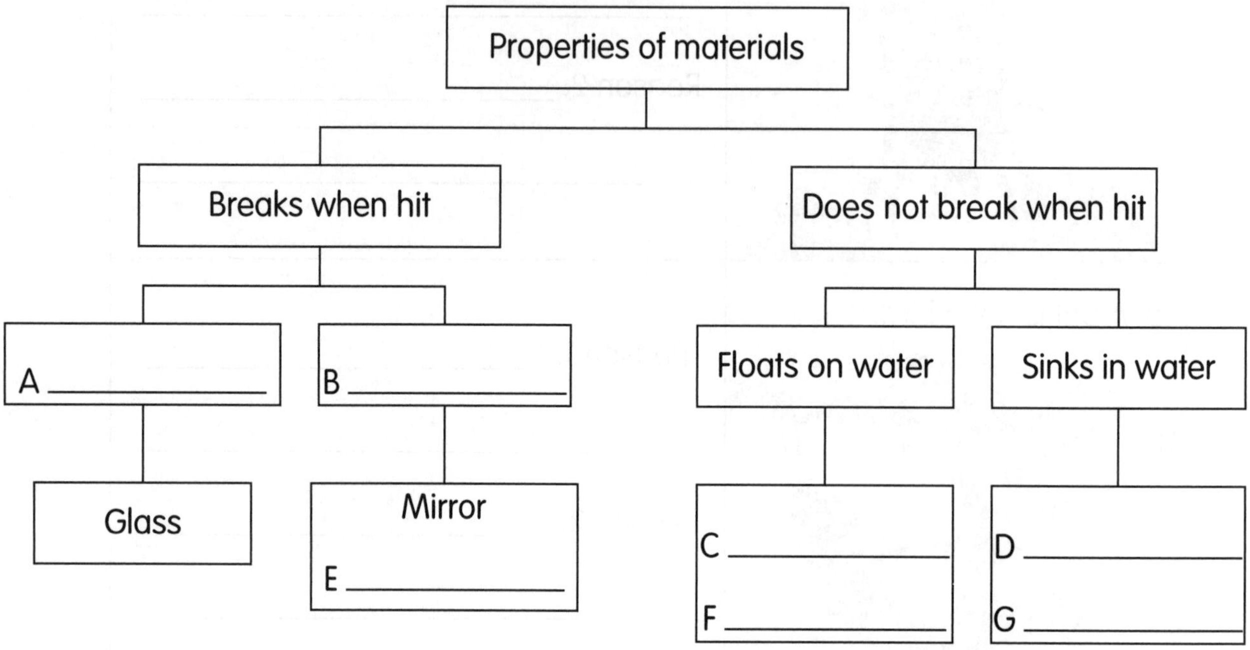

End of Paper

Marks:

/50

Test 4 Cycles

Topics:
- Life Cycles
- Life Cycles of Some Animals
- Life Cycles of Plants

Name: ______________________ Class: __________ Date: ______________

Section A (15 x 2 = 30 marks)

For each question, four options are given. Choose the correct answer and write down your choice, 1, 2, 3 or 4, in the brackets provided.

1. Which of the following statements about life cycle is correct?

    (A) A life cycle is a pattern that repeats itself in the lives of living things.
    (B) All living things have similar stages in their life cycles.
    (C) The life cycle of a bird consists of the egg, chick and adult stages.
    (D) A life cycle shows the order of the different stages.

    (1) A and B only
    (2) B and C only
    (3) A, C and D only
    (4) A, B, C and D ( )

2. Which two animals below have a four-stage life cycle?

(1)	Butterfly	Housefly
(2)	Housefly	Cockroach
(3)	Grasshopper	Housefly
(4)	Cockroach	Butterfly

( )

3. Which of the following are characteristics of a caterpillar?

(A) It looks like its parents.
(B) It grows very fast.
(C) It feeds on the leaves of plants.
(D) It moults as it grows.

(1) A and B only
(2) C and D only
(3) B, C and D only
(4) A, B, C and D ( )

4. In which stage of its life cycle does the mosquito not live in water?

(1) Egg
(2) Larva
(3) Pupa
(4) Adult ( )

5. For an insect with a four-stage life cycle, which of the following comes after the larval stage?

(1) Egg
(2) Pupa
(3) Nymph
(4) Adult ( )

6. Animal X does not take care of its young. Which of the following statements shows a characteristic that Animal X is likely to have?

(1) The adult usually lays many eggs at one time.
(2) Most of the eggs do not have any form of protection from being eaten.
(3) The life cycles of these animals consists of three stages.
(4) The eggs are usually laid on land. ( )

7. The diagrams below show the same plant at different times.

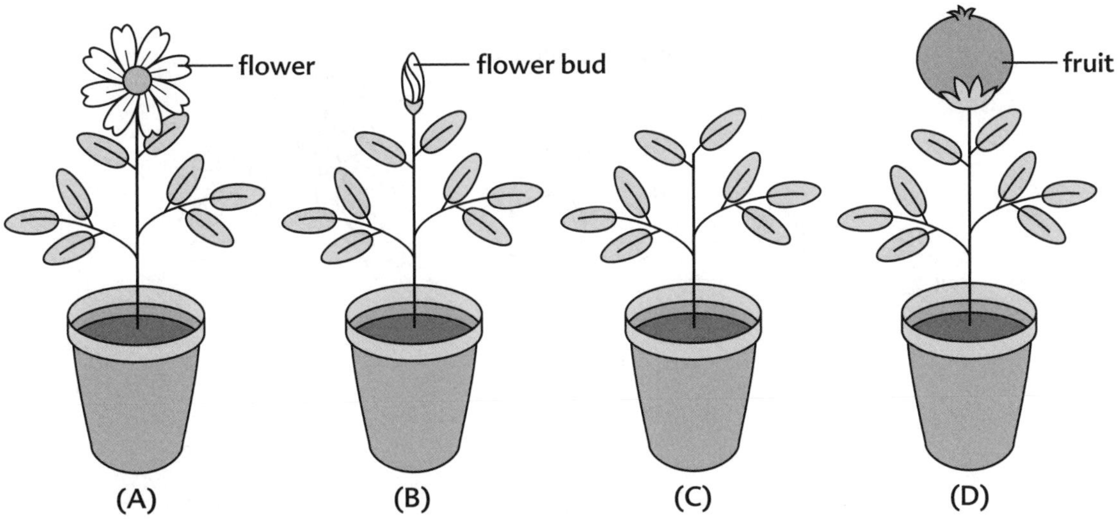

Which of the following correctly shows the sequence in time?

(1) A ⟶ B ⟶ C ⟶ D
(2) B ⟶ A ⟶ C ⟶ D
(3) C ⟶ A ⟶ D ⟶ B
(4) C ⟶ B ⟶ A ⟶ D ( )

8. Animals have different stages in their life cycle. Which of the following is correct?

	Three-stage life cycle	Four-stage life cycle
(1)	Frog	Butterfly
(2)	Housefly	Moth
(3)	Cockroach	Grasshopper
(4)	Beetle	Chicken

( )

9. The diagrams below show the life stages of a bean plant and a tomato plant.

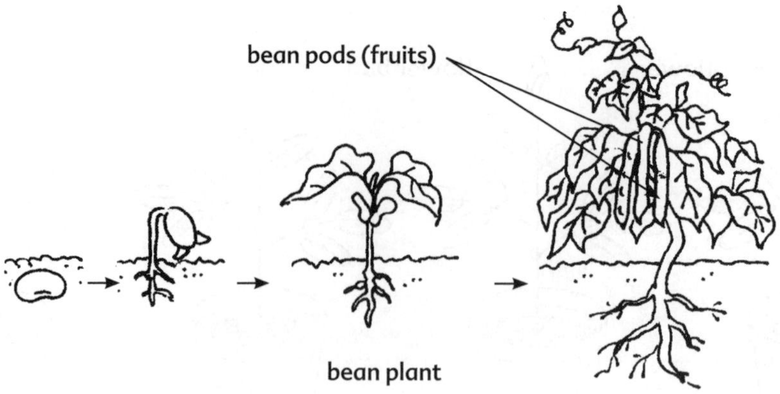

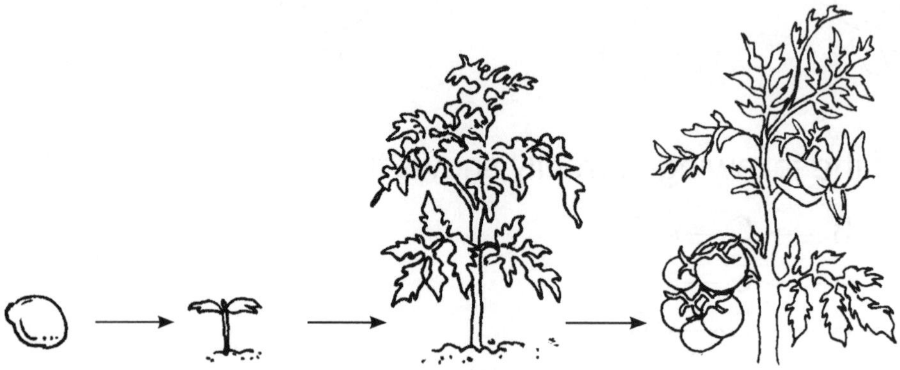

Which of the following statements about both plants is true?

(A) The plants have the same number of stages in their life cycle.
(B) The fruits of both plants contain more than one seed.
(C) Both the tomato and the bean are flowering plants.
(D) Both plants take the same amount of time to complete their life cycle.

(1) A and B only
(2) C and D only
(3) A, B and C only
(4) B, C and D only ( )

10. The diagram below shows the life cycle of a crocodile.

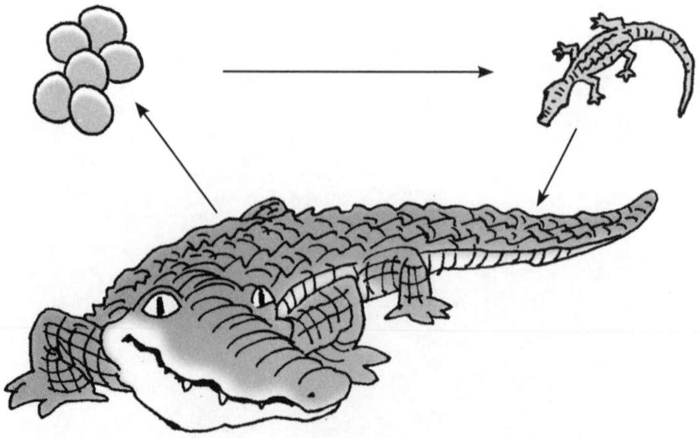

Which of the following animals have the same life cycle as a crocodile?

(A) Snake
(B) Turtle
(C) Cat
(D) Whale

(1) A and B only
(2) C and D only
(3) A, B and D only
(4) A, B, C and D ( )

11. Which of the animals below have the same life cycle as the baboon?

(1) Donkey, kangaroo, hen
(2) Prawn, penguin, elephant
(3) Lion, zebra, tiger
(4) Giraffe, scorpion, goat ( )

12. A dragonfly is an insect. It reproduces by ________.

(1) giving birth to its young alive
(2) producing spores
(3) laying eggs
(4) dividing itself into two ( )

13. Which of the following is part of a life cycle?

(A) egg ⟶ larva
(B) seed ⟶ seedling
(C) day ⟶ night
(D) pupa ⟶ adult

(1) A and B only
(2) A, B and D only
(3) B, C and D only
(4) A, B, C and D ( )

14. Which of the following animals goes through a four-stage life cycle?

(A) Cockroach nymph

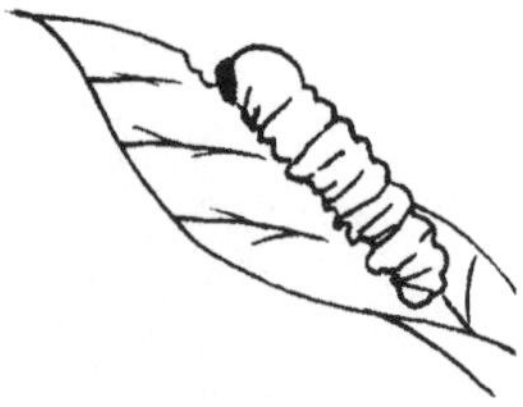

(B) Caterpillar

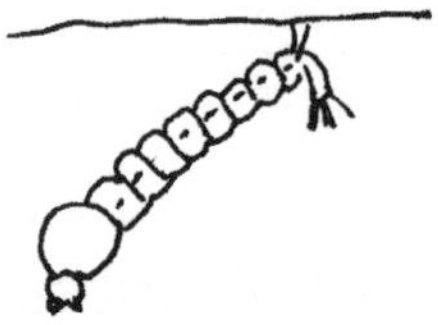

(C) Wriggler of mosquito

(D) Maggot of housefly

(1) A and C only
(2) A, B and D only
(3) A, C and D only
(4) B, C and D only ( )

15. The diagram below shows the life cycle of a papaya plant.

(A)

(B)

(C)

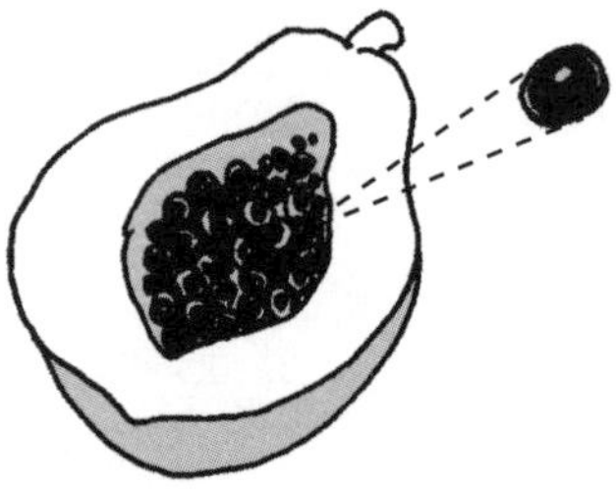

(D)

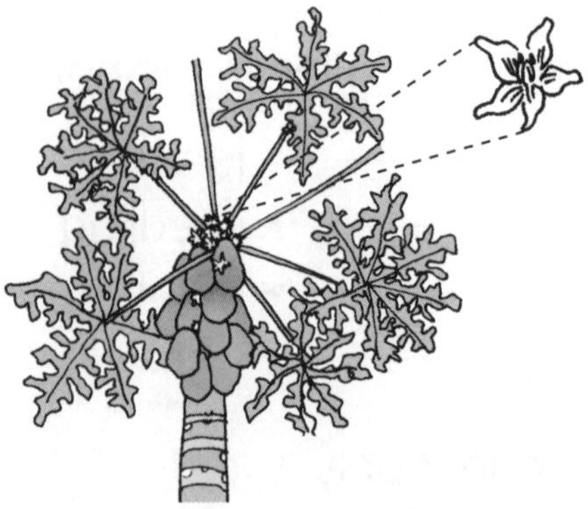

Which of the following correctly represents the order of its life cycle?

(1) A → C → B → D
(2) D → B → C → A
(3) B → C → A → D
(4) C → B → D → A ( )

Section B (20 marks)

Write your answers for each question in the blank spaces provided.

16. Circle TRUE or FALSE for each statement. [3]

(a) Insects may have three-stage or four-stage life cycles. TRUE / FALSE

(b) A housefly and a butterfly have different numbers of stages in their life cycle. TRUE / FALSE

(c) Different animals have different life spans. TRUE / FALSE

17. The table below shows the stages of growth of a human. Arrange the stages by writing the correct number for each stage, starting with (1) for the newborn. [4]

Stages of growth in a human	
Toddler	
Pre-teen	
Newborn	1
Teenager	
Child	
Adult	
Elderly person	
Baby	

18. The diagram below shows the life cycle of an imaginary animal X.

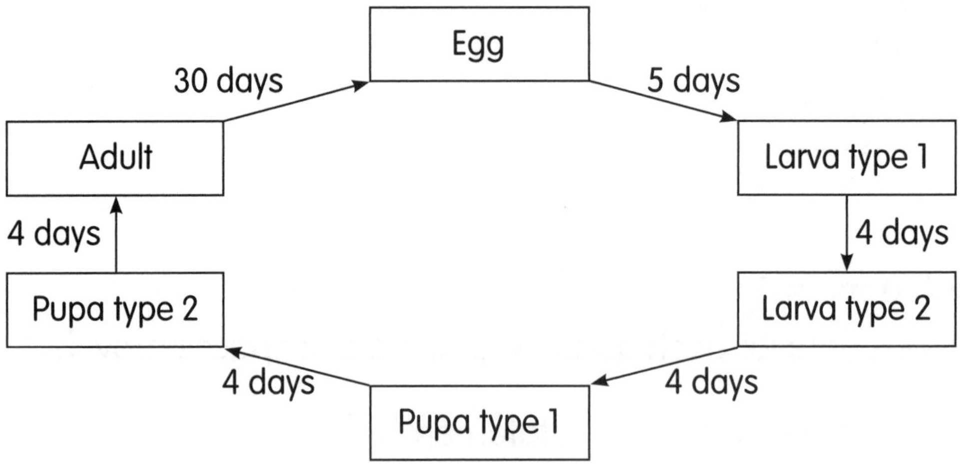

(a) How many stages are there in the life cycle of animal X? [1]

___

(b) How long does the egg take to hatch? [1]

___

(c) What is the similarity between the larval and the pupal stages? [1]

___

(d) How long does the animal take to become an adult? [1]

___

19. The diagram below shows the germination of a seed into a seedling.

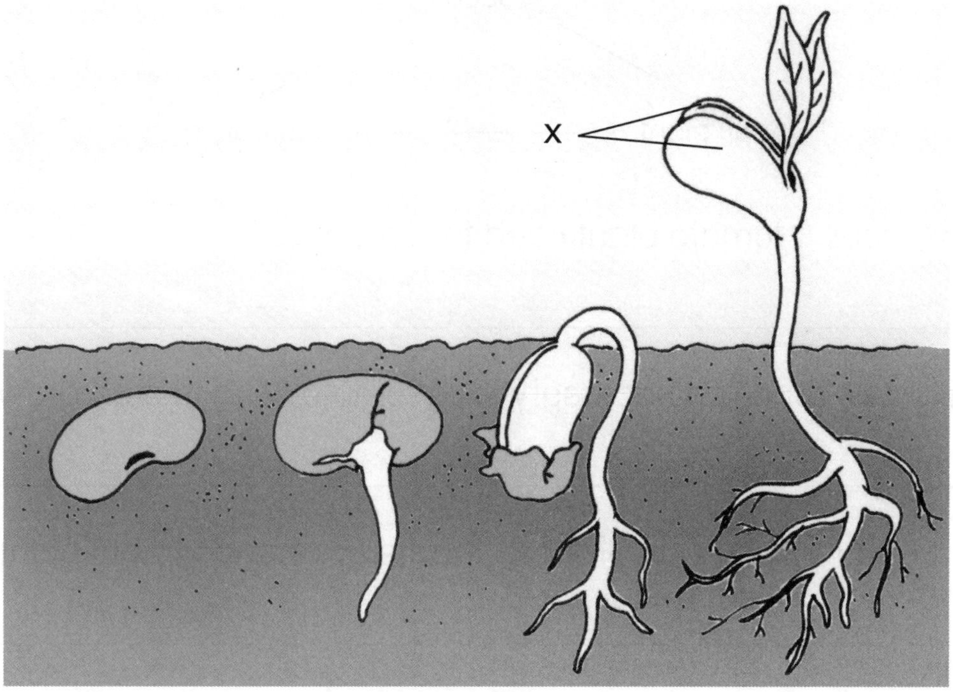

(a) (i) When the seed germinates, which part appears first? [1]

____

(ii) What is its function? [1]

____

(b) What is the function of X? [1]

____

(c) What happens to X when the seedling grows bigger? [1]

____

20. The diagram below shows the life cycle of a tomato plant.

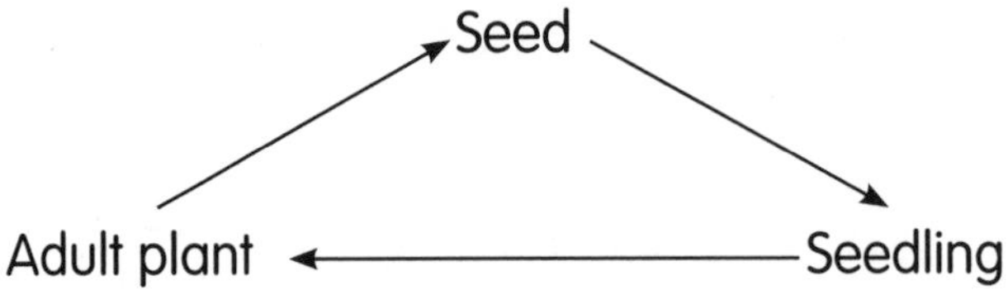

(a) Why does a tomato plant need to reproduce? [1]

____

(b) Give one condition necessary for a tomato seed to start growing. [1]

____

(c) How many stages are there in the life cycle of a tomato plant? [1]

____

(d) The diagram shows an adult tomato plant.

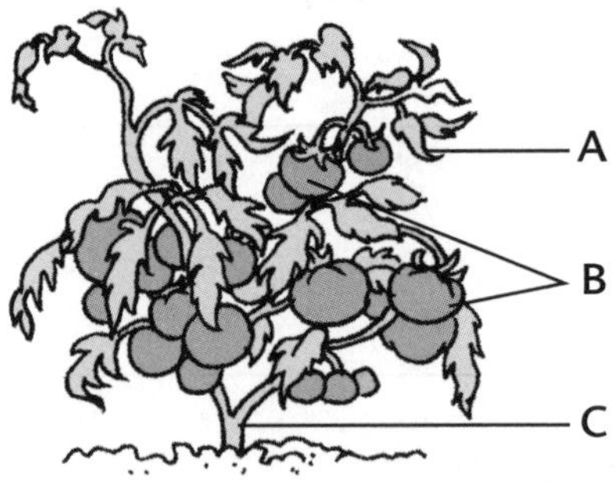

(i) In which structure, A, B or C, are the seeds found? [1]

____

(ii) Before the tomato plant can bear structure B, what must the plant produce? [1]

____

End of Paper

Test 5
Cycles

Marks: /50

Topics:
- What is Matter?
- The Three States of Matter

Name: ______________ Class: ________ Date: ____________

Section A (15 x 2 = 30 marks)

For each question, four options are given. Choose the correct answer and write down your choice, 1, 2, 3 or 4, in the brackets provided.

1. Are light and clouds matter?

	Is light matter?	Are clouds matter?
(1)	Yes	Yes
(2)	Yes	No
(3)	No	No
(4)	No	Yes

( )

2. Which of the following groups are examples of matter?

(1) Glue, paint, ice
(2) Music, water, paper
(3) Sugar, shadow, soap
(4) Syrup, shoe, thunder ( )

3. Which of the following items can be classified as matter?

(A) Dust
(B) Rain
(C) Steam
(D) Sound

(1) A and B only
(2) C and D only
(3) A, B and C only
(4) A, B, C and D ( )

4. Study the classification table below.

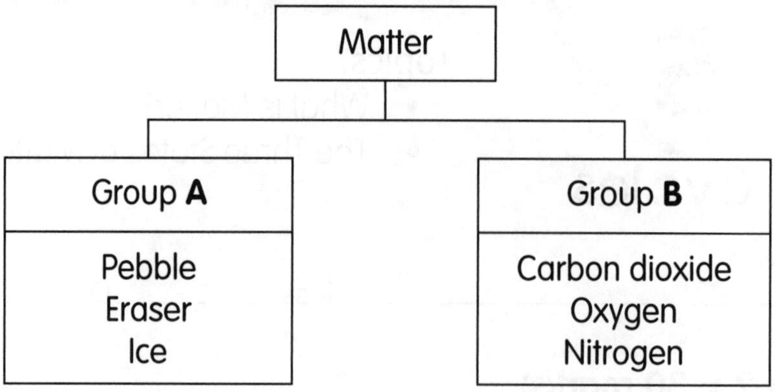

The substances are classified according to whether they __________.

(A) can be compressed or not
(B) have a definite volume or not
(C) have a definite mass or not
(D) occupy space or not

(1) A and B only
(2) C and D only
(3) A, B and D only
(4) B, C and D only ( )

5. Which of the following pairs of substances are similar in state?

(A) Salt and vinegar.
(B) Tofu and jelly.
(C) Marble and coin.
(D) Ketchup and ice.

(1) A and D only
(2) B and C only
(3) A, B and D only
(4) A, B, C and D ( )

6. Study the diagrams below carefully.

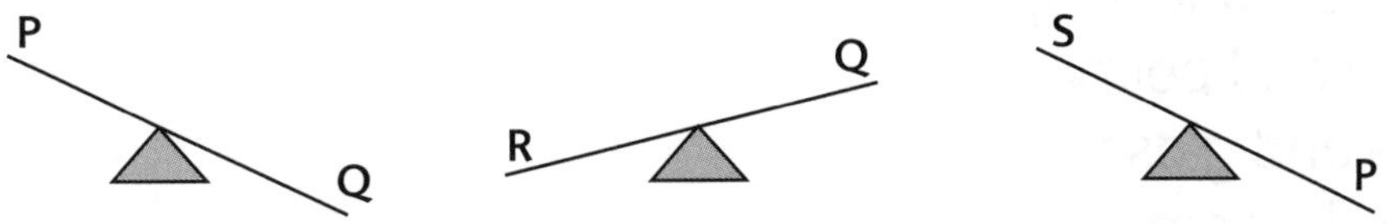

Which of the following arranges the objects' masses from the smallest to the biggest?

(1) P ⟶ Q ⟶ R ⟶ S
(2) Q ⟶ R ⟶ P ⟶ S
(3) S ⟶ P ⟶ Q ⟶ R
(4) R ⟶ P ⟶ Q ⟶ S ( )

7. Two objects, A and B, are placed on a lever balance as shown below.

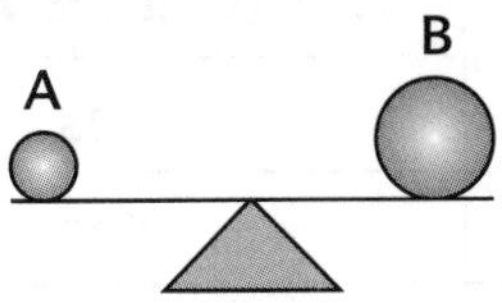

Which of the following statements is true?

(A) A and B have the same mass.
(B) A and B have the same volume.
(C) B has a larger volume than A.
(D) A and B are matter.

(1) A and C only
(2) B and D only
(3) A, C and D only
(4) A, B and D only ( )

8. Which of the following statements about air is correct?

(A) Air takes up space.
(B) Air has weight.
(C) Air does not have a definite shape.
(D) Air can be compressed.

(1) A and D only
(2) B and C only
(3) A, C and D only
(4) A, B, C and D ( )

9. Which of the following pairs consists of a solid and a liquid?

(1) Spaghetti and soup.
(2) Honey and petrol.
(3) Stone and glass.
(4) Ice and steam. ( )

10. Liquid cannot be compressed because it has ______________.

(1) a definite mass
(2) a definite volume
(3) no definite shape
(4) no definite size ( )

11. The table below shows the properties of **A**, **B** and **C**.

	Has definite shape	Has definite volume	Can be compressed
A	Yes	Yes	No
B	No	Yes	No
C	No	No	Yes

Which of the following correctly represents **A**, **B** and **C**?

	A	B	C
(1)	Oxygen	Orange juice	Syringe
(2)	Marble	Ice	Water
(3)	Stone	Milk	Steam
(4)	Coin	Tea	Creamer

( )

12. What can you conclude from the diagram below?

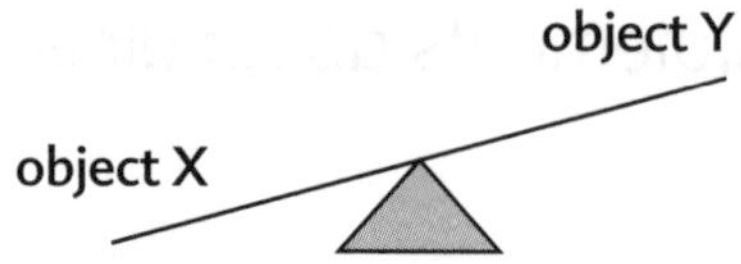

(1) Objects X and Y are made of different materials.
(2) Object X has more mass than object Y.
(3) Object X has the same shape as object Y.
(4) Object X has the same volume as object Y. ( )

13. Study the diagram below carefully.

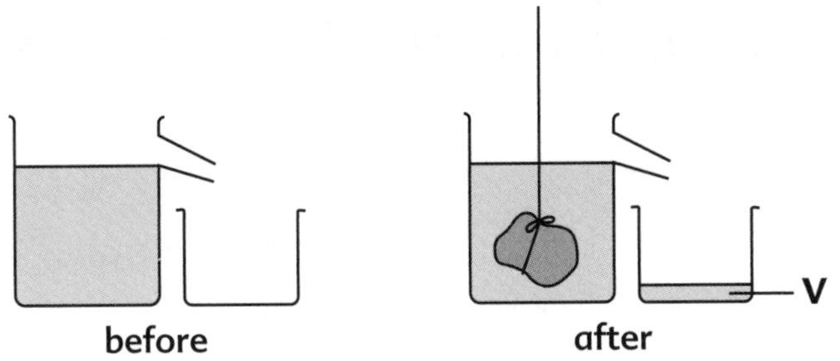

What does **V** represent?

(1) Mass of the stone.
(2) Volume of the stone.
(3) Mass and volume of the stone.
(4) The state of matter of the stone. ( )

14. Three liquids X, Y and Z were mixed together. After a while, the liquids separated into three layers, as shown in the diagram below.

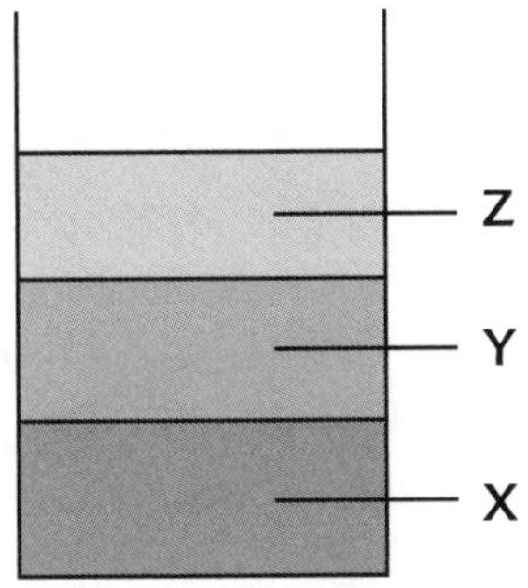

The experiment shows that ______________.

(A) X is the heaviest liquid
(B) Z is the lightest liquid
(C) Y is lighter than X but heavier than Z
(D) when liquids are mixed, they separate out randomly

(1) D only
(2) A and C only
(3) A and B only
(4) A, B and C only ( )

15. The diagrams below show some apparatus used to measure the volume of liquids. Which of the following correctly arranges the apparatus according to the volumes of liquid they can measure from the largest to the smallest?

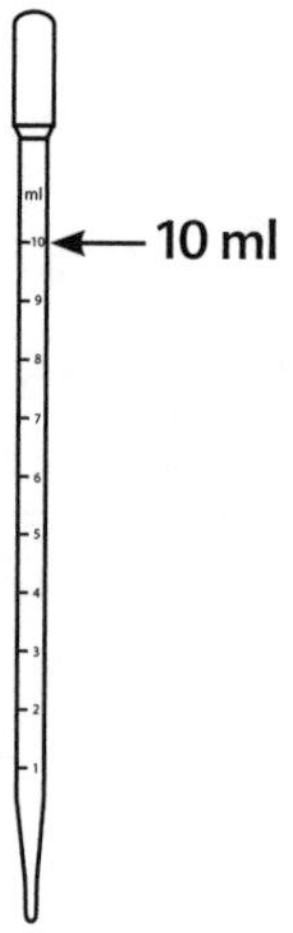

P

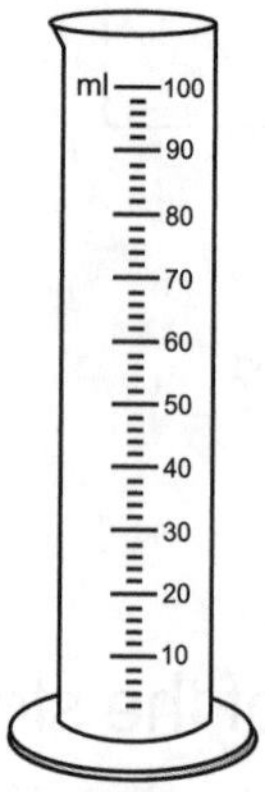

Q

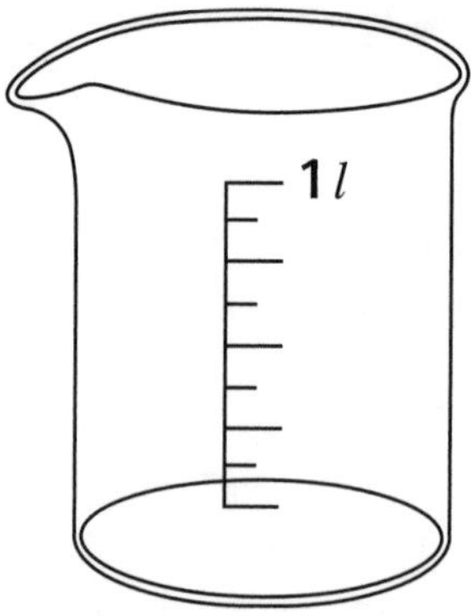

R

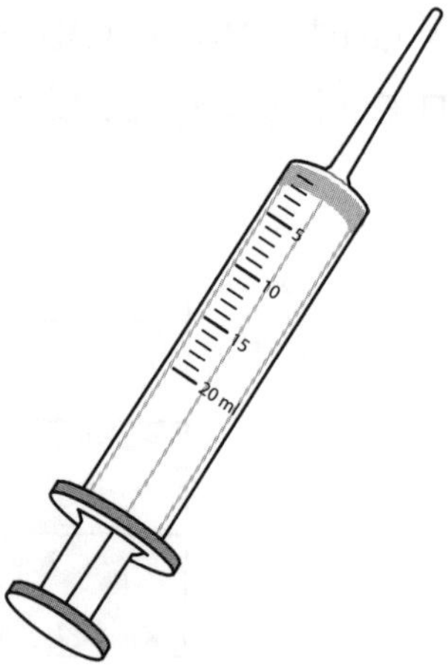

S

Largest ⟶ Smallest

(1) P ⟶ S ⟶ Q ⟶ R
(2) R ⟶ Q ⟶ S ⟶ P
(3) Q ⟶ P ⟶ R ⟶ S
(4) S ⟶ R ⟶ P ⟶ Q

( )

Section B (20 marks)

Write your answers for each question in the blank spaces provided.

16. Circle TRUE or FALSE for each statement. [3]

(a) All matter has mass and occupies space. TRUE / FALSE

(b) Matter is in the liquid state if it has a definite volume and shape. TRUE / FALSE

(c) Root beer is made up of two states of matter. TRUE / FALSE

17. Complete the graphic organiser using the words below. [3]

Solid	**Flour**	**Liquid**
Honey	**Gas**	**Carbon dioxide**

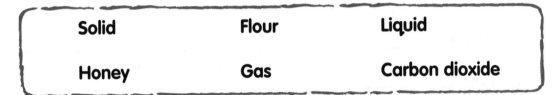

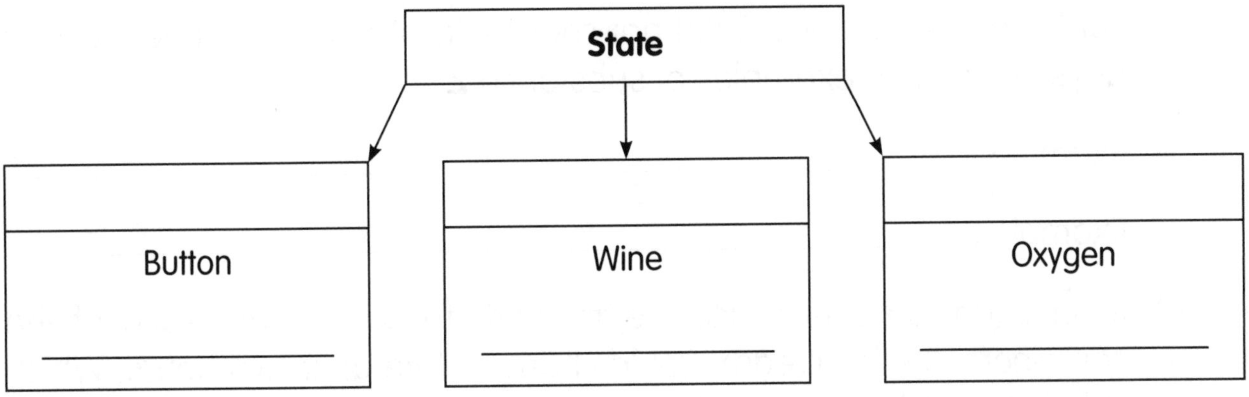

18. Study the four containers shown below.

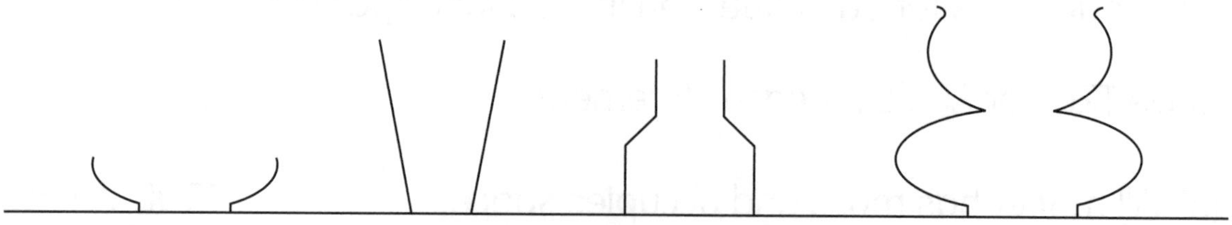

(a) All the containers appear empty, but they are not. They contain a substance **X**. What is substance **X**? [1]

____

(b) When an equal amount of substance **Y** is placed into each of the containers, substance **Y** took the shape of each of the containers. Name two examples of substance **Y**. [2]

Example 1 _______________________________________

Example 2 _______________________________________

(c) When an equal amount of substance **Z** is placed into each of the containers, substance **Z** did not change its shape, even after several days. Name two examples of substance **Z**. [2]

Example 1 _______________________________________

Example 2 _______________________________________

(d) If an equal amount of ice cream were to be put into each of the containers, the ice cream would change state after two hours. Which substance, **X**, **Y** or **Z**, would have the same state as the ice cream after two hours? [1]

____

19. Mei Mei mixed some flour with water to form a dough. She moulded the dough into a rabbit, then a snake and then a frog, one at a time.

(a) Which property of the dough is changed when it is moulded? Circle your answer. [1]

Colour **Volume** **Mass** **Shape**

(b) Which state of matter is the dough in? [1]

____

(c) Name one other substance that behaves like dough. [1]

____

20. Irwin set up an experiment as shown in the diagram below.

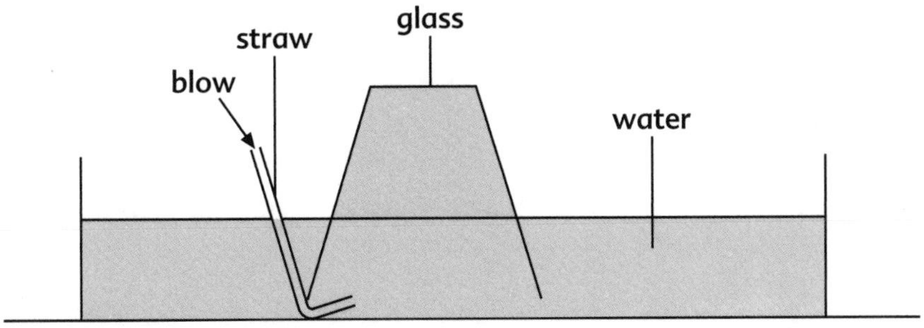

(a) What three observations can Irwin make when he blows into the straw? [3]

Observation 1 ___________________________________

Observation 2 ___________________________________

Observation 3 ___________________________________

(b) What does this experiment show? Tick your answers. [2]

- ☐ Water occupies space.
- ☐ Water has mass.
- ☐ Air occupies space.
- ☐ Air has mass.

End of Paper

BLANK

Thematic Assessment 2

Marks: /100

Cycles

Name: ______________________ Class: __________ Date: ______________

Section A (30 x 2 = 60 marks)

For each question, four options are given. Choose the correct answer and write down your choice, 1, 2, 3 or 4, in the brackets provided.

1. Which one of the following is grouped wrongly?

	Three-stage life cycle	Four-stage life cycle
(1)	Chicken	Mosquito
(2)	Duck	Housefly
(3)	Snake	Grasshopper
(4)	Tortoise	Butterfly

( )

2. Study the following classification chart carefully.

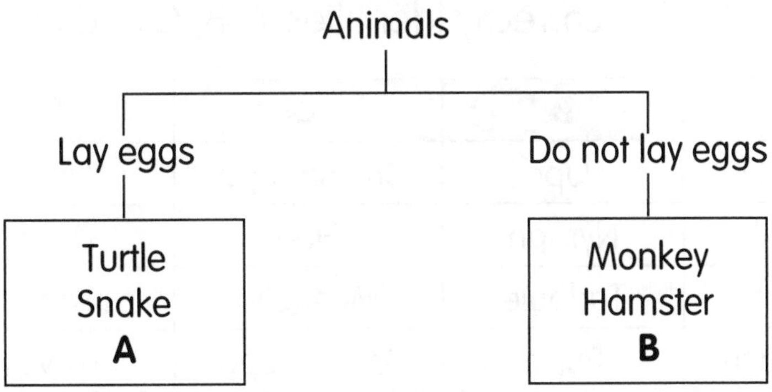

What would animals A and B be?

	A	B
(1)	Frog	Hen
(2)	Lizard	Rabbit
(3)	Butterfly	Duck
(4)	Goose	Moth

( )

3. A frog and a fish are alike because they ________.
   (1) lay eggs
   (2) are covered in scales
   (3) eat plants
   (4) look after their young ( )

4. Which of the following correctly classifies the animals?

	Lay eggs	Live in water	Lay eggs and live in water
(1)	Chicken	Octopus	Frog
(2)	Seal	Prawn	Flea
(3)	Rabbit	Turtle	Snail
(4)	Sparrow	Dragonfly	Shark

( )

5. The diagrams below show the life cycle of two different kinds of insects.

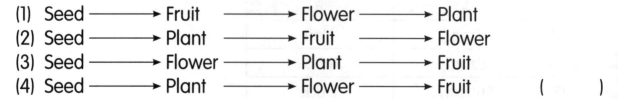

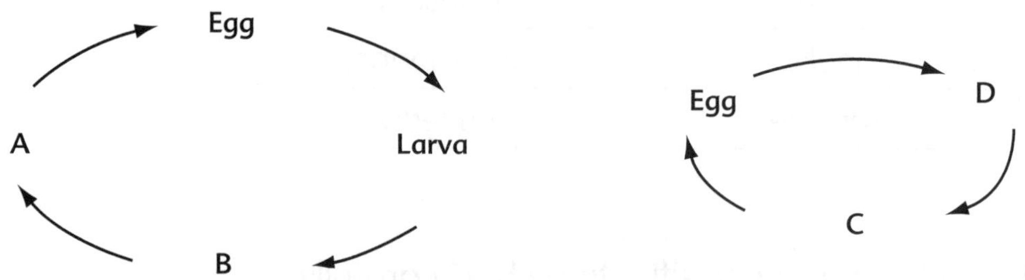

Which of the following correctly identifies A, B, C and D?

	A	B	C	D
(1)	Butterfly	Pupa	Grasshopper	Nymph
(2)	Housefly	Nymph	Hen	Chick
(3)	Python	Tadpole	Mosquito	Nymph
(4)	Cockroach	Pupa	Grasshopper	Larva

( )

6. Which of the following correctly shows the life cycle of a cucumber plant?
   (1) Seed → Fruit → Flower → Plant
   (2) Seed → Plant → Fruit → Flower
   (3) Seed → Flower → Plant → Fruit
   (4) Seed → Plant → Flower → Fruit ( )

7. Study the diagrams below carefully.

The animals shown above are similar in that ____________.

(A) the parents look after the young
(B) the young looks like the parent
(C) their life cycles have same number of stages
(D) they reproduce to ensure continuity of their kind

(1) A and B only
(2) C and D only
(3) A, C and D only
(4) A, B, C and D ( )

8. Which of the following is the function of a seed?

(1) Grows into a new plant.
(2) Stores food for the adult plant.
(3) Takes in water for the plant.
(4) Allows the leaves to make food for the plant. ( )

9. Which of the following are true about life cycles?

(A) All living things have a life cycle.
(B) The stages in a life cycle can be different for different living things.
(C) The length of the life cycle is similar for all insects.
(D) The life cycle of a human is different from that of all other living things.

(1) A and B only
(2) C and D only
(3) A, B and D only
(4) B, C and D only ( )

10. Study the concept map below.

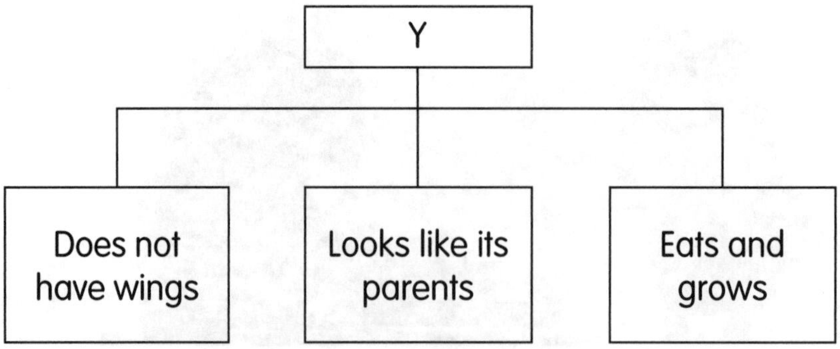

Y is the young of a ____________.

(1) mosquito
(2) housefly
(3) beetle
(4) cockroach ( )

11. The animals in the table below are grouped according to ____________.

Group A	Group B
Beetle	Whale
Butterfly	Rabbit
Mosquito	Hamster

(A) where they live
(B) how they reproduce
(C) the stages of their life cycle
(D) the food they eat

(1) A and D only
(2) B and C only
(3) A, B and C only
(4) A, C and D only ( )

12. Which is the most suitable characteristic for A and B?

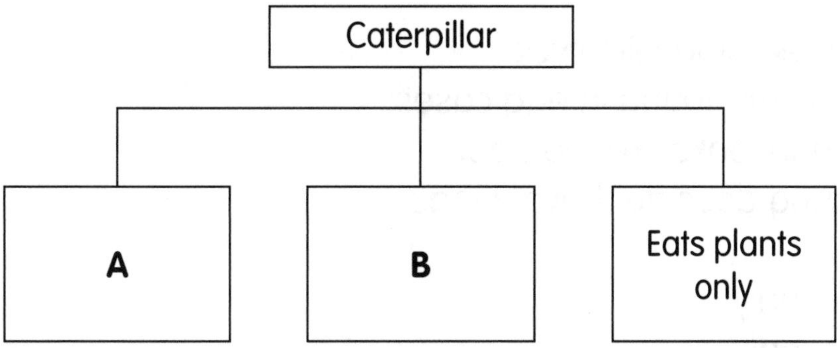

	A	B
(1)	Does not have wings.	Looks like the adult.
(2)	Does not have wings.	Does not look like the adult.
(3)	Has wings.	Does not look like the adult.
(4)	Has wings.	Looks like the adult.

( )

13. Which of the following changes when a chick develops into a hen?
(A) Weight
(B) Shape
(C) Size
(D) Colour of the feathers

(1) A and B only
(2) C and D only
(3) A, C and D only
(4) A, B, C and D ( )

14. Which of the following correctly shows the developments in the life cycle of a frog?
(1) Egg → Tadpole without legs → Tadpole with four legs → Frog
(2) Egg → Tadpole with forelegs → Tadpole with four legs → Frog
(3) Egg → Tadpole with hindlegs → Tadpole with four legs → Frog
(4) Egg → Tadpole with four legs → Frog ( )

15. Which of the following statements is true about the life cycle of a cockroach?

(A) It is a three-stage life cycle.
(B) The eggs are found in egg cases.
(C) The young looks like the adult.
(D) The young does not have wings.

(1) A and B only
(2) B and C only
(3) A and C only
(4) A, B, C and D ( )

16. Study the diagrams below carefully.

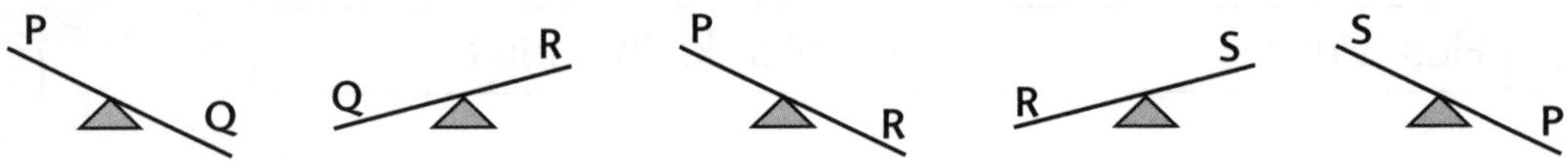

Which of the following arranges the objects' masses from the biggest to the smallest?

(1) P, Q, R, S
(2) Q, R, P, S
(3) S, P, Q, R
(4) R, P, Q, S ( )

17. Soap and water ____________.

(A) have mass
(B) have definite shapes
(C) do not have definite volumes
(D) occupy space

(1) A and D only
(2) B and C only
(3) A, B and D only
(4) B, C and D only ( )

18. A ball was inflated and its mass measured as shown in diagram A. More air is then pumped into the ball and its mass is measured as shown in diagram B.

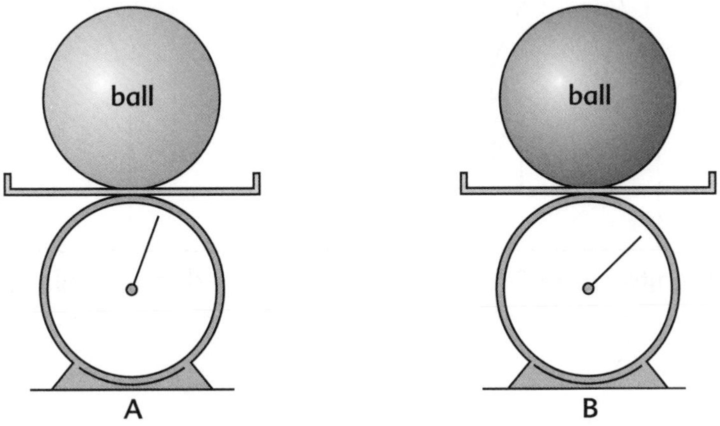

What does the experiment show?

(A) Air has mass.
(B) Air has a definite shape.
(C) Air can be compressed.
(D) Air does not occupy space.

(1) A and C only
(2) B and D only
(3) A, C and D only
(4) A, B and C only ( )

19. Which of the following groups consists of only one state of matter?

(1) Pebbles, sand, sea water
(2) Wine, lime juice, oil
(3) Oxygen, blood, plaster
(4) Paint, nail polish, nail ( )

Refer to the diagrams below to answer Questions 20 to 22.

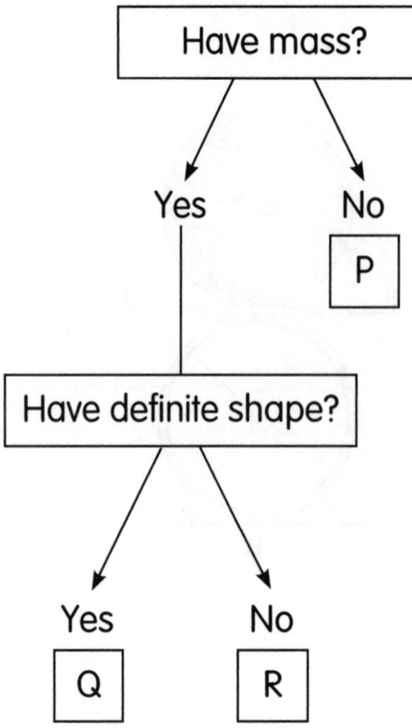

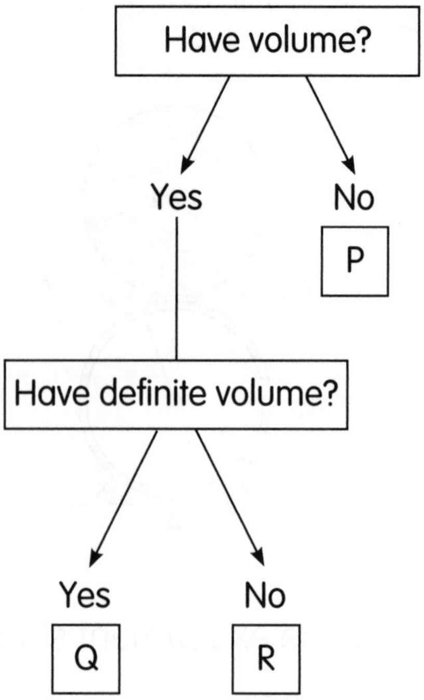

20. Which of the following is likely to be P?

(1) Rain
(2) Cloud
(3) Music
(4) Water vapour ( )

21. Which of the following is likely to be Q?

(1) Light
(2) Battery water
(3) Carbon dioxide
(4) Steel wire ( )

22. Which of the statements below are true about R?

(A) R is a gas.
(B) It has mass.
(C) It has volume.
(D) It does not have a definite shape.

(1) A and B only
(2) C and D only
(3) A, B and D only
(4) A, B, C and D ( )

23. Which of the following describes the similarities between a solid, a liquid and a gas?

(1) They have mass and take up space.
(2) They have definite volume.
(3) They have definite shape.
(4) They have no definite volume. ( )

24. Jenny put some ice into a beaker. After some time, she noticed the ice had melted into water. When she heated the beaker of water over a burner, all the water disappeared after some time. Which of the following is correct?

(A) Water can exist in three states.
(B) Water can change from one state to another.
(C) Water in the gas state has no definite shape.
(D) Water in the solid state is ice.

(1) A and B only
(2) C and D only
(3) A, C and D only
(4) A, B, C and D ( )

25. Which of the following groups of substances are classified according to their states?

(1)

Group 1	Group 2
Magnet	Clay
Iron filings	Coffee

(2)

Group 1	Group 2
Sand	Ink
Paper	Milk

(3)

Group 1	Group 2
Thread	Golf club
String	Air

(4)

Group 1	Group 2
Hot chocolate	Fork
Muffin	Creamer

( )

26. At which state does matter have fixed shape?

(1) Solid only
(2) Solid and liquid only
(3) Liquid and gaseous only
(4) Solid, liquid and gaseous ( )

27. Study the diagram below carefully.

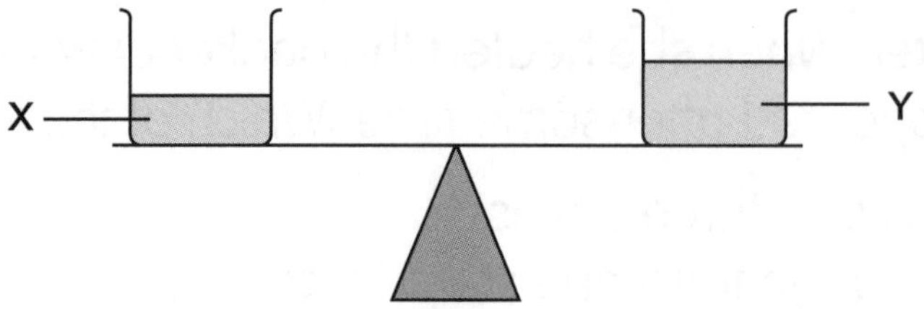

Which of the following statements is true about liquids X and Y?

(1) Liquid X and liquid Y have the same mass.
(2) Liquid X and liquid Y have the same volume.
(3) Liquid X occupies the same amount of space as liquid Y.
(4) Liquid X can be compressed; liquid Y cannot be compressed. ( )

28. Which of the following is true about matter?

(1) Matter of the same volume must have the same mass.
(2) Matter of the same shape must have same volume.
(3) Matter with a definite shape must be a solid.
(4) Matter with no definite mass must be a gas. ( )

29. Which of the following groups of substances have definite volume?

(1) Medicated oil, cooking oil, syrup
(2) Rice, steam, noodles
(3) Oxygen, water vapour, carbon dioxide
(4) Brush, shampoo, carbon dioxide ( )

30. A gas is different from a solid because it ____________.

(1) has mass
(2) occupies space
(3) can be compressed
(4) has a definite volume ( )

Section B (40 marks)

Write your answers for each question in the blank spaces provided.

31. In modern farms today, chicks are hatched from eggs by keeping the eggs in special boxes.

(a) What do these special boxes provide the eggs with? [1]

____

(b) What performs the same function as these boxes? [1]

____

(c) In the space provided below, draw the life cycle of a chicken. [3]

32. (a) In the graphic organiser below, state the similarities and differences between the life cycles of a duck and a frog. [4]

Two similarities
(a) ______________________
(b) ______________________

Life cycle of duck | Life cycle of frog

Two differences	
(a) ______________	______________
(b) ______________	______________

(b) Which part of the young of a frog helps it to move about? [1]

____

33. (a) What is the name for the larva of a butterfly? [1]

____

(b) State two characteristics of the larva of a butterfly. [2]

____

(c) The pupal stage of a butterfly is different from its adult stage. State two differences. [2]

____

____

(d) Which two other insects' life cycle is similar to that of a butterfly's? [2]

____

____

34. An experiment was set up to investigate the germination of maize. Five maize seeds were placed on damp cotton wool in dish A and another five maize seeds were placed on dry cotton wool in dish B as shown below. The petri dishes were placed side by side in a corner of the classroom. The cotton wool in dish A was kept moist throughout the experiment.

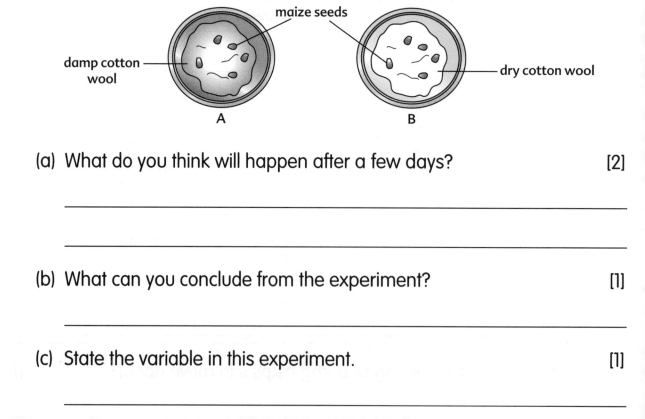

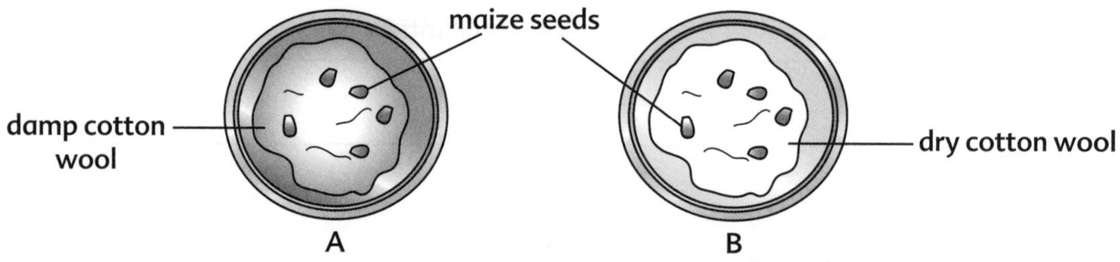

(a) What do you think will happen after a few days? [2]

____

____

(b) What can you conclude from the experiment? [1]

____

(c) State the variable in this experiment. [1]

____

(d) Name two factors that were kept constant (the same) for dish A and dish B. [2]

____

____

(e) What was the purpose of dish B. [1]

____

35. Study the concept map below and answer the questions that follow.

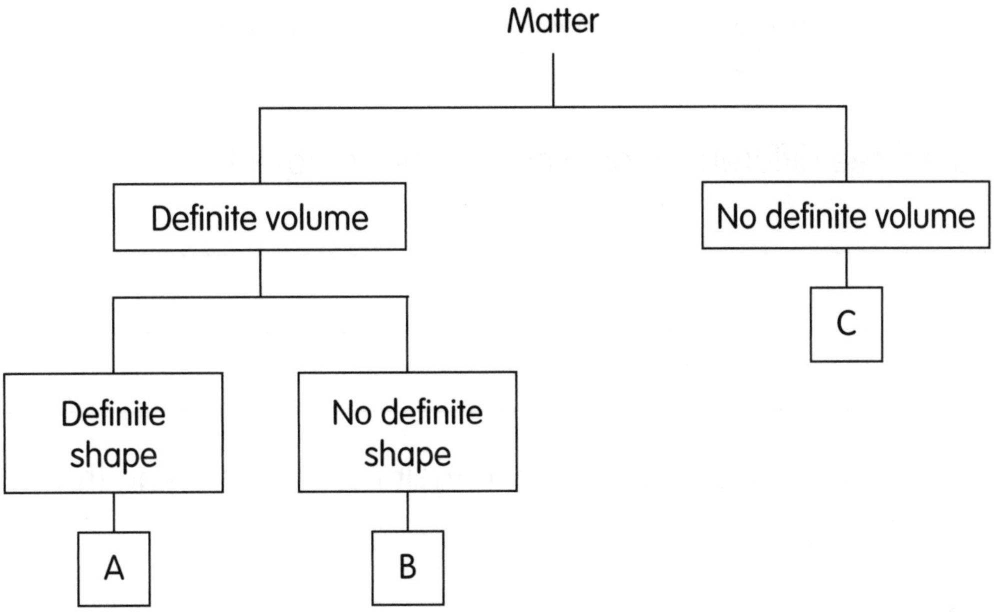

(a) State two properties of: [3]

A: ____

B: ____

C: ____

(b) Give an example each of: [3]

A: ____

B: ____

C: ____

(c) What two characterisitics are common to A, B and C? [2]

A, B and C all: (i) ______________________________

(ii) ______________________________

36. The diagrams below show three objects.

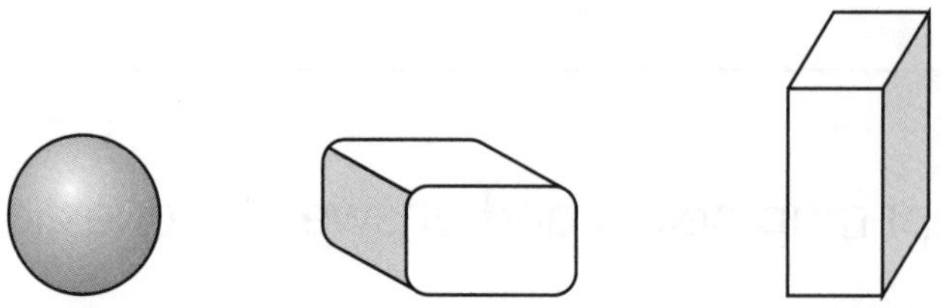

(a) State three differences between the three objects. [3]

____

____

____

(b) Arrange the objects according to their masses, starting from the smallest. [1]

____

(c) If you are given a measuring cylinder and some water, describe how you would find the volume of the glass ball. [3]

____

____

____

(d) Can the volume of the styrofoam slab be measured in the same way as in (c)? Why? [1]

____

End of Paper

Test 6 Systems

Marks:

/50

Topics:
- What is a system?
- Your amazing body

Name: ________________________ Class: ________ Date: ____________

Section A (15 x 2 = 30 marks)

For each question, four options are given. Choose the correct answer and write down your choice, 1, 2, 3 or 4, in the brackets provided.

1. We are able to bend our elbows because of the contraction and relaxation of our __________.

   (1) bones
   (2) muscles
   (3) tendons
   (4) ligaments ( )

2. Which of the following protect our brain and our heart?

	Brain is protected by:	Heart is protected by:
(1)	Skull	Backbone
(2)	Head	Thigh bone
(3)	Skull	Ribcage
(4)	Head	Shoulder bone

( )

3. Which of the following activities causes the heart to beat faster?

   (1) Sleeping
   (2) Running
   (3) Listening to classical music.
   (4) Resting ( )

4. Which of the following gases are found in our lungs?

(A) Oxygen
(B) Carbon dioxide
(C) Methane
(D) Water vapour

(1) A and B
(2) C and D
(3) A, B and D
(4) A, B, C and D ( )

5. Which of the following are parts of the Karaoke system?

(A) Screen
(B) Compact discs
(C) Microphone
(D) Disc player

(1) A and B only
(2) B and C only
(3) A, C and D only
(4) A, B, C and D ( )

6. Which of the following is **not** a system?

(1) Remote control
(2) Marble
(3) Tape recorder
(4) Camera ( )

7. The diagram shows a bottle of liquid eraser.

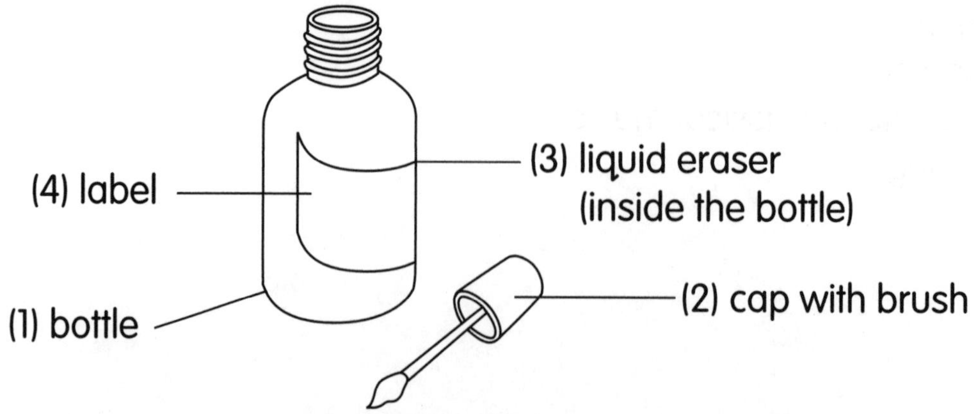

Which of the parts, when removed, will **not** affect its function? ( )

8. Study the graphic organiser below carefully.

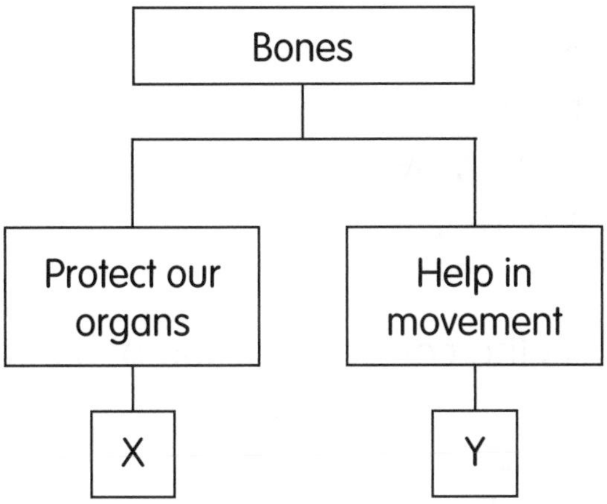

Which of the following correctly represents X and Y?

	X	Y
(1)	Skull	Finger bone
(2)	Toe bone	Ribs
(3)	Arm bone	Backbone
(4)	Finger bone	Leg bone

( )

9. Which of the following is true?

(1) Bones can move on their own.
(2) Saliva helps to digest food.
(3) Out of the many bones in our body, only a few are connected.
(4) A system is made up of not more than five parts. ( )

10. Which of the following processes is incorrectly matched to the body parts?

	Process	Body part
(1)	Oxygen is absorbed and carbon dioxide is removed.	Lungs
(2)	Food is digested and absorbed into the blood stream.	Stomach
(3)	Allow us to watch our favourite television programme.	Eyes
(4)	Prevents germs from entering our body.	Skin

( )

11. Which of the following explains why muscles are attached to bones at our joints?

(1) To support the body.
(2) To give a shape to the body.
(3) To allow the bones to move.
(4) To strengthen the bones. ( )

12. Which diagram shows the correct direction of blood flow in our circulatory system?

(1)
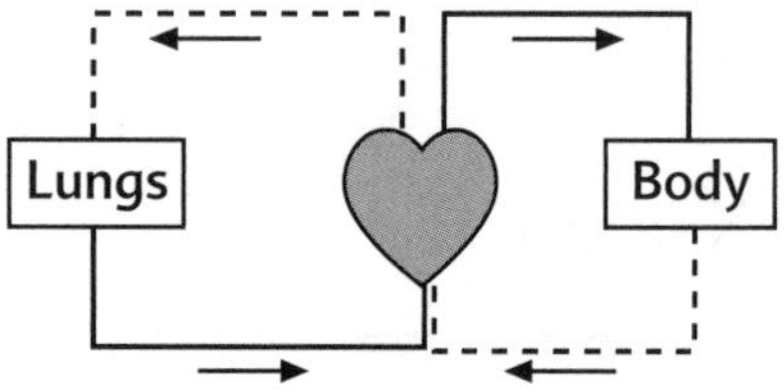

(2)
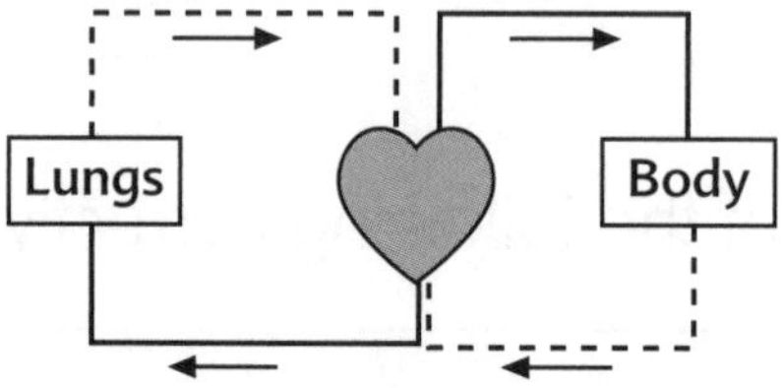

(3)
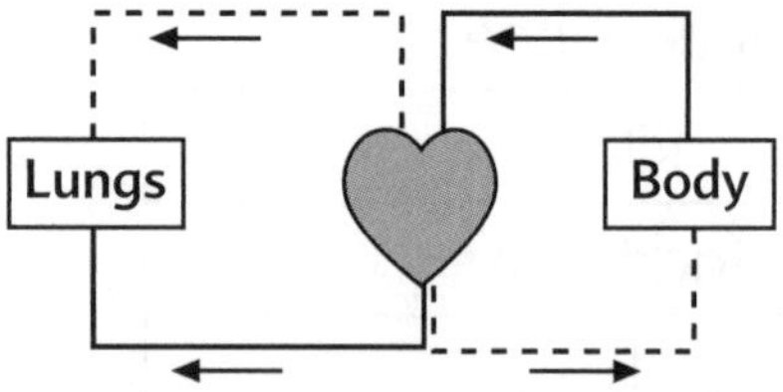

(4)
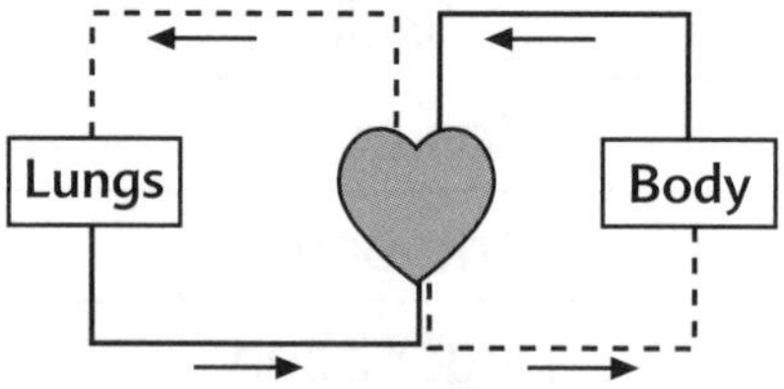

(Dotted lines represent blood rich in carbon dioxide; complete lines represent blood rich in oxygen.) ( )

13. Which organ controls each and every part of our body?

(1) Heart
(2) Lungs
(3) Brain
(4) Liver ( )

14. Which of the following activities makes use of only one of our senses?

(1) Making a telephone call.
(2) Listening to heavy-metal music.
(3) Eating a red apple.
(4) Baking a cake. ( )

15. Which of the following activities does not involve the bending of our joints?

(1) Cycling on an exercise bicycle.
(2) Playing a tennis game.
(3) Typing on the computer.
(4) Yawning ( )

Section B (20 marks)

Write your answers for each question in the blank spaces provided.

16. Circle TRUE or FALSE for each statement. [3]

    (a) Muscles and bones work together to make movement possible. TRUE / FALSE

    (b) Our heart pumps blood to all parts of the body. TRUE / FALSE

    (c) When we exercise, our breathing becomes faster. TRUE / FALSE

17. In the table below, list three things that are carried by the blood in our body. Indicate (with a tick) whether they are useful or not useful. [3]

Things carried by our blood	Useful	Not useful
1.		
2.		
3.		

18. Complete the graphic organiser below. [6]

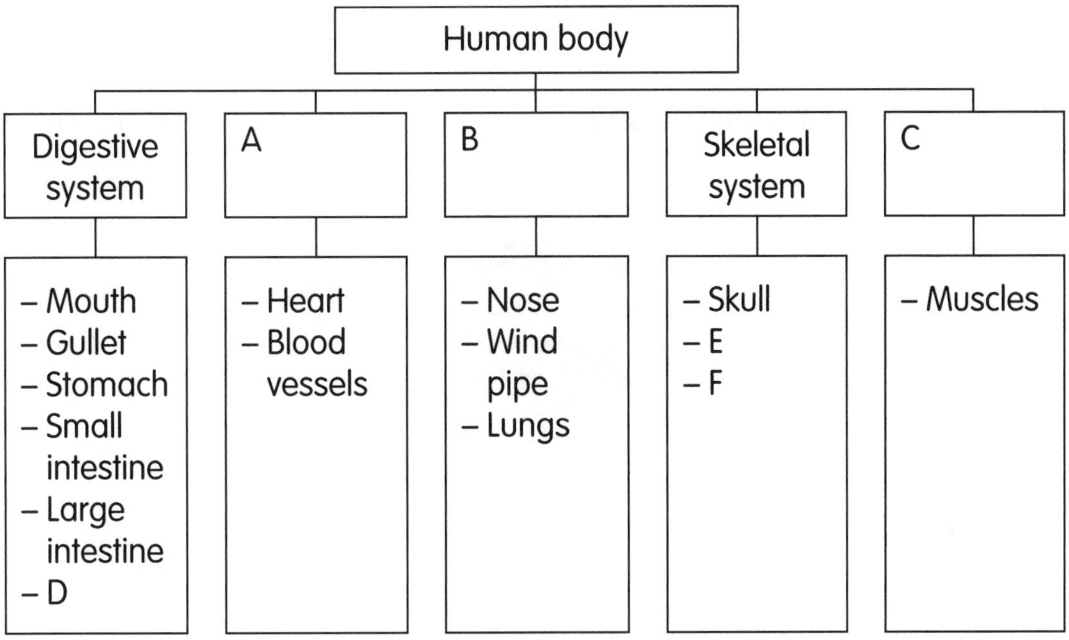

A: ____________ D: ____________

B: ____________ E: ____________

C: ____________ F: ____________

19. The diagram shows a model of our circulatory system.

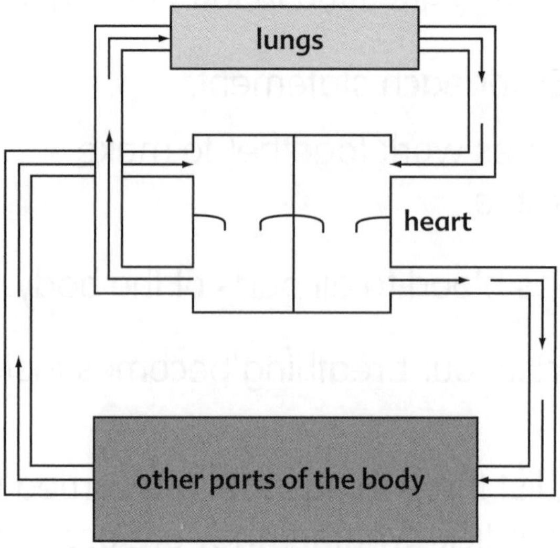

(a) What are the functions of our circulatory system? [2]

____

____

(b) How is our circulatory system similar to our digestive and respiratory systems? [2]

____

____

20. The following is a picture of an MP3 player, which stores and plays music.

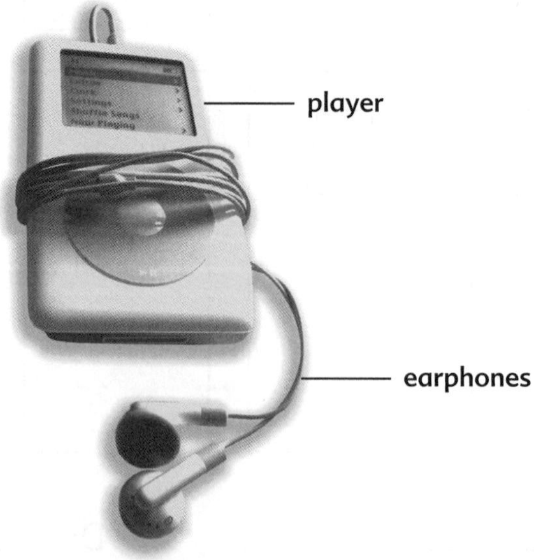

(a) Why is the MP3 player an example of a system? [1]

____

____

(b) Name three parts of the MP3 player system and state their functions. [3]

	Part	Function
(i)		
(ii)		
(iii)		

End of Paper

BLANK

Test 7
Systems

Marks: /50

Topics:
- The digestive system
- Plants and their parts

Name: ______________________ Class: __________ Date: ______________

Section A (15 x 2 = 30 marks)

For each question, four options are given. Choose the correct answer and write down your choice, 1, 2, 3 or 4, in the brackets provided.

1. What is the usual function of the stem of a plant?

   (1) To hold up the plant and reach out for sunlight.
   (2) To absorb water and minerals.
   (3) To receive light energy to make food.
   (4) To reproduce. ( )

2. Which of the following describes the functions of leaves?

	Take in	Give out
(A)	Oxygen	Carbon dioxide
(B)	Carbon dioxide	Oxygen
(C)	Water	Nutrients
(D)	Nutrients	Water vapour

   (1) A and B only
   (2) C and D only
   (3) A, C and D only
   (4) A, B and D only ( )

3. When we eat the potato and ginger, which part of the plant are we eating?

   (1) Root
   (2) Stem
   (3) Leaf
   (4) Fruit ( )

4. Which of the following statements about flowers is true?

(A) Flowers can grow singly or in bunches.
(B) Flowers may be brightly coloured or dull.
(C) Plants produce flowers so that they can attract insects.
(D) Some flowers are edible while others are poisonous.

(1) A and B only
(2) C and D only
(3) A, B and D only
(4) A, B, C and D ( )

5. The diagram below shows the classification of X and Y.

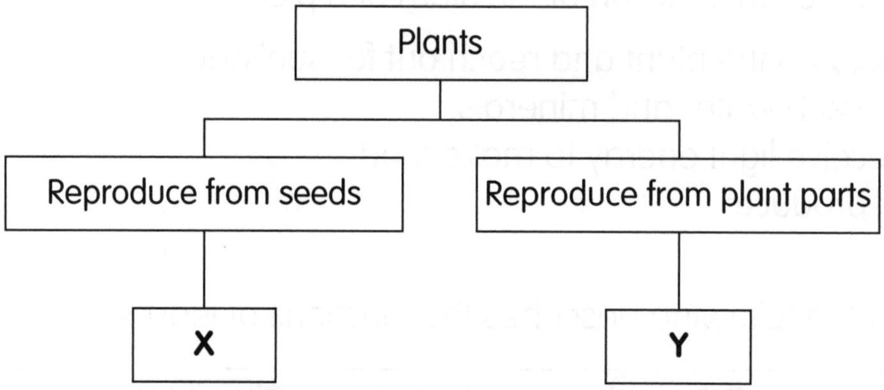

Which of the following are likely to be X and Y?

	X	Y
(1)	String bean	Sugar cane
(2)	Tapioca	Ginger
(3)	Tomato	Chilli
(4)	Ginger	Banana

( )

6. Study the classification chart below.

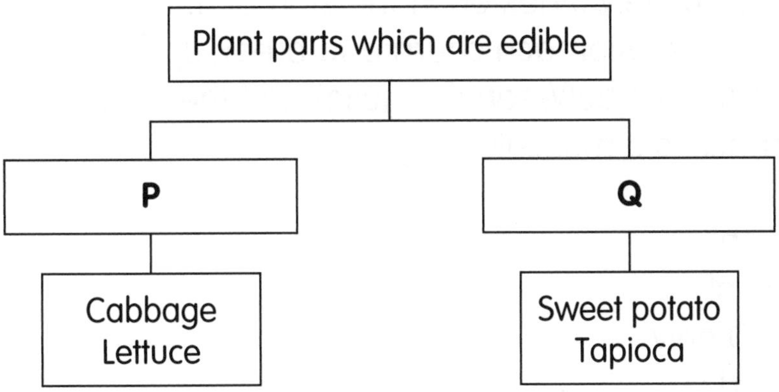

Which of the following is correct about P and Q?

	P	Q
(1)	Stems	Flowers
(2)	Flowers	Leaves
(3)	Leaves	Roots
(4)	Roots	Seeds

( )

7. The cucumber is a fruit because it ____________.

(1) is formed when the plant is mature
(2) is edible
(3) is the last stage in the plant's life cycle
(4) contains the seeds ( )

8. Which of the following statements about digestion is correct?

(A) Digestion is the process of breaking down food into simpler substances for absorption and conversion into energy.
(B) Digestion takes place in the stomach and small intestine.
(C) Blood carries the digested food to all parts of the body.
(D) Undigested food is passed out of the body through the anus.

(1) A and C only
(2) B and D only
(3) A, C and D only
(4) A, B, C and D ( )

9. Which of the following statements is true about the stomach?

(A) Food is completely digested in the stomach.
(B) The walls of the stomach churn and break up food.
(C) The stomach lies between the gullet and the small intestine.
(D) The stomach is a muscular organ.

(1) A and B only
(2) C and D only
(3) B, C and D only
(4) A, B, C and D ( )

10. Which of the following statements is true about the large intestine?

(A) The large intestine is between the small intestine and the stomach.
(B) Absorption of water happens in the large intestine.
(C) Digestion is completed in the large intestine.
(D) The large intestine is a muscular organ.

(1) A and C only
(2) B and D only
(3) A, B and D only
(4) B, C and D only ( )

11. Which of the following describes what happens to food in the mouth?

(A) Food is chewed into small pieces.
(B) Food is mixed with saliva and partially digested.
(C) Food is softened to make swallowing easier.
(D) Some absorption of digested food take place.

(1) A and B only
(2) C and D only
(3) A, B and C only
(4) A, B, C and D ( )

12. Which of the following fits the description of a long, narrow muscular tube with a rich supply of blood vessels?

(1) Gullet
(2) Small intestine
(3) Large intestine
(4) Anus ( )

13. Which of the following describes the difference between the small and large intestines?

	Small intestine	Large intestine
(A)	Digestion takes place	No digestion takes place
(B)	Absorption of digested food takes place	Absorption of water takes place
(C)	Muscular	Not muscular
(D)	Longer and narrower	Shorter and broader

(1) A and C only
(2) B and D only
(3) A, B and D only
(4) A, B, C and D ( )

14. If we eat more than we need, the digested food which is not used up by the body will be stored as body ________.

(1) muscle
(2) fat
(3) tissues
(4) fluid ( )

15. Which of the following explains why food must be completely digested before it can pass into the blood stream?

(1) Undigested food particles are too big to pass through the walls of the small intestine into the blood stream.
(2) Undigested food particles are too big to be carried in the blood.
(3) Undigested food particles contains waste materials that may poison the blood.
(4) Absorption into the blood stream will not start unless all the food is digested. ( )

Section B (20 marks)

Write your answers for each question in the blank spaces provided.

16. Circle TRUE or FALSE for each statement. [3]

(a) Digestion starts in the mouth and ends in the large intestine. TRUE / FALSE

(b) Normal faeces are solid. TRUE / FALSE

(c) Flowers are not part of a plant system. TRUE / FALSE

17. The flowchart below shows the flow of food from the mouth to the anus.

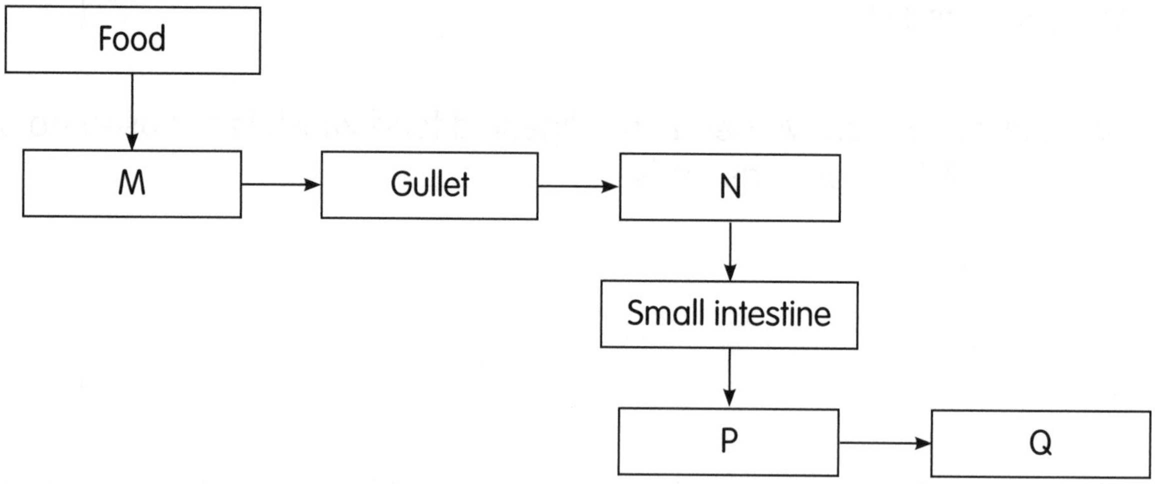

(a) Complete the flowchart by filling in the boxes with the appropriate body part. [4]

M: ____________________

N: ____________________

P: ____________________

Q: ____________________

(b) What happens to food when it is in "M"? [1]

____

(c) What process takes place at "P"? [1]

____

18. The following diagrams show edible plant parts. For each, identify the part of the plant that we eat. [6]

Plant part we eat	Name of the plant part

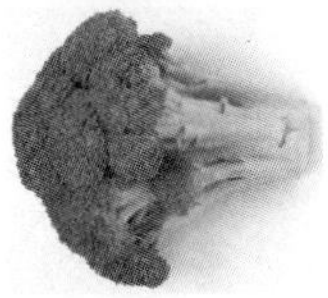	

19. State what will happen when each of the following parts is missing in a plant. [5]

Plant part	What will happen if it is missing?
Roots	
Leaves	
Flowers	
Fruits	
Seeds	

End of Paper

BLANK

Thematic Assessment 3

Marks: /100

Systems

Name: ______________________ Class: __________ Date: ______________

Section A (30 x 2 = 60 marks)

For each question, four options are given. Choose the correct answer and write down your choice, 1, 2, 3 or 4, in the brackets provided.

1. Which of the following are essential parts of the computer system?

   (A) CPU
   (B) Monitor
   (C) Printer
   (D) Keyboard

   (1) A and C only
   (2) B and D only
   (3) A, B and D only
   (4) A, B, C and D ( )

2. The following shows the parts of a plane system.

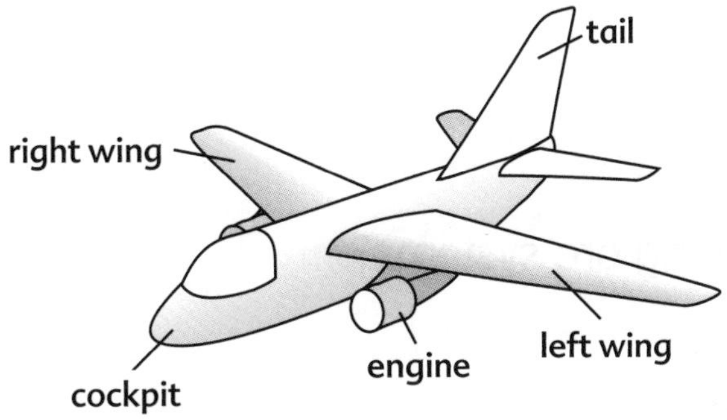

The (a) ____________ push(es) the plane forward while the (b) ____________ help(s) it glide in the air.

	(A)	(B)
(1)	Cockpit	Left and right wings
(2)	Engines	Left and right wings
(3)	Cockpit	Tail
(4)	Engines	Tail

( )

3. May makes the following model of a plane. Which of the following parts have to function in order for the model plane to fly?

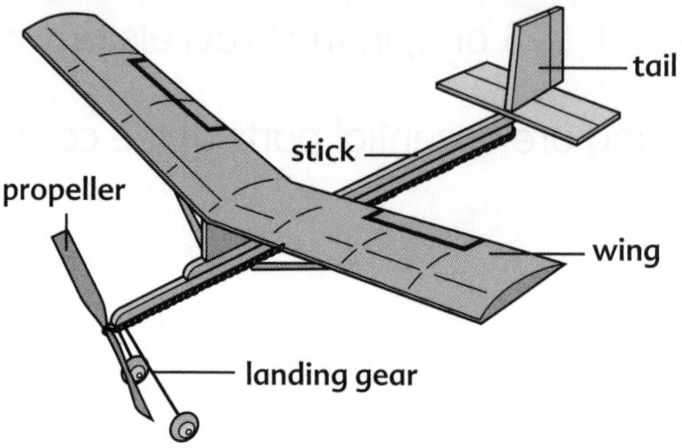

(A) Propeller
(B) Stick
(C) Wings
(D) Tail ( )

(1) A only
(2) A and C only
(3) A, B, C and D
(4) C only ( )

4. Which of the following are systems?

(A) A coin
(B) A pair of glasses
(C) An animal
(D) A stone

(1) A and D only
(2) B and C only
(3) A, B and D only
(4) A, B, C and D ( )

5. The diagram shows a mechanical pencil.

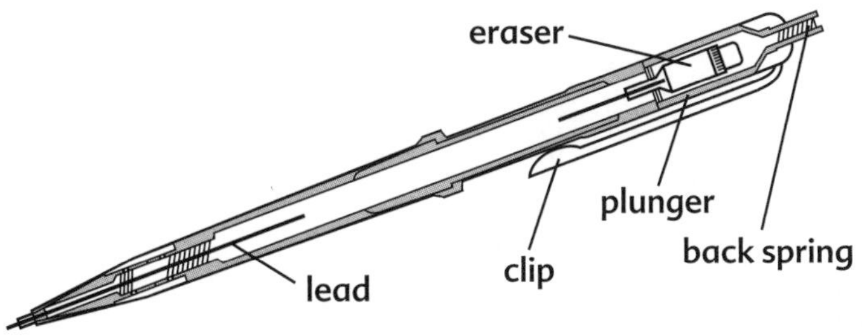

Which of the following parts, when removed from the mechanical pencil, will prevent the pencil from fulfiling its main function?

(A) Back spring
(B) Clip
(C) Eraser
(D) Plunger

(1) A and B only
(2) B and C only
(3) C and D only
(4) A and D only ( )

6. A page of a science book illustrates the following body systems.

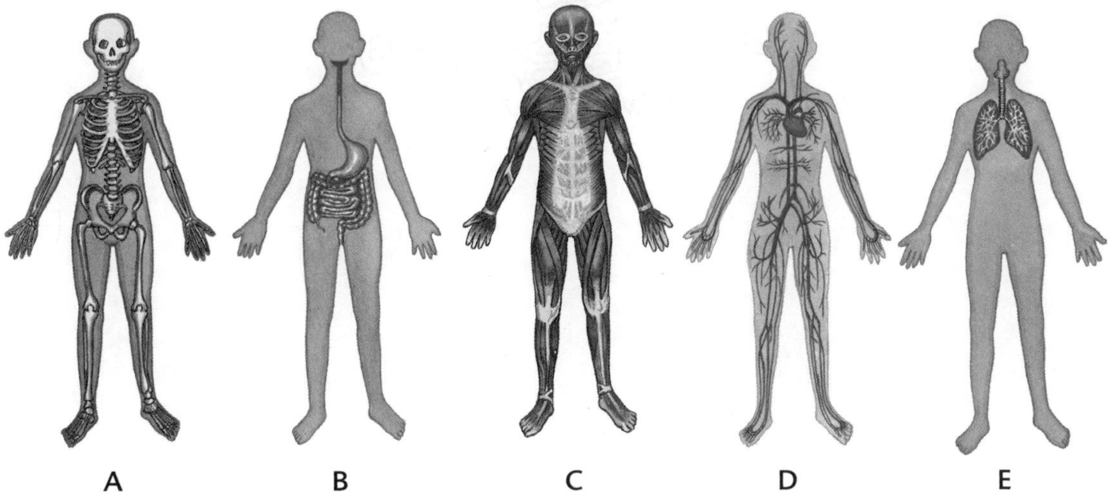

Which of the above two systems work together to produce movement of the limbs?

(1) A and C
(2) B and D
(3) A and E
(4) C and E ( )

7. Which of the following are parts of a balsam plant?

(A) Leaf
(B) Stem
(C) Flower
(D) Fruit

(1) A and B only
(2) C and D only
(3) A, C and D only
(4) A, B, C and D ( )

8. The diagram below shows the digestive system. In which part does absorption of water take place?

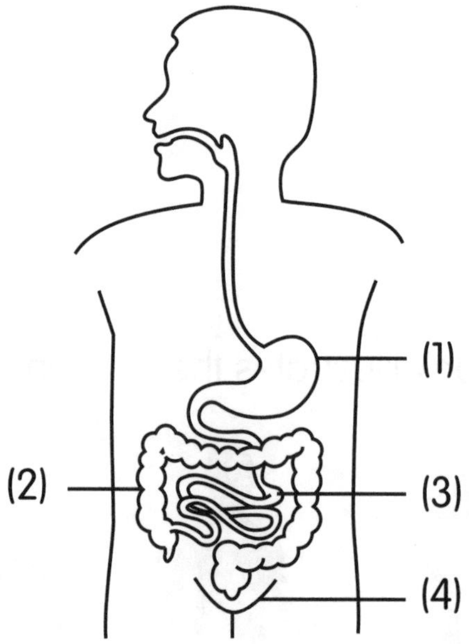

( )

The following shows a simplified diagram of a system in the human body. Questions 9 to 11 refer to this diagram.

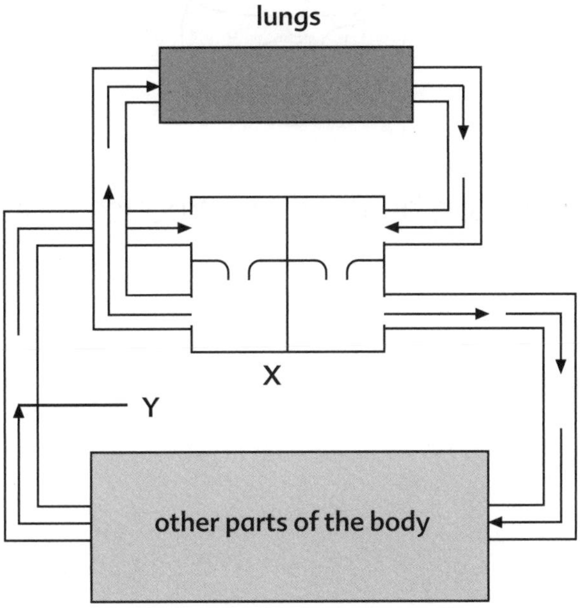

9. The diagram shows the ____________ system.

   (1) circulatory
   (2) respiratory
   (3) digestive
   (4) skeletal ( )

10. What is X?

    (1) Nose
    (2) Stomach
    (3) Heart
    (4) Muscle ( )

11. What is substance Y flowing in the system?

    (1) Air
    (2) Blood
    (3) Mucus
    (4) Food ( )

12. A fish is swimming in the following fish bowl.

Which of the following can be used to introduce more dissolved oxygen into the water?

(A) Stones
(B) Air pump
(C) Hydrilla
(D) Another fish

(1) A and C only
(2) B and C only
(3) A, C and D only
(4) B, C and D only ( )

13. Sharks use gills to take in dissolved oxygen from the water.

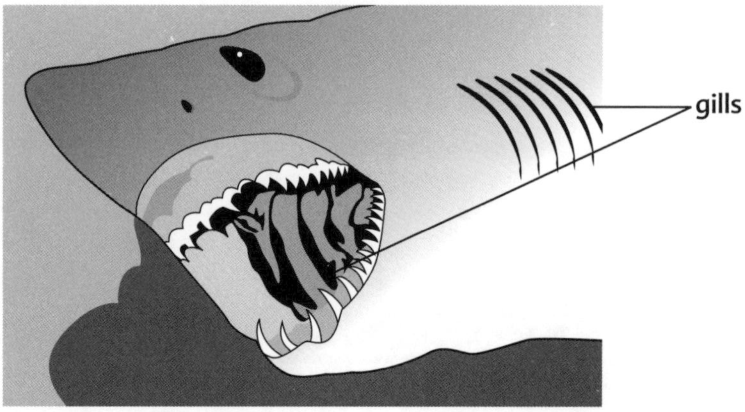

Gills are part of the ____________ system of sharks.

(1) circulatory
(2) respiratory
(3) digestive
(4) skeletal ( )

14. Which of the following will turn iodine blue-black? (Iodine changes from brown to blue-black when starch is present.)

(A) Tapioca paste
(B) Orange juice
(C) Fish meat
(D) Congee (porridge)

(1) A and D only
(2) B and C only
(3) A, C and D only
(4) B, C and D only ( )

The following shows a cactus. Questions 15 and 16 refer to this diagram.

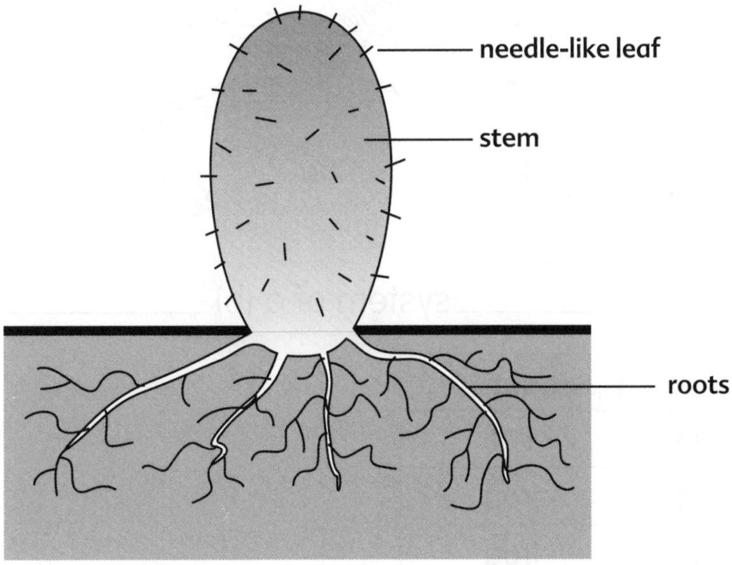

15. It has a large network of (a) _________ to collect as much (b) _________ as possible.

	(a)	(b)
(1)	needle-like leaves	oxygen
(2)	needle-like leaves	water
(3)	roots	oxygen
(4)	roots	water

( )

16. To reduce water loss in the dry desert climate, the cactus has needle-like leaves. How can it make its own food like other plants with normal leaves?

(1) Its roots can absorb a lot of nutrients from the sand.
(2) Its needle-like leaves can kill insects and suck nutrients from them.
(3) The chlorophyll on its stem can trap light energy and make food.
(4) It does not need food to survive. ( )

17. The following diagram is taken from a science book.

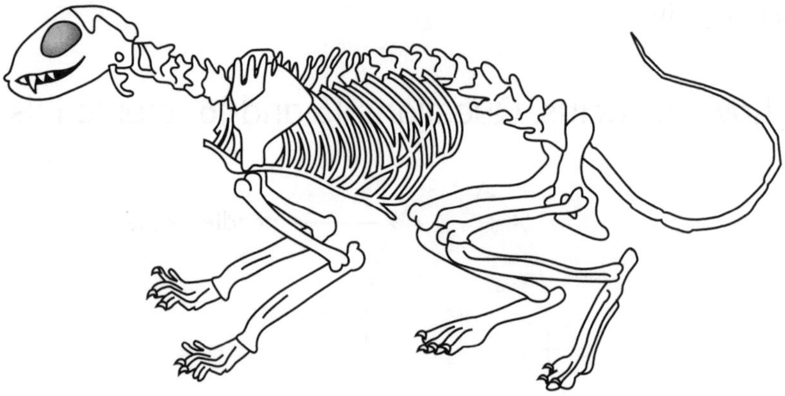

It shows the (a) __________ system of a (b) __________.

	(a)	(b)
(1)	muscular	cat
(2)	skeletal	frog
(3)	muscular	frog
(4)	skeletal	cat

( )

18. Tommy has made the following model of a human system. Which system does his model represent?

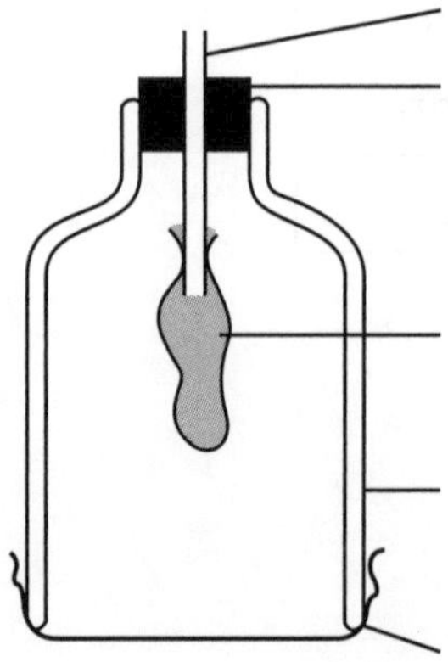

(1) Circulatory system
(2) Respiratory system
(3) Digestive system
(4) Skeletal system ( )

19. Which organs are parts of the digestive system?

(A) Brain
(B) Stomach
(C) Small intestine
(D) Large intestine

(1) A and B only
(2) B and D only
(3) A, B and C only
(4) B, C and D only ( )

20. Joe does the following experiment:

- He crumbles a cracker onto Plate 1 and adds a drop of iodine.
- Then he takes another cracker and chews it in his mouth five times before spitting the chewed-up cracker onto Plate 2. Next, he puts a drop of iodine on the cracker on Plate 2.

Which of the following observations will Joe make?

(1)

	Crumbled cracker on Plate 1	Chewed-up cracker on Plate 2
Colour of cracker + iodine	Brown	Brown

(2)

	Crumbled cracker on Plate 1	Chewed-up cracker on Plate 2
Colour of cracker + iodine	Blue-black	Blue-black

(3)

	Crumbled cracker on Plate 1	Chewed-up cracker on Plate 2
Colour of cracker + iodine	Blue-black	Brown

(4)

	Crumbled cracker on Plate 1	Chewed-up cracker on Plate 2
Colour of cracker + iodine	Brown	Blue-black

( )

Ling performs an experiment on a certain type of indoor plant. Questions 21 and 22 refer to the following results from Ling's experiment.

Plant group	Amount of light per day (hours)	Average growth in one week (centimetres)
 (1)	4	1
 (2)	6	4
 (3)	8	6
 (4)	10	3

21. What conclusion can Ling draw from her results?
    (1) The more the amount of light, the faster the plants grow.
    (2) The lesser the number of plants placed together, the faster they grow.
    (3) The plants grow best with eight hours of light per day.
    (4) The plants can only grow in indoor settings. ( )

22. Which variables must she keep constant to make her experiment fair?
    (A) Amount of water.
    (B) Type and amount of soil.
    (C) Type of plants.
    (D) Colour of light.

    (1) A, B and C only
    (2) B, C and D only
    (3) A, C and D only
    (4) A, B, C and D ( )

23. What are the functions of the stomach?

	Food crushed	Food digested	Food absorbed into bloodstream
(1)	Yes	No	No
(2)	Yes	Yes	No
(3)	Yes	Yes	Yes
(4)	No	No	Yes

( )

24. What are the functions of the small intestine?

	Food digested	Food absorbed into bloodstream
(1)	Yes	Yes
(2)	Yes	No
(3)	No	Yes
(4)	No	No

( )

25. What are the functions of the large intestine?

	Food digested	Food absorbed into bloodstream	Water absorbed into bloodstream
(1)	No	No	No
(2)	No	No	Yes
(3)	No	Yes	Yes
(4)	Yes	Yes	Yes

( )

26. The following diagram shows a body system of an elephant.

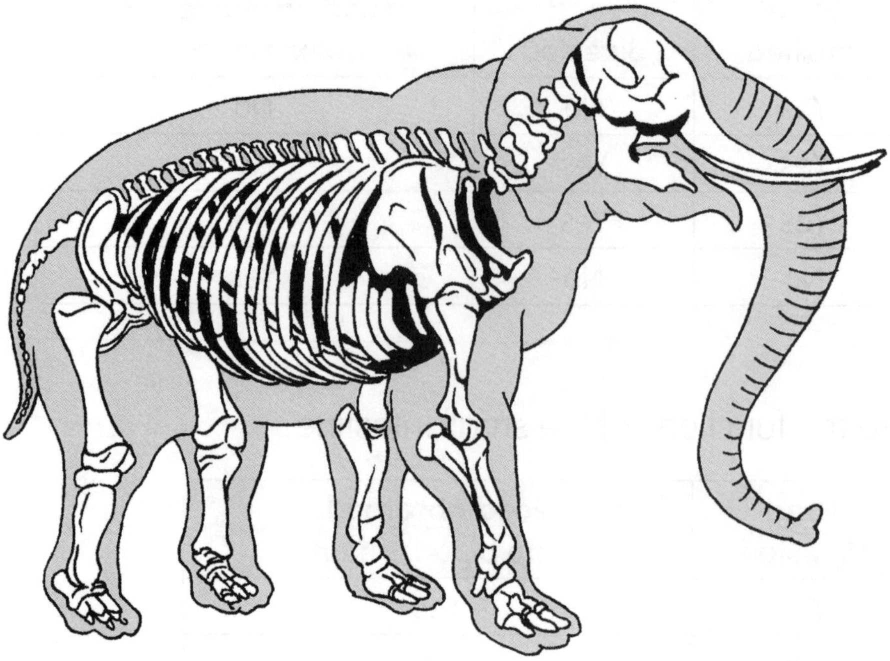

How does an elephant curl its trunk?

(1) By means of the skeletal system.
(2) By means of the muscular system.
(3) By means of the skeletal and muscular systems working together.
(4) By means of the respiratory system. ( )

27. What is the function of leaves?

(1) To hold the plant upright and reach out for sunlight.
(2) To absorb water and minerals.
(3) To receive light energy to make food.
(4) To reproduce. ( )

28. Which of the following statements about Systems is true?

(A) Systems are found in both living and non-living things.
(B) Systems are made up of parts which work together to perform a function.
(C) A system will not function properly if one or more parts are missing.
(D) The nose, windpipe, heart, brain and lungs form our respiratory system.

(1) A and B only
(2) C and D only
(3) A, B and C only
(4) A, B, C and D ( )

29. Which of the following is not a function of the skeletal system?

(1) Protects the internal organs.
(2) Helps in movement.
(3) Ensures the removal of waste products.
(4) Gives the body shape. ( )

30. Which of the following takes place after food is completely digested?

(1) It passes from the stomach to the small intestine.
(2) It passes from the small intestine to the large intestine.
(3) It is carried by the blood to all parts of the body.
(4) It passes out of the body through the anus. ( )

Section B (40 marks)

Write your answers for each question in the blank spaces provided.

31. Peter is blind. All his other sense organs are working normally. For each case, state whether he is able to tell the difference between the two given items. Explain your answers.

(a) Green tea and iced orange juice. [1]

____

(b) A floral perfume spray and an insecticide spray. [1]

____

(c) A red magic pen and a green magic pen from the same box of magic pens. [1]

____

32. The following shows a mobile phone.

(a) Why is the mobile phone an example of a system? [1]

____

(b) Name three parts of the system and state their functions. [3]

	Part	Function
(i)		
(ii)		
(iii)		

(c) The following shows a notebook.

State two similarities between a mobile phone and a notebook. [2]

Similarity 1: ____

Similarity 2: ____

(d) For a mobile phone, each key on the key pad can contain a number of characters such as those shown below.

1	2abc	3def

Give one reason why the keys on the key pad of a mobile phone are not made like the keys on the notebook. [1]

____

33. The crossword puzzle below contains the names of the different body systems. Use the clues in the table below to complete the crossword puzzle. (b) has been done for you.

	Clues
(a)	Ben rested while fishing. Suddenly the fish line tightened. Ben became excited. His heart beat faster.
(b)	Ben stood up at once. The fish line pulled with even stronger force, nearly making Ben fall into the water. He maintained his balance and stood firm against the force of the fish line.
(c)	Ben exerted all his force in his arm muscles to pull the fish line. The tug of war went on for a long time before he managed to pull a large fish up. His muscles were aching by then.
(d)	Ben was very tired. He panted very hard for air.
(e)	Ben barbecued the fish and had a satisfying meal. He belched.

[4]

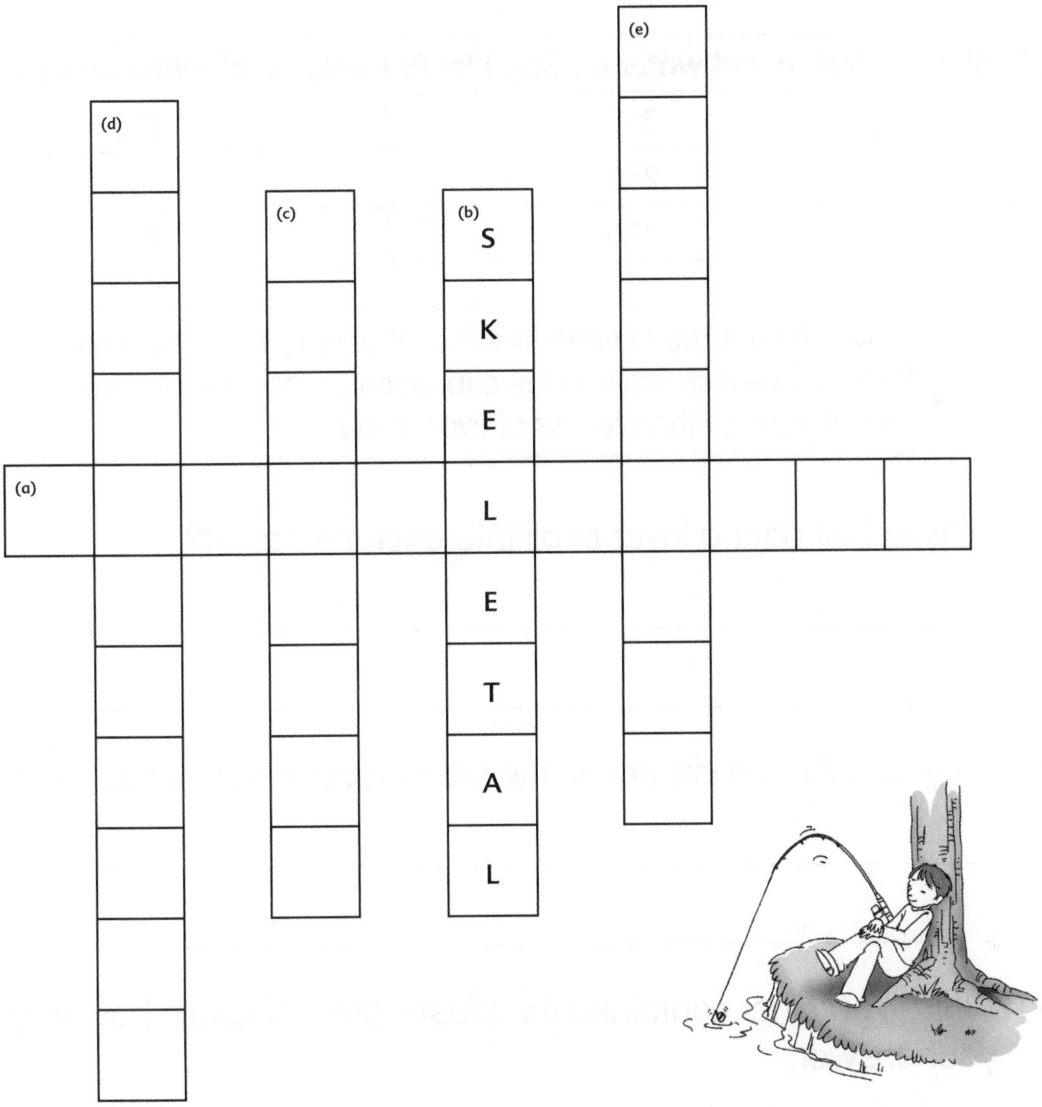

34. Ahmad said, "All living things need water to survive." Ali did not believe this statement and did the following experiment:

Ali placed one plastic plant and two real plants into three identical containers, A, B and C. He filled each container with 250 cm^3 of water. Next he poured a layer of oil into each container.

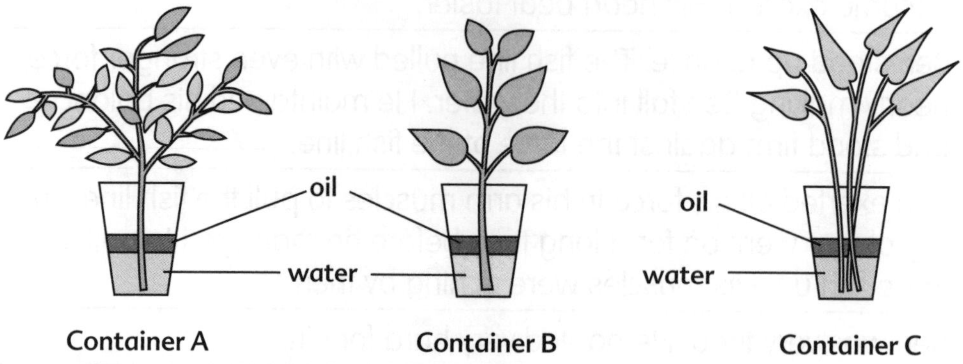

After one week, Ali recorded the volume of water in each container and tabulated his readings as shown.

Container	Volume of water on Day 1 (cm^3)	Volume of water on Day 7 (cm^3)
A	250	230
B	250	250
C	250	225

Note: When a cup of water is left on the table for a few days, there will be less water in the cup, because some water will be lost through the process of evaporation.

(a) Why did Ali pour a layer of oil into each container? [1]

____

____

(b) Why was there a change in the water level in two of the containers? [1]

____

____

(c) Which container contained the plastic plant? Explain how you got your answer. [2]

____

____

(d) What can Ali conclude from his experiment? [1]

____

Ahmad said, "Your experiment does not change what I think."

Ali said, "Why? My experiment is a fair one."

Ahmad said, "Your experiment does not show that living things will die without water."

(e) Is Ahmad's last statement true? Why? [3]

____

____

____

35. Circle TRUE or FALSE for each statement. [4]

(a) All living things are systems. TRUE / FALSE

(b) All animals use lungs to breathe. TRUE / FALSE

(c) The heart is part of the digestive system. TRUE / FALSE

(d) Chlorophyll traps energy from light. TRUE / FALSE

36. (a) Label the three parts of the leaf below. [3]

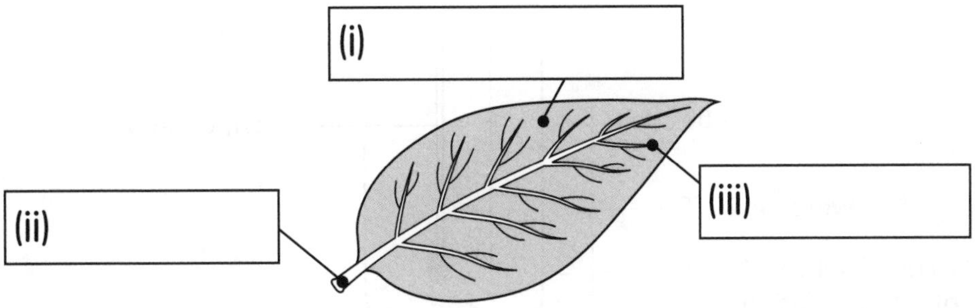

(b) Here are leaves of two different tropical plants.

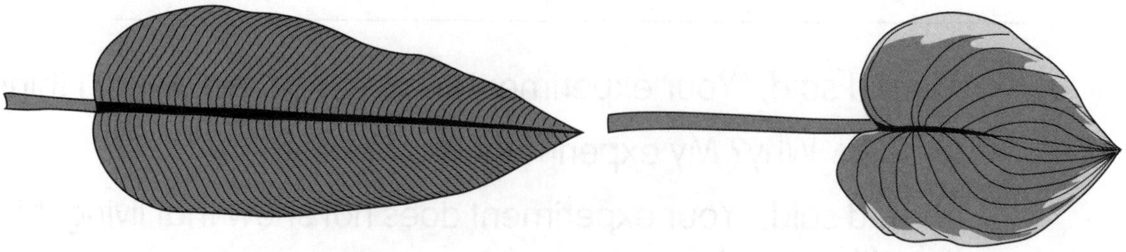

State one similarity and two differences between the leaves. [3]

Similarity
(a) ____________________

Bird of paradise leaf — Hosta leaf

Two differences	
(a) __________	__________
(b) __________	__________

37. Sam added 2 cm^3 of saliva to 10 cm^3 of starch solution at 20 °C as shown below.

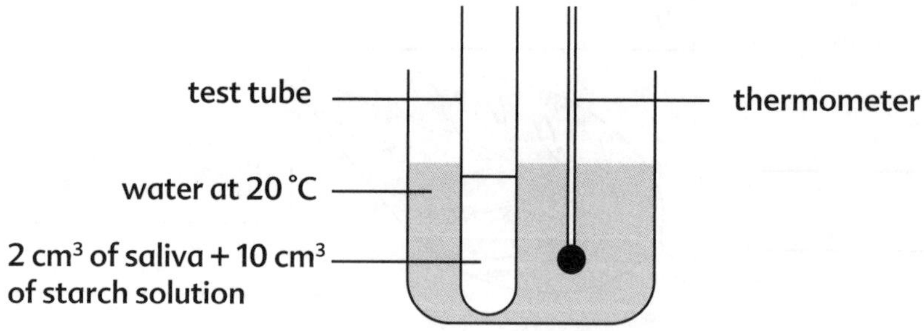

Every 30 seconds, Sam takes out a drop of liquid from the test tube and tests it for starch with iodine solution. Iodine turns blue-black if starch is present, and remains brown if starch is absent.

Sam then repeated his experiment, this time at 40 °C. The following are his results.

Time (s)		30	60	90	120	150	180	210
Colour of the iodine test	20 °C	Blue-black	Blue-black	Blue-black	Blue-black	Blue-black	Blue-black	Brown
	40 °C	Blue-black	Blue black	Blue-black	Brown	Brown	Brown	Brown

(a) In the human body:

(i) Where is saliva found? [1]

____

(ii) What is its function? [1]

____

(b) In Sam's experiment, when did the iodine stop turning blue-black at:

(i) 20 °C? [1]

____

(ii) 40 °C? [1]

____

(c) Why did the iodine stop turning blue-black? [2]

____

____

(d) Which temperature, 20 °C or 40 °C, is the better temperature for saliva to act on starch? Explain your answer. [2]

____

____

End of Paper

BLANK

Test 8
Interactions

Marks: /50

Topics:
- Magnets and their characteristics
- Making magnets
- Magnets, magnets, everywhere

Name: ________________ Class: ________ Date: ____________

Section A (15 x 2 = 30 marks)

For each question, four options are given. Choose the correct answer and write down your choice, 1, 2, 3 or 4, in the brackets provided.

1. Which one of the following is attracted to a magnet?

   (1) Plastic keychain
   (2) Wooden ruler
   (3) Steel tie pin
   (4) Eraser ( )

2. Which direction will a freely hung magnet point to?

   (1) North–South
   (2) South–East
   (3) East–West
   (4) West–North ( )

3. Which of the following is true about a magnet?

   (A) Magnets attract magnetic materials.
   (B) All magnets have two poles — north and south.
   (C) Like poles of a magnet attract.
   (D) Magnets can only be made from iron.

   (1) A and B only
   (2) C and D only
   (3) A and D only
   (4) B and C only ( )

4. Which of the following actions will destroy a magnet?

(1) Dropping it once.
(2) Hammering it many times.
(3) Putting it in ice.
(4) Letting it interact with non-magnetic materials. ( )

5. What are lodestones?

(A) Natural magnets
(B) Temporary magnets
(C) Permanent magnets
(D) Special stones

(1) A and B only
(2) C and D only
(3) A and C only
(4) B and D only ( )

6. A magnet was used to stroke nails made of four different materials.

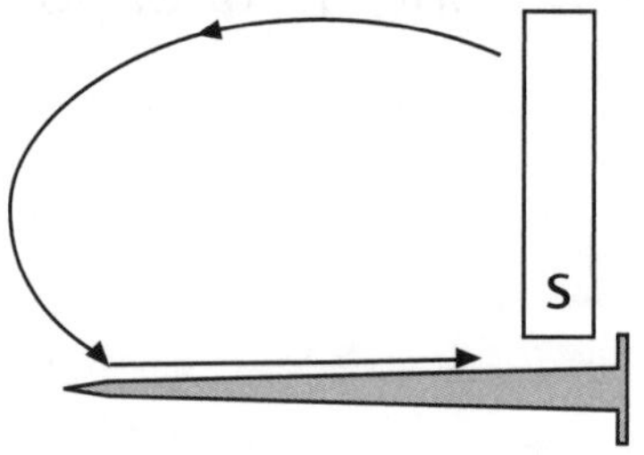

Which of the following will become a magnet?

(A) Copper nail
(B) Iron nail
(C) Steel nail
(D) Nickel nail

(1) A and D only
(2) B and C only
(3) B, C and D only
(4) A, B and D only ( )

7. The following experiment was set up to find out the identity of bar P.

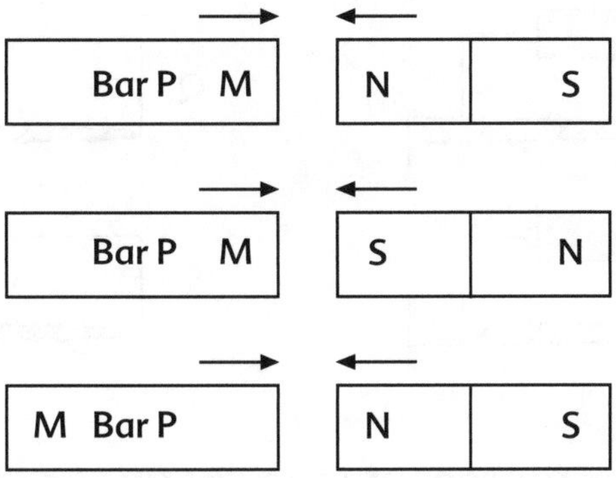

Bar P was pulled towards the magnet in all three set-ups.
Which of the following is a probable conclusion for the experiment?

(A) Bar P is a magnet.
(B) M is the south-pole of Bar P.
(C) Bar P is made of magnetic material.
(D) The magnet used in the experiment is not functioning properly.

(1) C only
(2) D only
(3) A and B only
(4) C and D only ( )

8. Which of the following is not a use of magnets?

(1) To keep lids closed in bags.
(2) To enable compasses to work.
(3) To separate good conductors of heat from poor conductors of heat.
(4) To enable ATM cards to store information. ( )

9. Study the experimental set-up below.

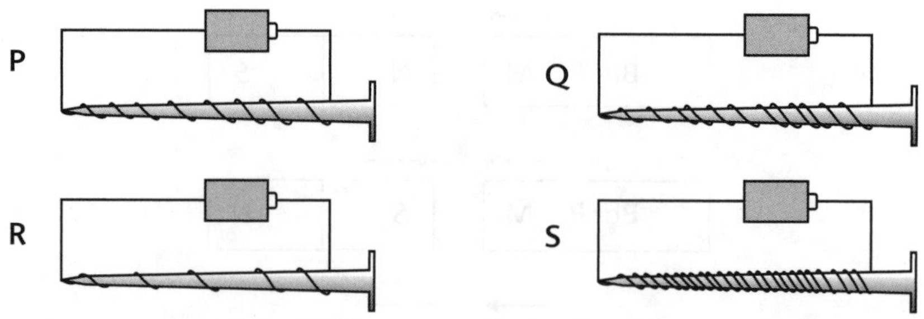

Which of the following represents the magnetic strength of the nail, from the weakest to the strongest?

(1) SPQR
(2) RPQS
(3) PQRS
(4) QRSP ( )

10. Two bar magnets are placed near each other as shown in the diagram.

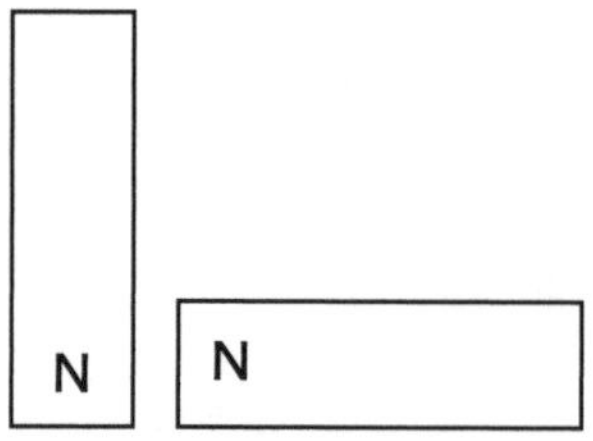

What would the reactions of the magnets be?

(1) They will attract each other.
(2) They will repel each other.
(3) Nothing will happen.
(4) They will move towards the left. ( )

11. Which of the following shows the response of a bar magnet which is placed near iron filings?

(1) 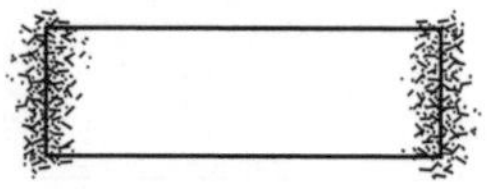

(2) 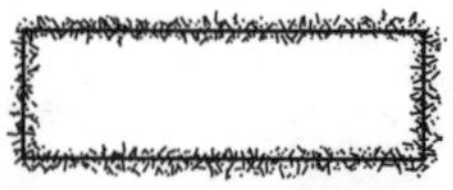

(3) 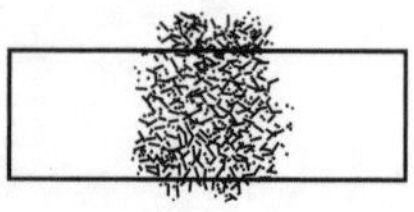

(4) 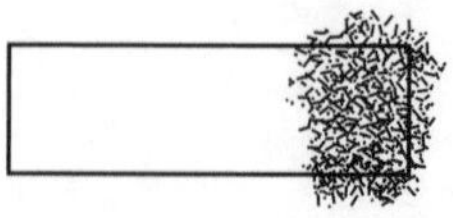

( )

12. The diagram below shows a U-shaped magnet and a horseshoe magnet.

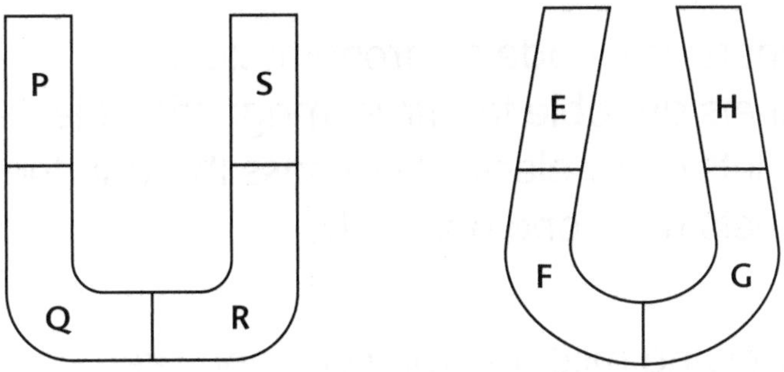

Which parts of the magnets have the strongest magnetic force?

	U-shaped magnet	Horseshoe magnet
(1)	PQ	EF
(2)	QR	FG
(3)	SR	HG
(4)	PS	EH

( )

13. Walter owns a very powerful magnet. He wanted to know which material, when placed between his magnet and the iron nails, will allow the magnet to attract the nails.

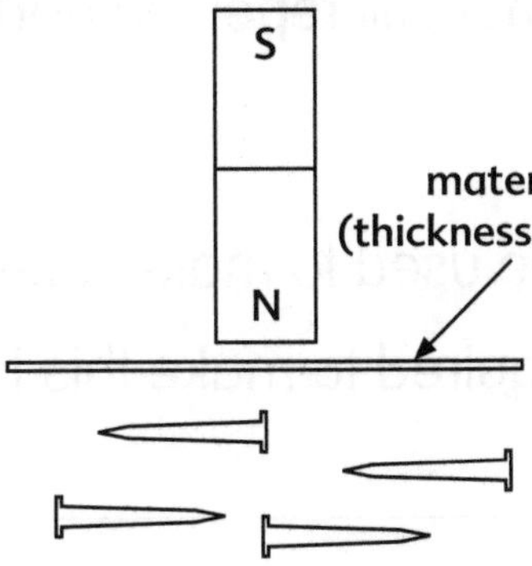

Note. A magnetic material will block the magnetic force of a magnet.

Which of the following is likely to be material X?

(A) Paper
(B) Plastic sheet
(C) Plywood
(D) Glass

(1) A and B only
(2) C and D only
(3) A and C only
(4) A, B, C and D ( )

14. Electromagnets are used to separate objects in dump yards. Which of the following explains why this is possible?

(1) Electromagnets are made of strong metals.
(2) Electromagnets are able to attract magnetic objects.
(3) Electromagnets allow electricity to pass through them.
(4) Electromagnets have one pole only. ( )

15. Which of the following mixtures may be separated by a magnet?

(1) Needles and iron nails.
(2) Copper and aluminium strips.
(3) Steel pins and sand.
(4) Plastic buttons and beans. ( )

Section B (20 marks)

Write your answers for each question in the blank spaces provided.

16. Circle TRUE or FALSE for each statement. [3]

(a) A horseshoe magnet has two poles. TRUE / FALSE

(b) A magnet may be made from any metal. TRUE / FALSE

(c) The north-pole of a magnet will repel the north-pole of another magnet. TRUE / FALSE

17. The electrical method may be used to make a temporary magnet.

(a) What three things are required to make this temporary magnet? [1]

____

(b) What is the name of a magnet made using the electrical method? [1]

____

(c) Explain how you can test if an iron rod has been magnetised. [2]

____

____

(d) Suggest two ways to increase the magnetic strength of the iron rod. [2]

____

____

18. You are given some iron nails and four bar magnets. In the space below, explain how you could conduct an experiment to find out which magnet is the strongest and which is the weakest. [3]

19. Study the graphic organiser below.

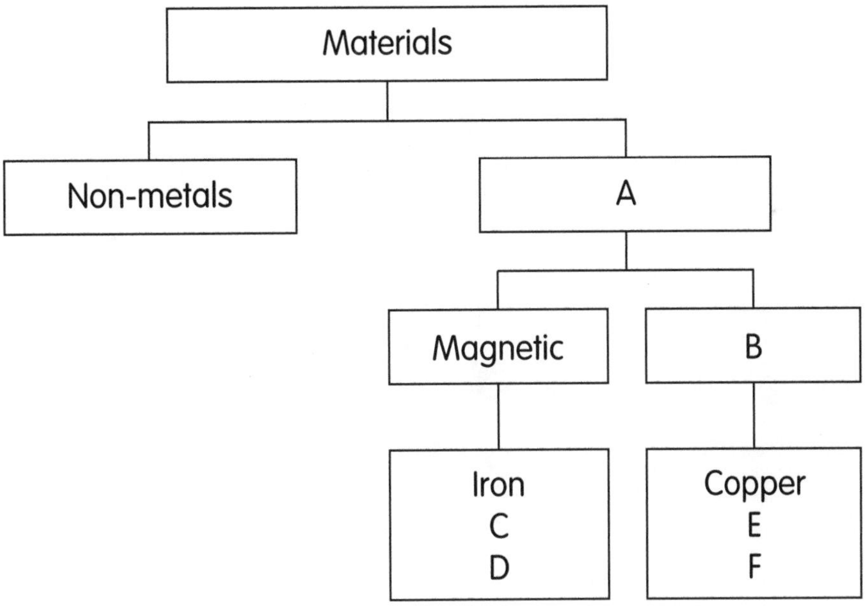

What could A, B, C, D, E and F be? [6]

A: ____________ D: ____________

B: ____________ E: ____________

C: ____________ F: ____________

End of Paper

BLANK

Thematic Assessment 4

Marks: /100

Interactions

Name: ______________________ Class: __________ Date: ______________

Section A (30 x 2 = 60 marks)

For each question, four options are given. Choose the correct answer and write down your choice, 1, 2, 3 or 4, in the brackets provided.

1. Which one of the following are not magnetic materials?

   (A) Copper
   (B) Steel
   (C) Iron
   (D) Aluminium

   (1) A and C only
   (2) B and D only
   (3) A and D only
   (4) B and C only ( )

2. Soo Feng bought a souvenir during her recent holidays. It was a colourful metallic brooch. When she brought the north-pole of her bar magnet near the brooch, nothing happened. Which of the following could be the reason?

   (1) The pole of the magnet used was incorrect.
   (2) The colours on the brooch prevented the magnet from attracting it.
   (3) The brooch was made of non-magnetic material.
   (4) The magnet used was very weak. ( )

3. Which of the following does not have a magnet in it?

   (1) Telephone
   (2) Torch
   (3) Computer
   (4) Mobile phone ( )

4. Which of the following will cause a magnet to lose its magnetism?

(A) Heating it.
(B) Using it constantly.
(C) Dropping it.
(D) Putting it in water.

(1) A and B only
(2) C and D only
(3) A and C only
(4) B and D only ( )

5. Which of the following is true about magnets?

(A) There are different types of magnets.
(B) Magnets attract objects made of magnetic materials.
(C) Every magnet has two poles.
(D) The attraction of a magnet is strongest at its poles.

(1) A and B only
(2) C and D only
(3) A, C and D only
(4) A, B, C and D ( )

6. Which of the following is true about the magnetic poles of a magnet?

(1) They exert the greatest magnetic force.
(2) They lose their magnetism first.
(3) They are the only part of the magnet that attract magnetic objects.
(4) They are sensitive to changes in temperature. ( )

7. Which of the following is true for a magnet that has been divided into two halves?

(1) The two halves are not magnets.
(2) Each of the halves is a stronger magnet than the original magnet.
(3) Each of the halves is a weaker magnet than the original magnet.
(4) Each of the halves has a north-pole and south-pole. ( )

8. Study the diagram below carefully.

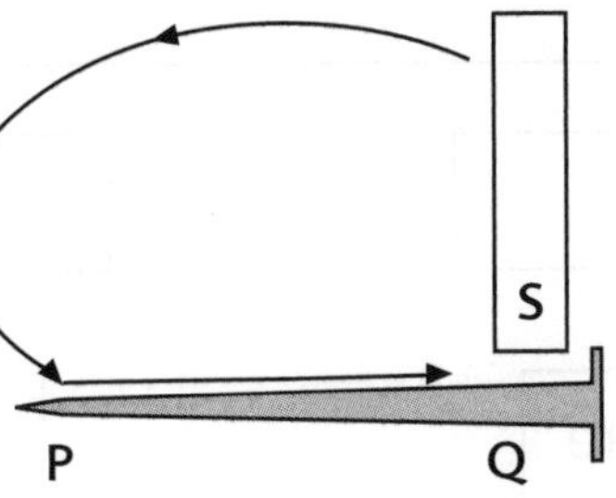

Which of the following is true of P and Q?

	P	Q
(1)	North-pole	North-pole
(2)	South-pole	North-pole
(3)	South-pole	South-pole
(4)	No established pole	No established pole

( )

9. Which of the following are ways to make a temporary magnet?

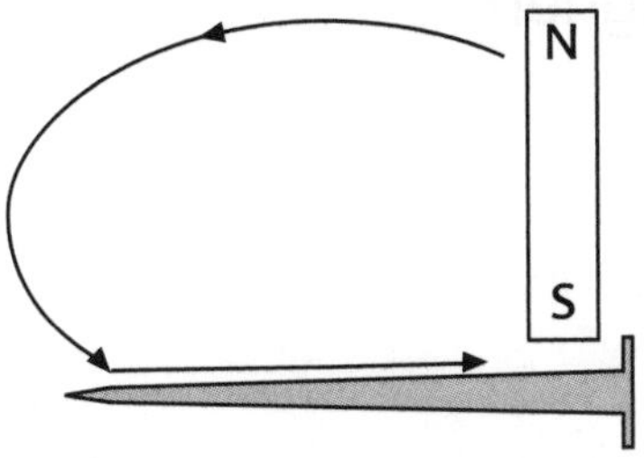

A

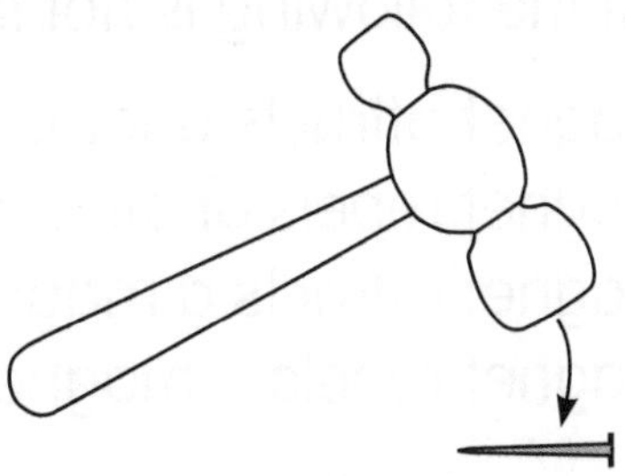

B

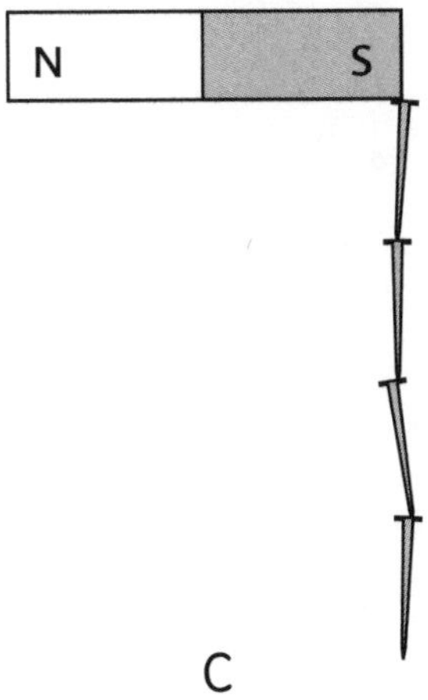

C

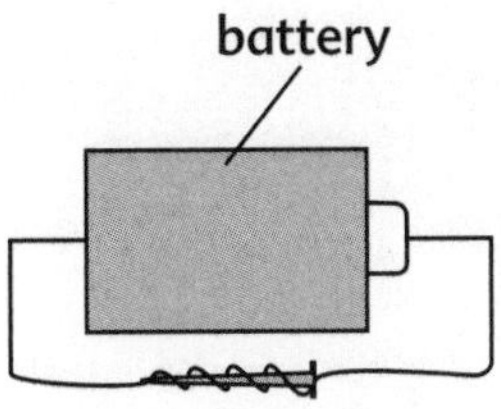

D

(1) A and C only
(2) B and C only
(3) B and D only
(4) A, C and D only

( )

10.

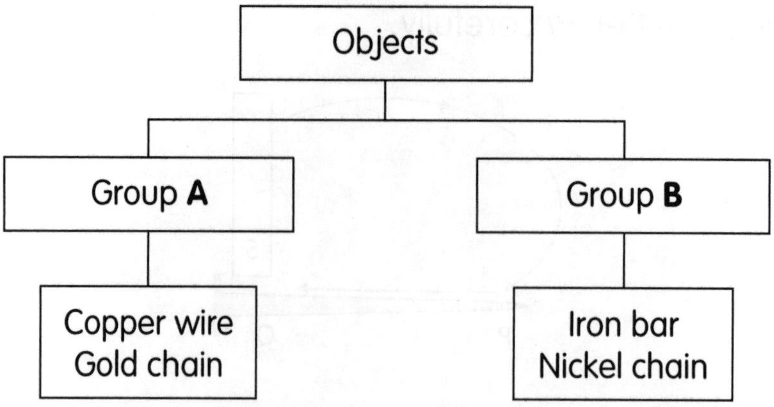

Which of the following may be placed in Groups A and B?

	Group A	Group B
(1)	Silver clip	Plastic band
(2)	Plastic band	Aluminium foil
(3)	Aluminium foil	Steel chip
(4)	Steel chip	Cobalt ring

( )

11. Which of the following is not true about a magnet?

(1) A magnet attracts another magnet.
(2) A magnet repels another magnet.
(3) A magnet attracts a magnetic object.
(4) A magnet repels a magnetic object. ( )

12. The diagram below shows five ring magnets looped through a wooden rod.

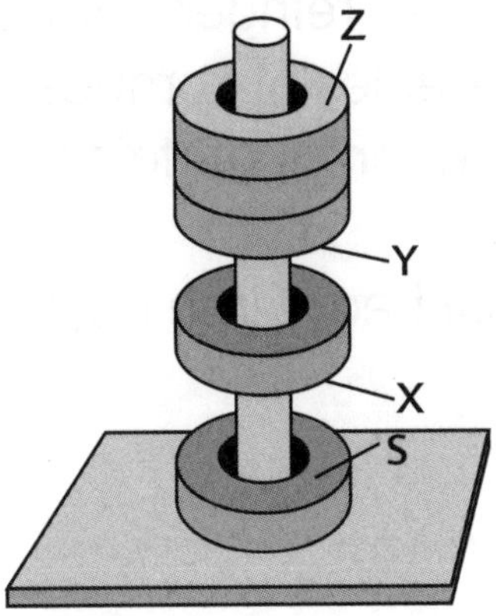

What are the poles labeled X, Y and Z?

	X	Y	Z
(1)	North	North	South
(2)	North	South	North
(3)	South	North	South
(4)	South	North	North

( )

13. The diagram below shows a bar magnet attracting two paper clips.

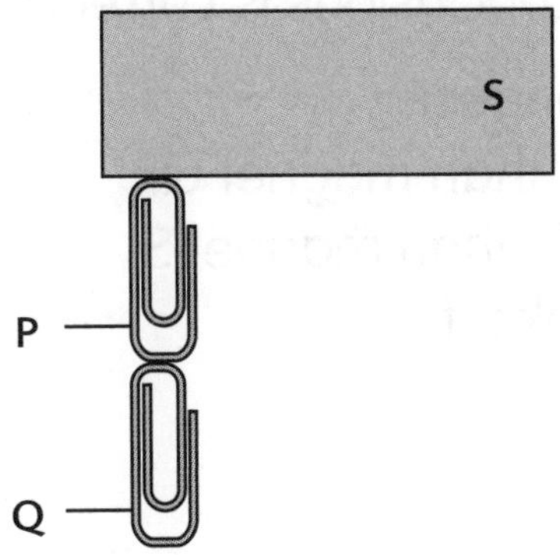

What are the poles P and Q?

	P	Q
(1)	North	North
(2)	North	South
(3)	South	North
(4)	South	South

( )

14. Which of the following are true about the uses of magnets?

(A) Magnets help the doors of refrigerators to remain shut.
(B) Magnets enable the needles of compasses to work properly.
(C) Magnets are used to separate metals from non-metals in dump yards.
(D) Magnets are used to lift heavy iron objects in factories.

(1) A and B only
(2) C and D only
(3) A, B and D only
(4) A, B, C and D ( )

15. An experiment was done to find out the strength of four magnets. The results are shown in the table below.

Magnet	Number of pins attracted
P	3
Q	5
R	6
S	2

Which of the following conclusions is correct?

(A) Magnet R is the strongest.
(B) Magnet P is weaker than magnet Q.
(C) Magnet Q is stronger than magnet S.
(D) Magnet S is the weakest.

(1) A and D only
(2) B and C only
(3) A, B and D only
(4) A, B, C and D ( )

16. Two magnets were brought near each other. Which one of the following is correct?

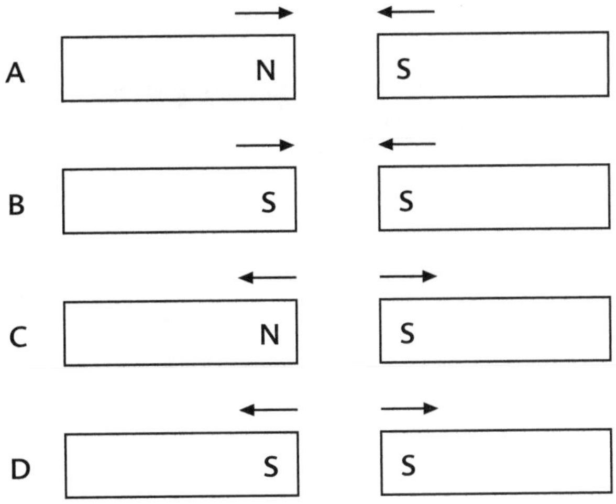

(1) A and B only
(2) C and D only
(3) A and D only
(4) B and C only ( )

17. Which nail will attract the greatest number of paper clips?

(1)
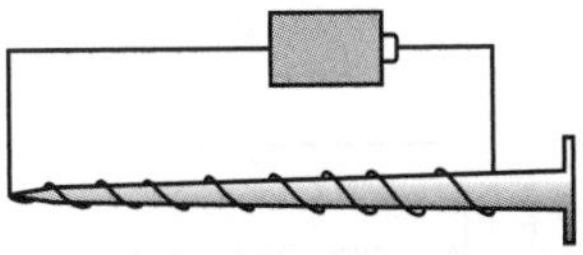

(2)
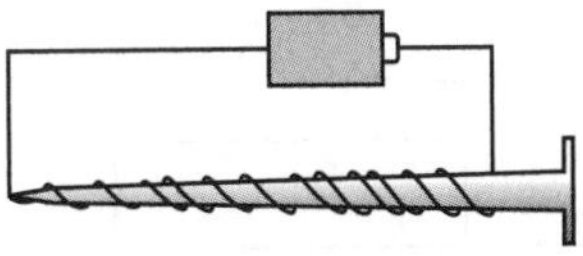

(3)
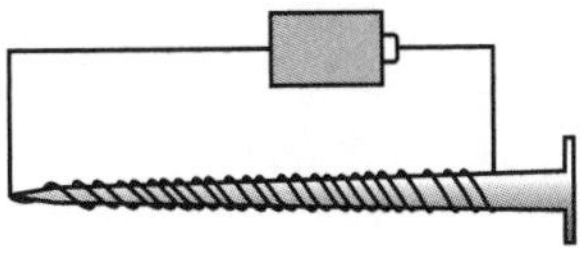

(4)
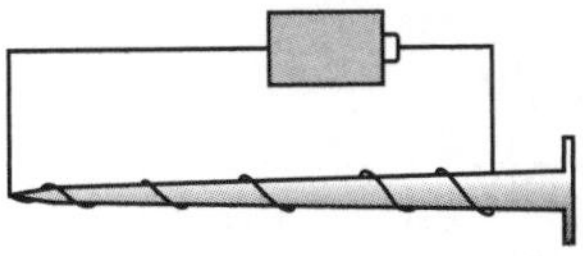

( )

18. Four rods were stroked using a bar magnet. Each rod was made from a different material. Which of the rods will become a magnet?

(1) Wooden rod
(2) Steel rod
(3) Plastic rod
(4) Aluminium rod ( )

19. The diagram shows a bar magnet hung such that it could turn freely. In which direction will it come to rest?

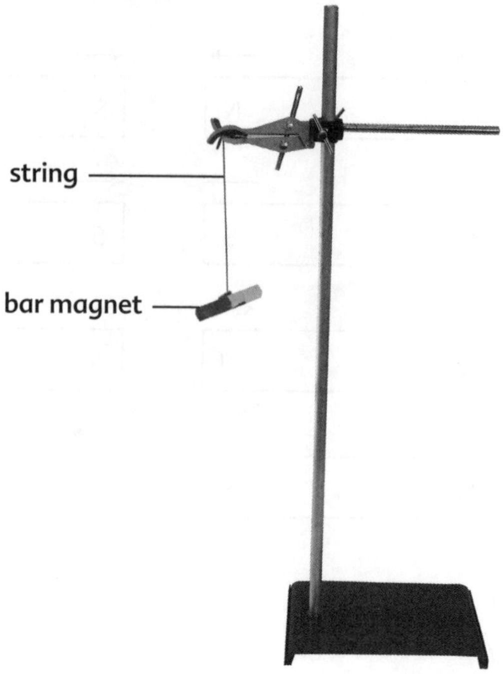

(1) North–South
(2) South–East
(3) East–West
(4) North–West

( )

20. You are given a magnet and an iron bar. Which of the following will occur?

(A)
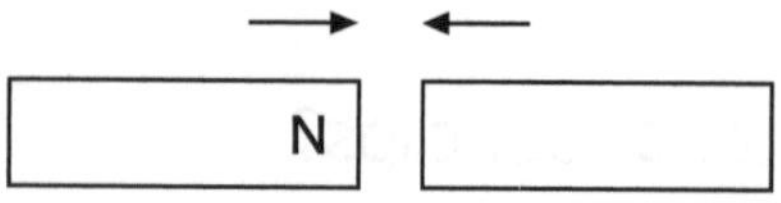

(B)
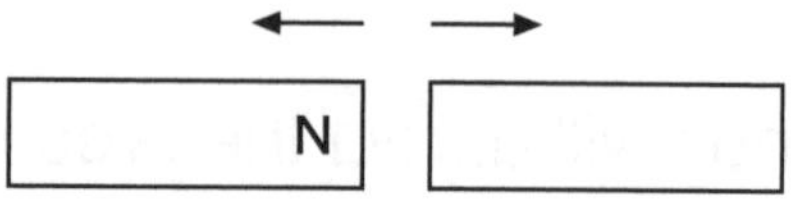

(C)
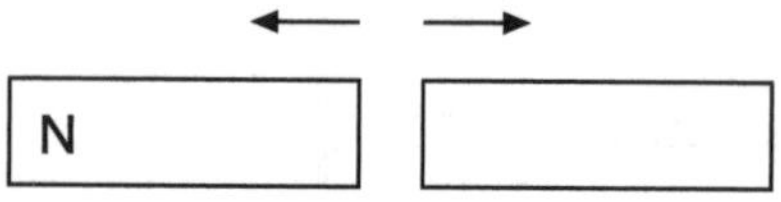

(D)
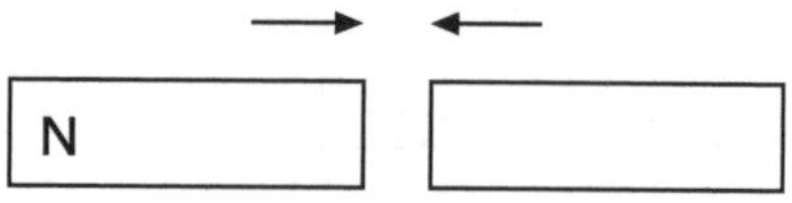

(1) A and B only
(2) C and D only
(3) A and D only
(4) B and C only

( )

21. A magnet is brought near four boxes made of four different kinds of materials as shown in the diagram below. In which of the boxes will the iron nails not respond to the magnet?

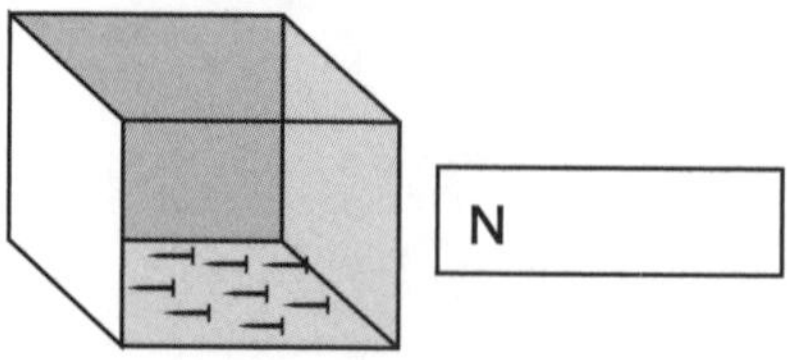

(1) Plastic box
(2) Glass box
(3) Paper box
(4) Iron box

( )

22. An iron nail was magnetised using the set-up given below.

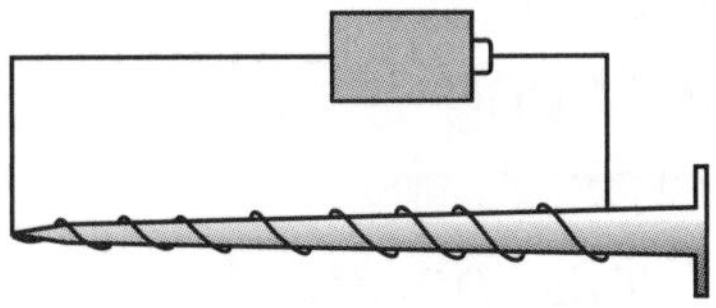

The iron nail was then removed from the set-up and placed near some iron filings. Which of the following is true?

(1) The iron filings will be attracted to the centre of the iron nail.
(2) The iron filings will be attracted to the two ends of the iron nail.
(3) The iron nail will not attract any iron filings.
(4) The iron nail will attract the iron filing for a short while only. ( )

23. Which of the following makes use of magnets?

(1) Computer mouse
(2) Scissors
(3) Washing machine
(4) Frying pan ( )

24. A strip of metal was found to be able to hold a piece of paper against white board A but not white board B. Which of the following is true?

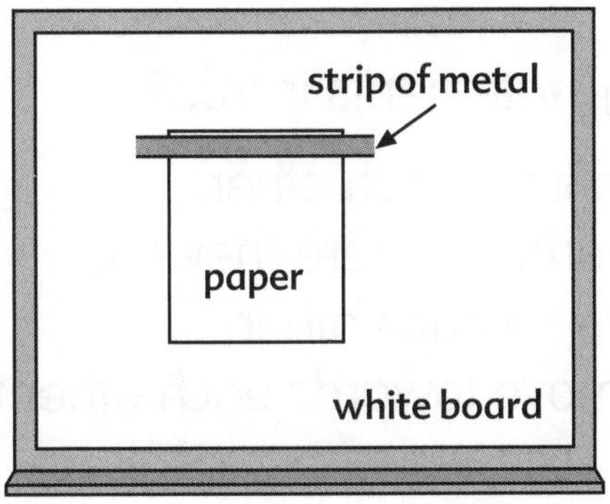

(A) White Board A is made of magnetic material.
(B) White Board B is made of non-magnetic material.
(C) The strip of metal is a magnet.
(D) The strip of metal is heavier than White Board B but lighter than White Board A.

(1) A and B only
(2) C and D only
(3) A, B and C only
(4) A, B, C and D ( )

25. Which one of the following groups of objects can be attracted by a magnet?

(1) Needle, safety pin, screws
(2) Cork, iron nails, rubber bung
(3) Stapler, paper clips, eraser
(4) Copper wire, thumb tacks, pendant ( )

26. Which of the following statements is correct?

(A) Magnetism from a magnet cannot pass through magnetic materials.
(B) Lodestones are temporary magnets.
(C) The most effective way of separating iron nails from steel nails is to use a magnet.
(D) A lodestone has only one pole.

(1) A only
(2) A and B only
(3) A and C only
(4) B and D only ( )

27. The diagram below shows two bar magnets which have been brought near each other.

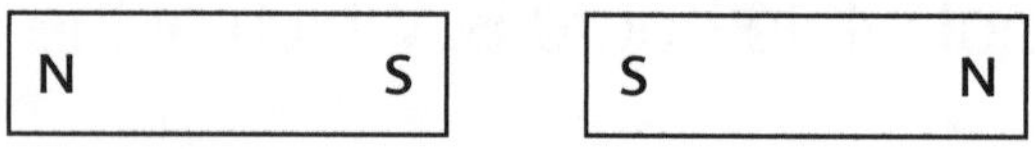

Which of the following statements is true?

(1) The magnets will attract each other.
(2) The magnets will remain where they are.
(3) The magnets will repel each other.
(4) The magnets will move towards each other first and then move away from each other. ( )

28. The diagram below shows four dishes filled with dust particles obtained from different metals.

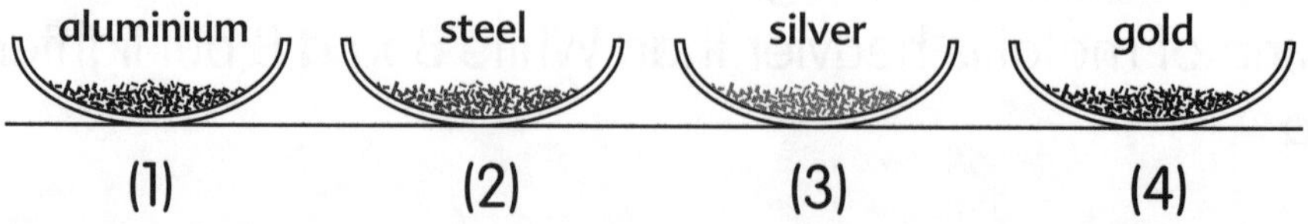

A magnet is lowered into each dish. From which dish would the contents be attracted to the magnet? ( )

29. Two iron nails were magnetised by two similar magnets as shown in the diagrams below.

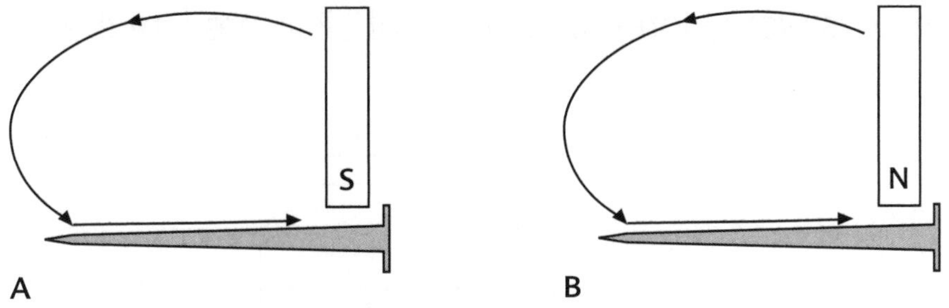

What would be the poles at A and B?

	A	B
(1)	North	North
(2)	South	South
(3)	North	South
(4)	South	North

( )

30. Which of the following is correct?

	Non-magnetic material	
	Metal	Non-metal
(1)	Iron	Rubber
(2)	Steel	Plastic
(3)	Aluminium	Styrofoam
(4)	Nickel	Wood

( )

Section B (40 marks)

Write your answers for each question in the blank spaces provided.

31. Some iron nails were stored in a bottle of oil to prevent the nails from rusting.

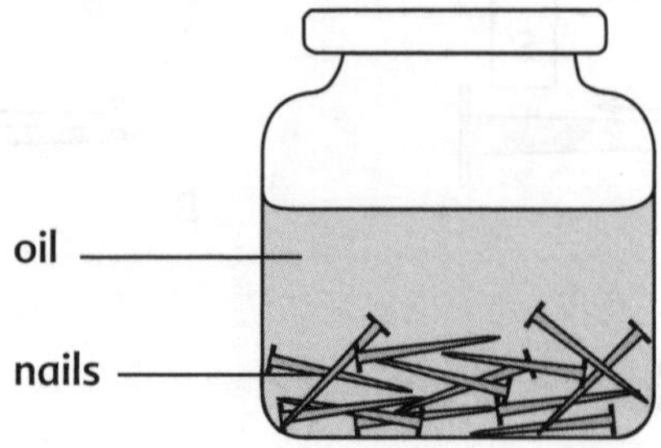

(a) What is the best way to remove a few nails without having to touch the oil in the bottle? [2]

____

____

(b) Which property of the iron nails allows them to be removed in this way? [1]

____

(c) Would the method in (a) work if another liquid such as water, instead of oil, was used to store the nails? [1]

____

(d) Can the same method be used if the objects in the oil were copper nails? Why? [2]

____

____

32. The diagram below shows three ring magnets.

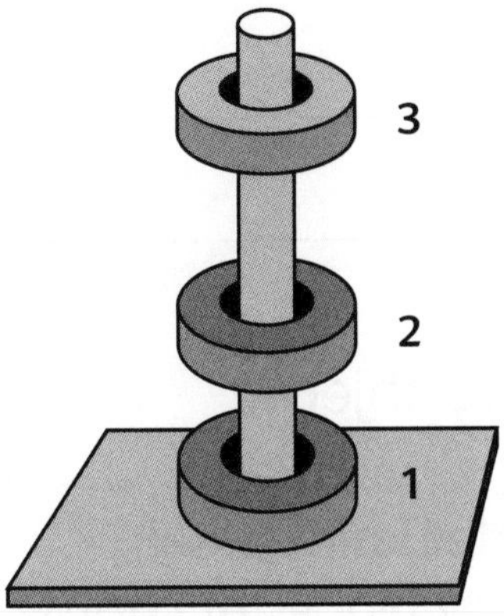

(a) Magnets 2 and 3 float. Why is this so? [3]

____

____

____

(b) What must be done to have all the magnets touching each other? [1]

____

33. You are given two bar magnets A and B as shown below.

(a) Describe a simple experiment you would carry out to find out which is the stronger magnet. Draw diagrams to support your answer. [3]

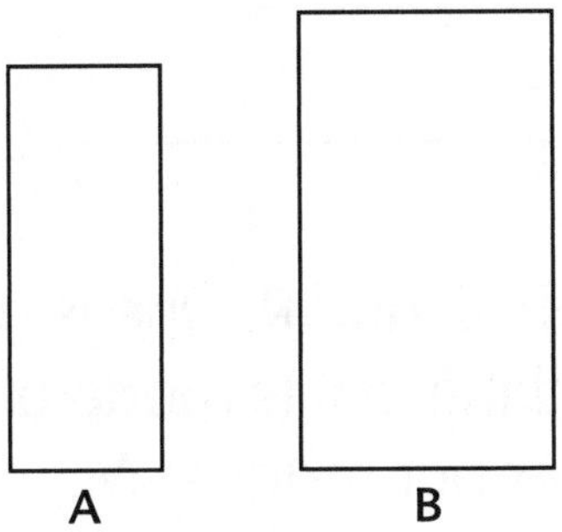

(b) What are two variables that must be kept constant for this experiment? [2]

____

____

34. You are given the following objects:

Plastic fork	**Butter knife (steel)**	**Steel needles**
Nickel clips	**Small pieces of copper wires**	**Nickel coins**
Silver pendant	**Aluminium cans**	**Steel nail clipper**
	Gold ring	

(a) Classify the objects above using the table below. [5]

Magnetic	Non-magnetic

(b) Describe how you would check that your classification is correct. [2]

____

____

35. You are given three bars P, Q and R. One is a magnet, another is made of magnetic material, and the last is made of non-magnetic material. You are also given another bar magnet M.

(a) Describe how you would find out which types of materials P, Q and R are made of. [4]

____

____

____

____

(b) Bar P was found to be made of magnetic material. How would you turn bar P into a temporary magnet, using only the materials given above? [1]

____

(c) State two precautions you must take in order for the procedure in (b) to be successful. [2]

____

____

36. An experiment was set up as shown in the diagram below. When different numbers of batteries were inserted into tube A, the temporary magnet could pick up different numbers of paper clips. The results are shown in the table below.

Number of batteries	Number of paper clips attracted
1	3
2	6
3	9
4	12
5	15

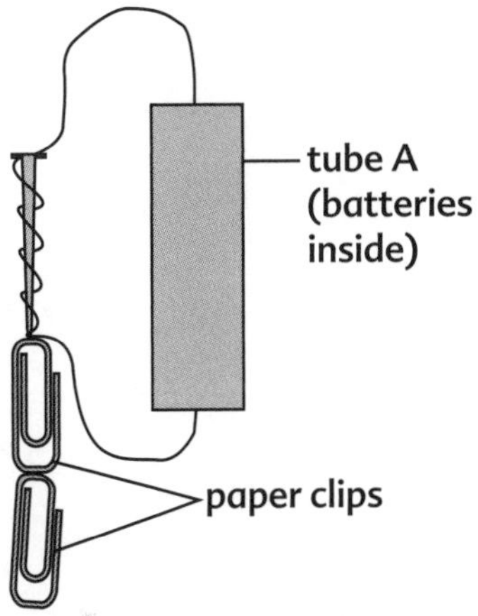

(a) Transfer the information from the table to the line graph below by:

(i) Labelling the axes of the graph. (Write in the boxes provided.) [2]

(ii) Plotting the points in the graph (one example has been done for you). [4]

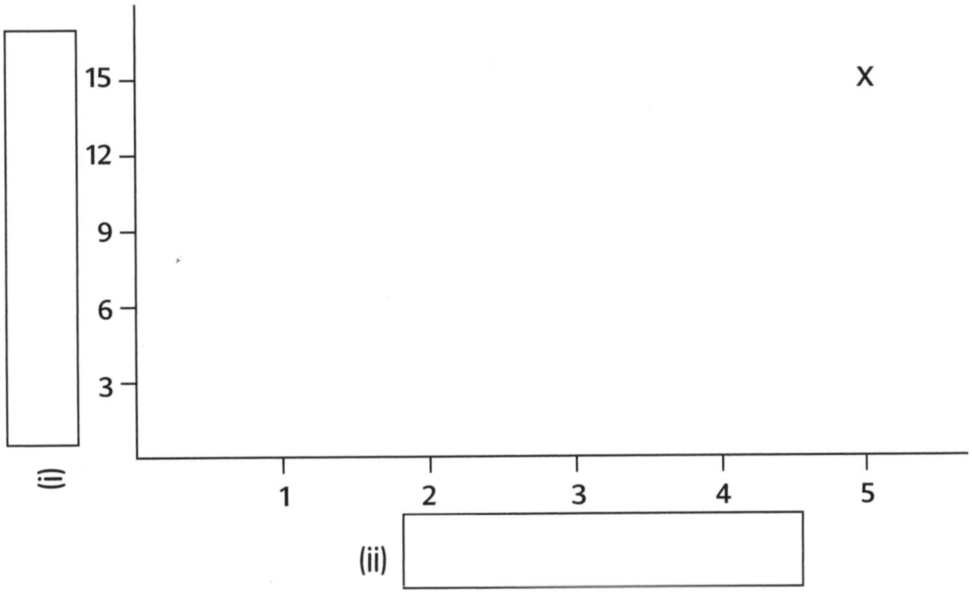

(b) What conclusion can you draw from this experiment? [1]

____

(c) A temporary magnet can also be made by stroking the iron nail with a bar magnet. An experiment was conducted with a temporary magnet made by the stroking method. Complete the table below using the numbers 8, 1, 3 and 12. [4]

Number of strokes	Number of paper clips attracted
10	
20	
40	
80	

End of Paper

Test 9

Energy

Marks:

/50

Topics:

- Light and shadows

Name: ______________________ Class: ________ Date: ______________

Section A (15 x 2 = 30 marks)

For each question, four options are given. Choose the correct answer and write down your choice, 1, 2, 3 or 4, in the brackets provided.

1. Are light and shadows energy?

	Is light energy?	Are shadows energy?
(1)	Yes	Yes
(2)	Yes	No
(3)	No	No
(4)	No	Yes

( )

2. Are light and shadows made up of matter?

	Is light made up of matter?	Are shadows made up of matter?
(1)	Yes	Yes
(2)	Yes	No
(3)	No	No
(4)	No	Yes

( )

3. Guan Heng holds up a wooden rod using a piece of plasticine. At which position should Guan Heng shine a torch to get the shadow in the diagram below?

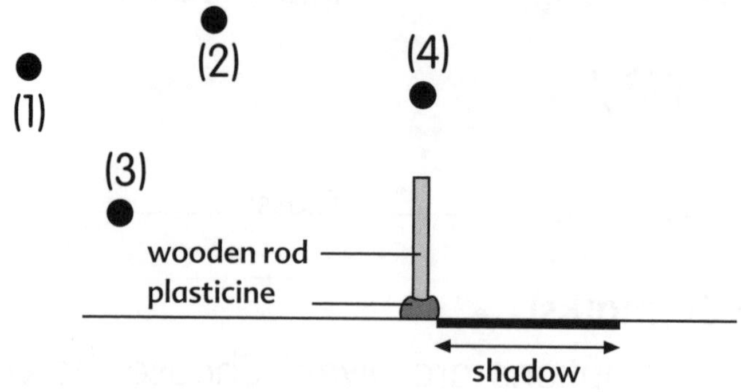

( )

4. Under which of the following conditions will a shadow form?

(1) Light from the sun travels through the wind shield of a car.
(2) Light from a street lamp is blocked by a passing car.
(3) There is no light at all in an enclosed room.
(4) Light from the sun enters the still (unmoving) water of a lake. ( )

5. The pictures below show the back of Anuar's hands.

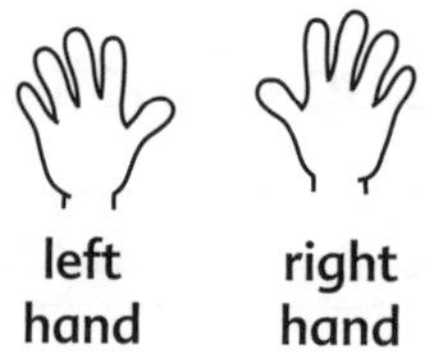

He puts one of his hands between a projector and a screen, with his palm facing the screen. A shadow is formed on the screen as shown. The shadow is almost the same size as Anuar's hand.

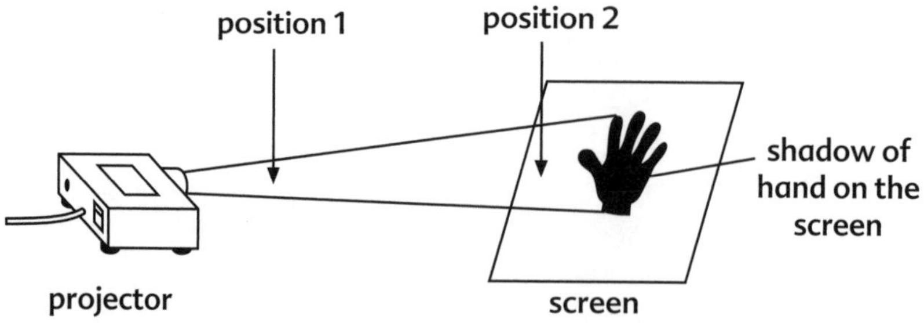

Which hand does Anuar use and where does he put his hand?

	Which hand does he use?	Where does he put his hand?
(1)	Left hand	Position 1
(2)	Right hand	Position 2
(3)	Right hand	Position 1
(4)	Left hand	Position 2

( )

6. The diagram below shows a ray of light, X, falling on a plane mirror. Which arrow correctly shows the direction in which the light is reflected?

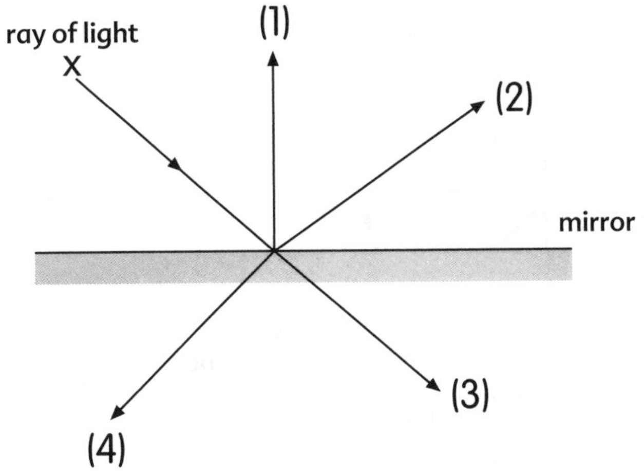

( )

7. The following show the shadows of a tea cup and a kettle.

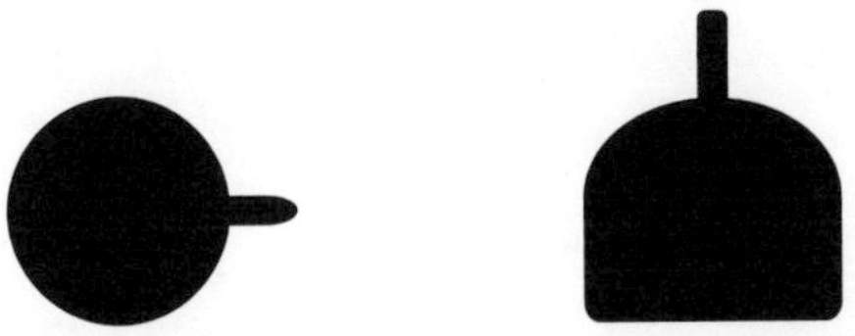

shadow of a cup shadow of a kettle

From which side of each object was the light shone, to form these shadows?

	Shadow of a cup	Shadow of a kettle
(1)	Top	Top
(2)	Side	Top
(3)	Side	Side
(4)	Top	Side

( )

8. Shawn's teacher asks him to place two mirrors in the bent tube, so that he can see the cube as shown below.

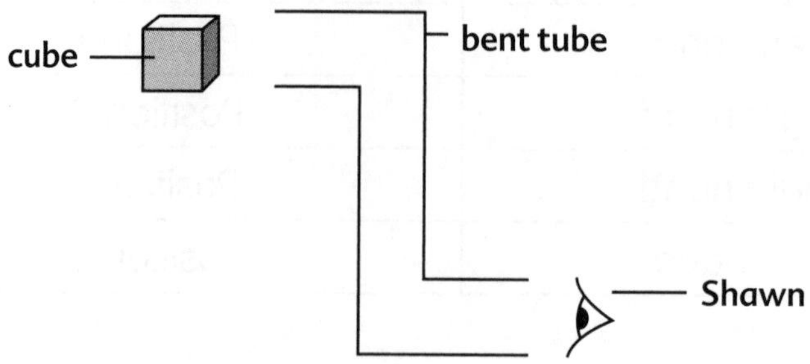

How should Shawn place the two mirrors?

(1)

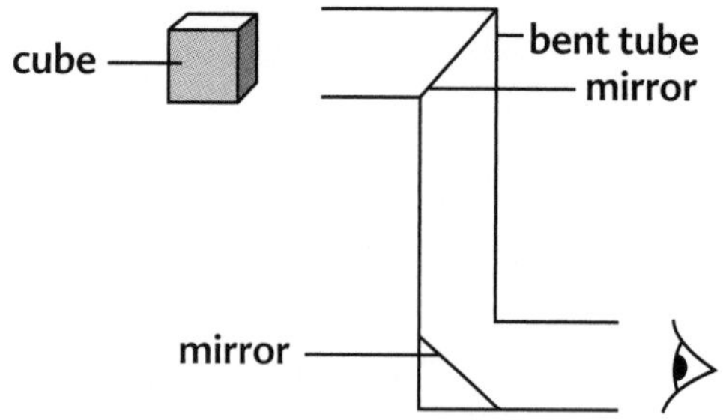

(2)

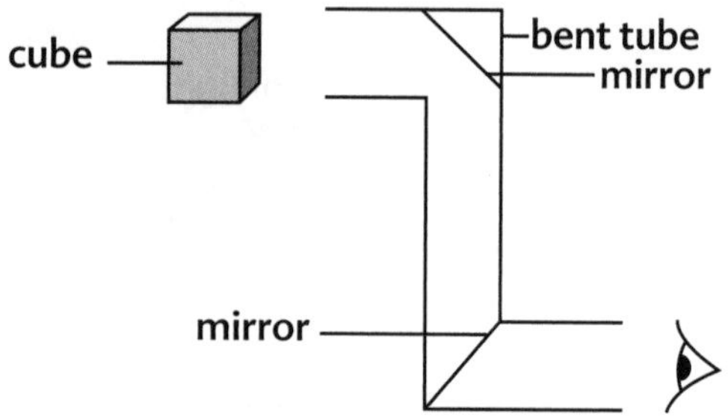

(3)

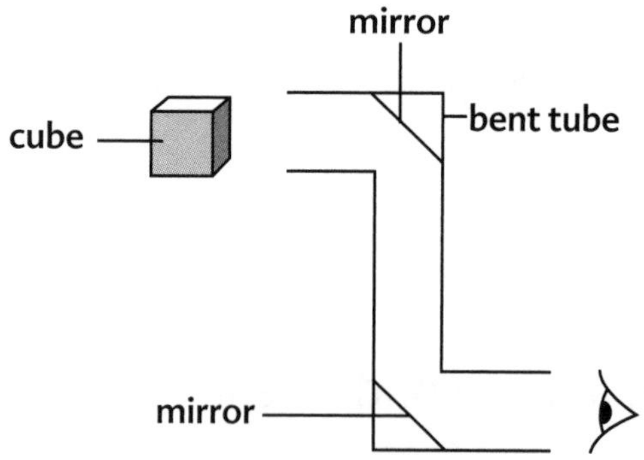

(4)

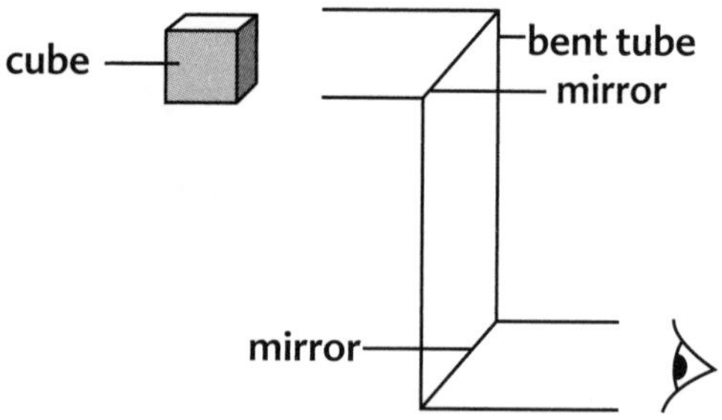

( )

9. Won sets up the following experiment. She places the block of wood at different positions, 1, 2, 3 and 4 and measures and records the height of the shadow.

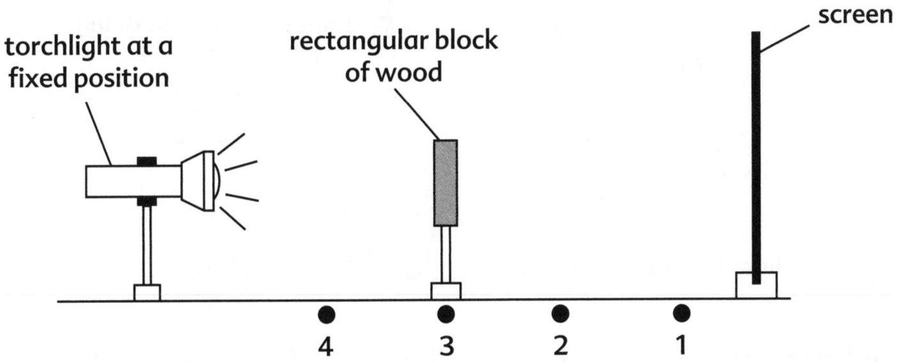

Which graph correctly shows how the height of the shadow changes with the position of the block of wood?

(1)
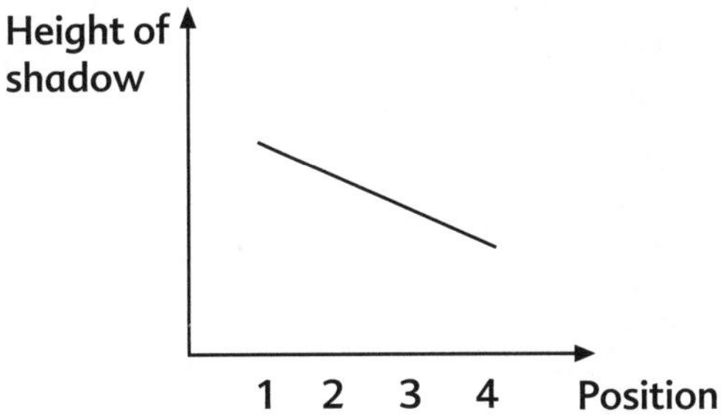

(2)
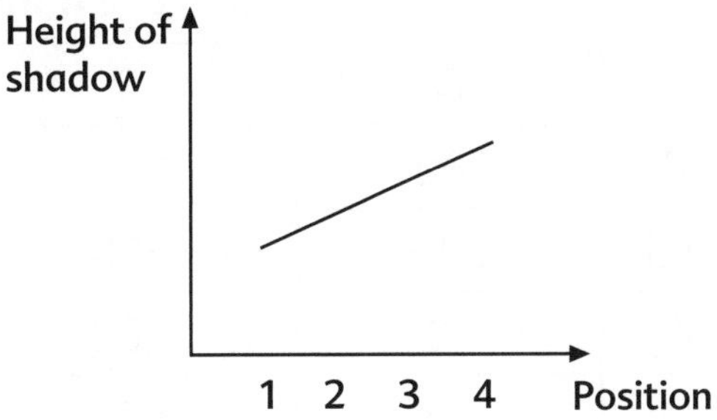

(3)
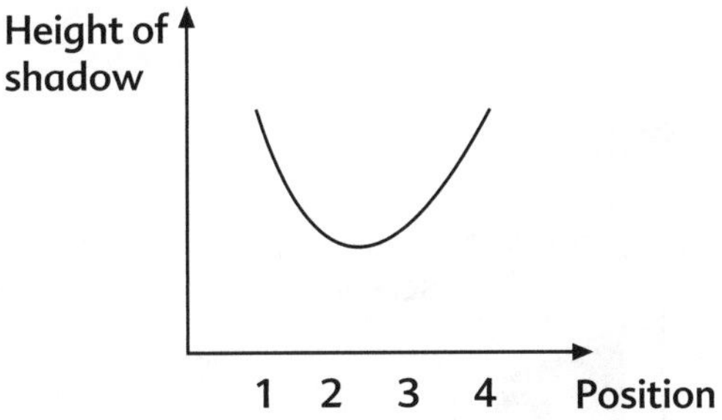

(4)
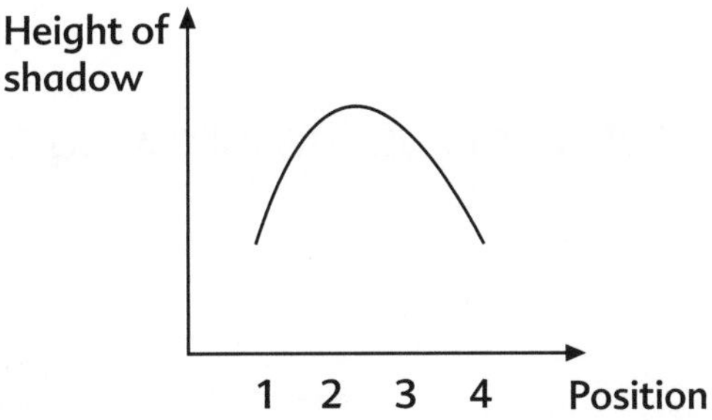

( )

10. Sarah sets up the following experiment. The depth of each liquid and the amount of light from each of the three torchlights are the same.

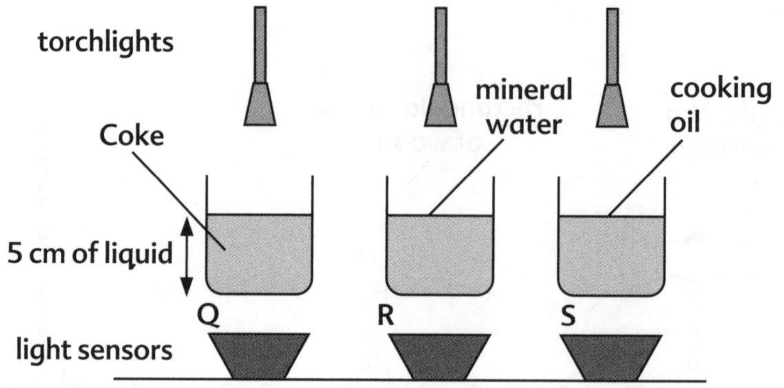

She uses light sensors to measure the light that passes through each of the three liquids. What will the readings from the sensors be? (More light will give a higher reading.)

	Units of light		
	Q	R	S
(1)	100	200	40
(2)	200	100	40
(3)	40	100	200
(4)	40	200	100

( )

11. Dorothy sets up the following experiment.

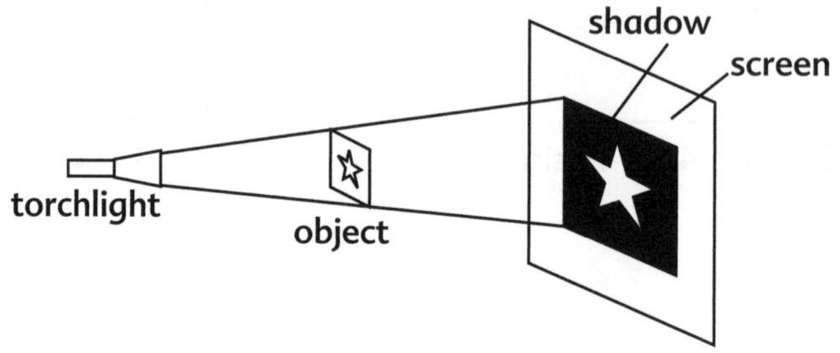

The screen and the torch are fixed in position. Dorothy moves the object towards the screen. What will happen to the size of the star in the shadow and the size of the square shadow?

	Size of the star in the shadow	Size of the square shadow
(1)	Increase	Increase
(2)	Increase	Decrease
(3)	Decrease	Increase
(4)	Decrease	Decrease

( )

12. Which of the following objects give off light?

(A) Filament lamp
(B) The moon
(C) A star

(1) A and B only
(2) B and C only
(3) A and C only
(4) A, B and C ( )

13. Amanda shines a lamp onto two poles, A and B, as shown. Both rods are of equal distance from the lamp.

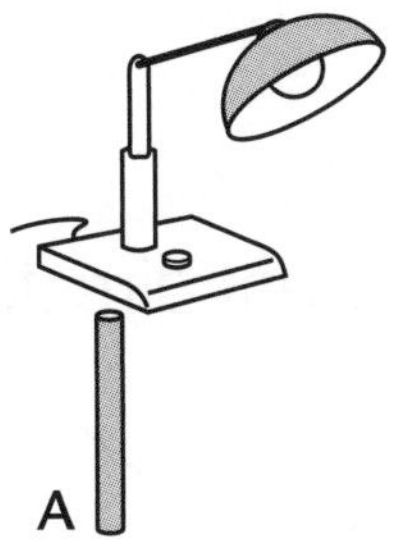

Which of the following shows the shadows formed by rods A and B?

(1)
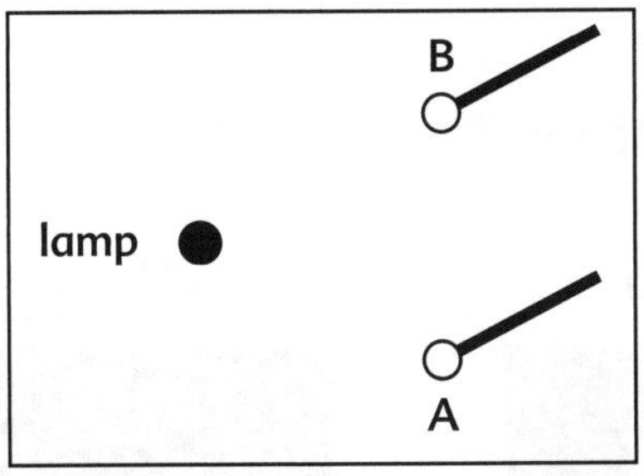

(2)
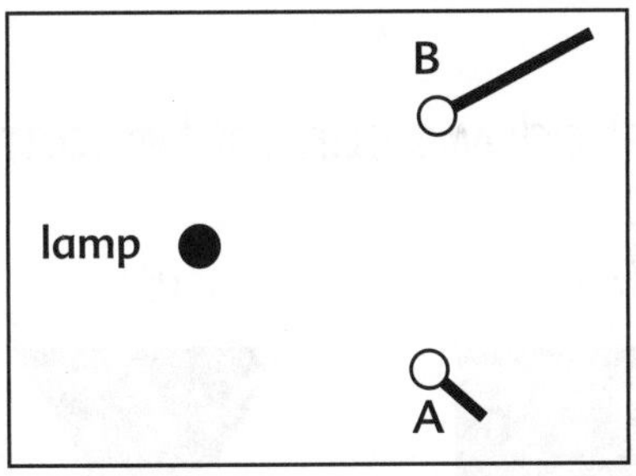

(3)
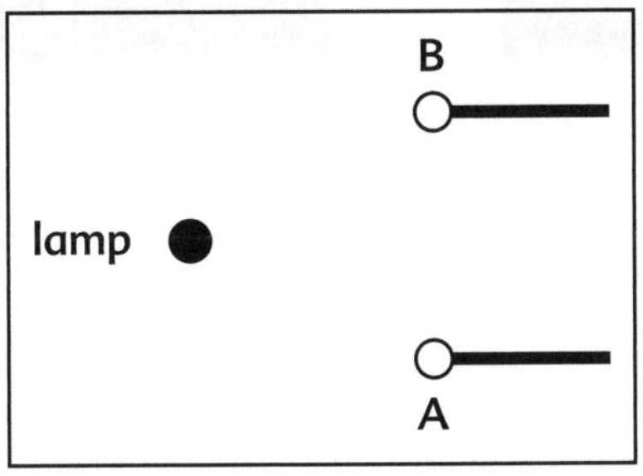

(4)
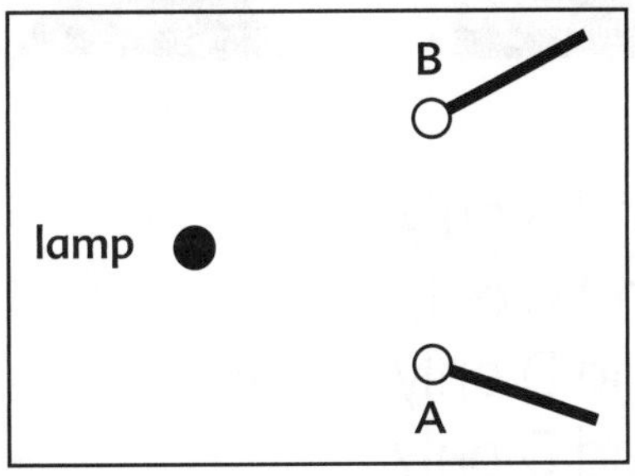

( )

14. Ryan does the following experiment using five identical cardboards.

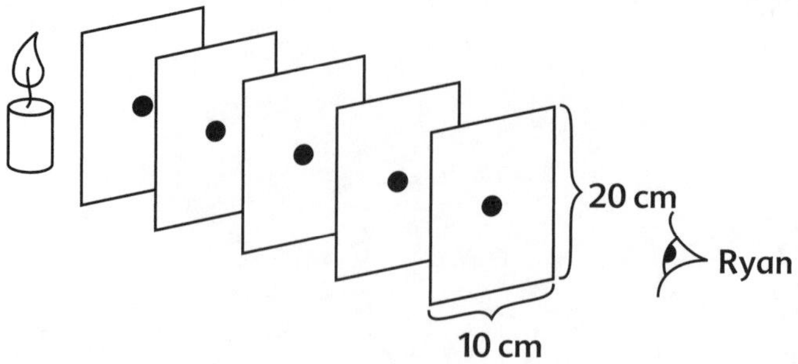

Which question is he trying to investigate?

(1) Where is the hottest part of a candle flame?
(2) Does light travel in a straight line?
(3) Can heat be transmitted by radiation from a candle flame?
(4) How fast does light travel? ( )

15. Melanie shines a torch from different directions on the following object.

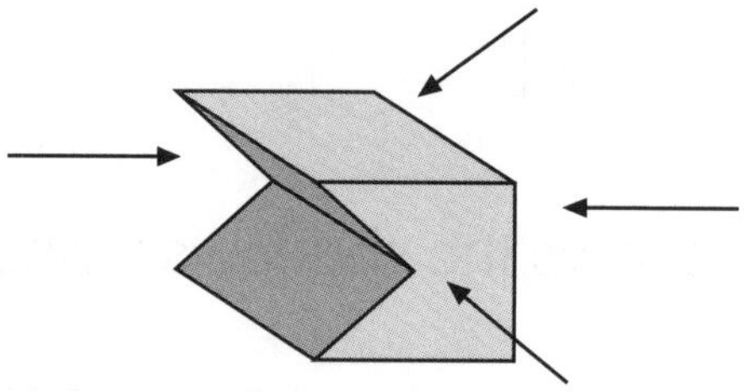

Which shadows cannot be formed by the object?

(A) (B) (C) (D)

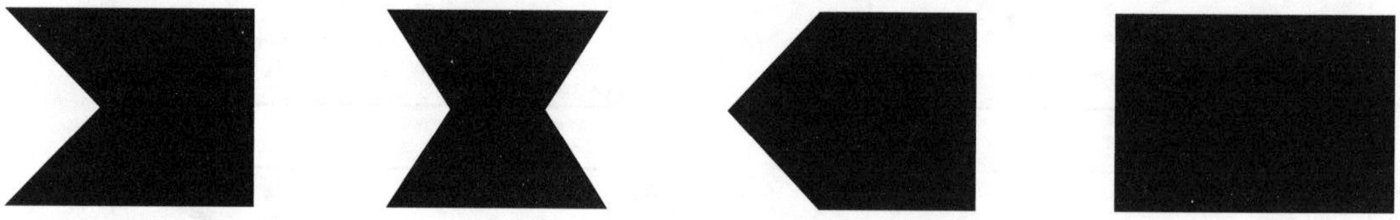

(1) A and B only
(2) B and C only
(3) C and D only
(4) A and D only ( )

Section B (20 marks)

Write your answers for each question in the blank spaces provided.

16. Circle TRUE or FALSE for each statement. [3]

(a) The face can be seen on a person's shadow. TRUE / FALSE

(b) Light travels in straight lines. TRUE / FALSE

(c) Light cannot be reflected. TRUE / FALSE

17. Create a table or a graphic organiser to classify the following objects into opaque, translucent and transparent. [3]

Storybook	Computer mouse	Spectacles
Wooden drawer	Clear glass	Frosted glass
Photograph	Worksheet	Bulb
School bag	Mobile phone	Tracing paper

18. You are given a screen and a light source. Describe how you would form the following shadows A, B and C. [3]

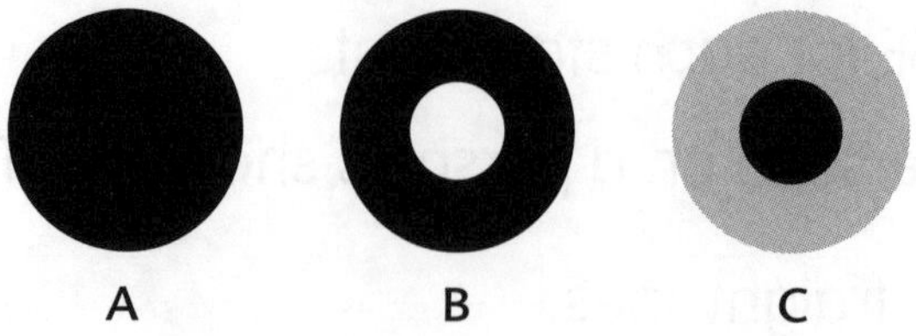

____

____

____

Draw your experimental set-up for (B) in the space below. [1]

19. Agnes sets up the following experiment. The object is opaque.

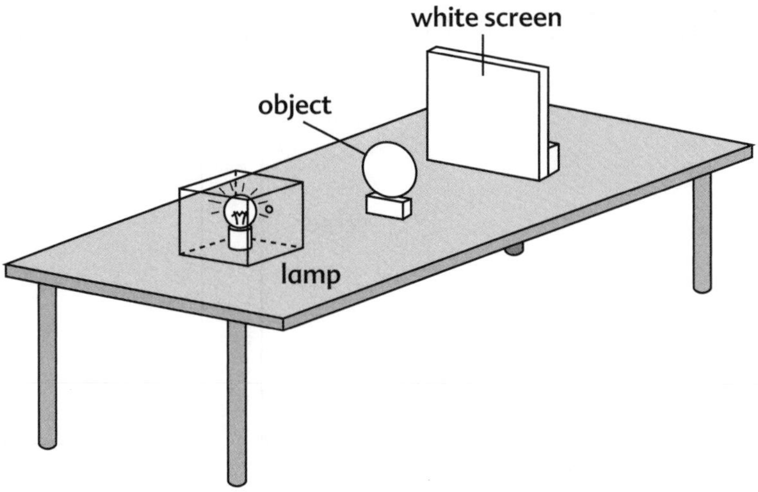

(a) In the space below, draw

(i) the shadow that forms on the screen. [1]

(ii) the shadow that forms when the object is rotated 90 degrees. [1]

(b) Describe how the shadow would change if

(i) the screen is moved towards the object. [1]

____

____

(ii) the lamp is moved away from the object. [1]

____

____

(c) Agnes replaces the object with a glass ball and a metal cube. She arranges the lamp, glass ball, metal cube and screen in a straight line as shown below. Draw, in the space provided, the shadow Agnes will see. [1]

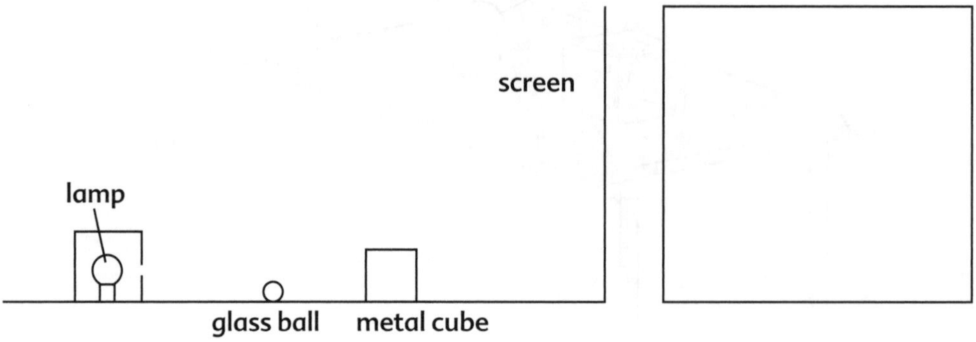

(d) Agnes replaces the glass ball and metal cube with a tennis ball and a rectangular piece of tracing paper as shown below. Draw, in the space provided, the shadow Agnes will see. [1]

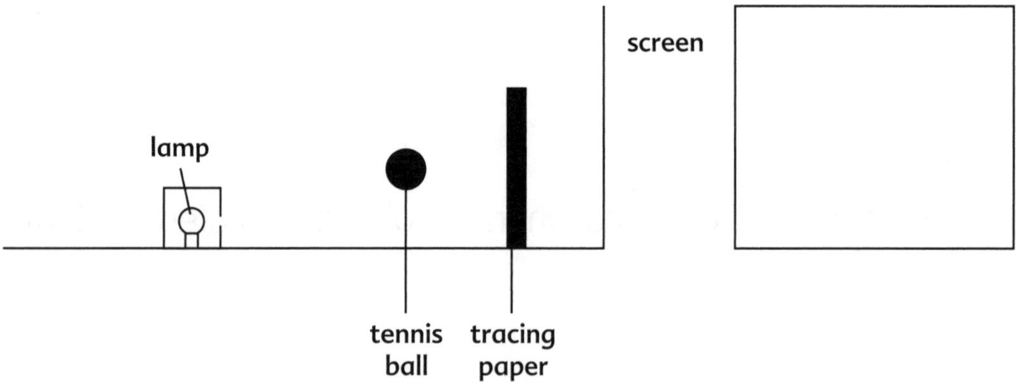

20. Grace uses a torch to shine on a soft drink can from position A and then from position B. A shadow is formed on Screen Y and then Screen X. In the spaces provided, draw the shape of the shadows that Grace will see. [2]

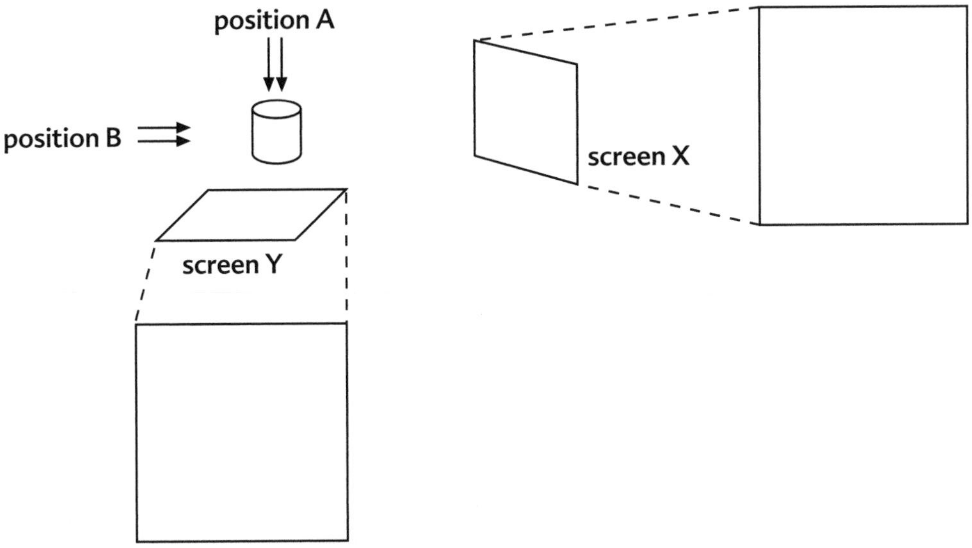

21. The diagram shows a shadow formed in the late afternoon. [2]

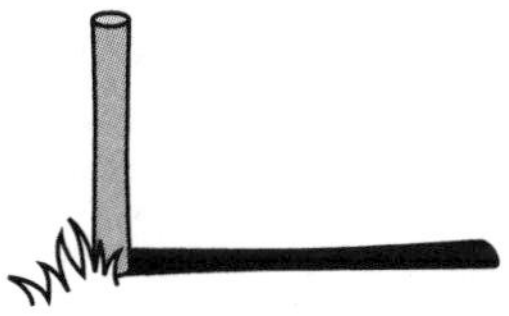

Draw the shadows formed at the different times shown below.

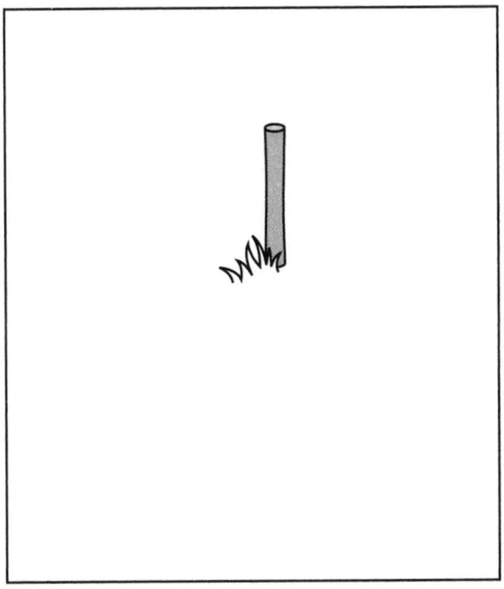

8 am

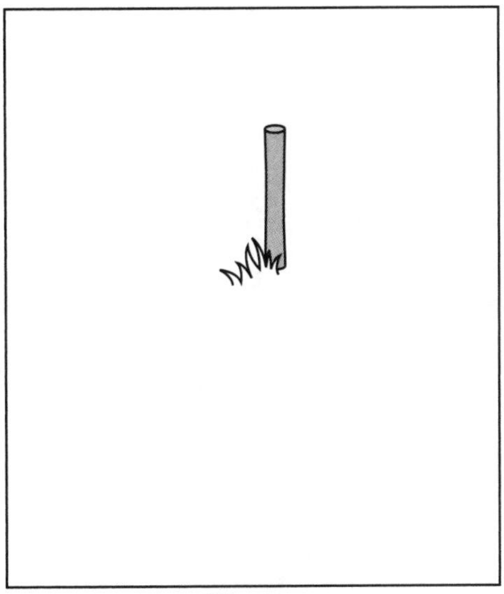

12 noon

End of Paper

BLANK

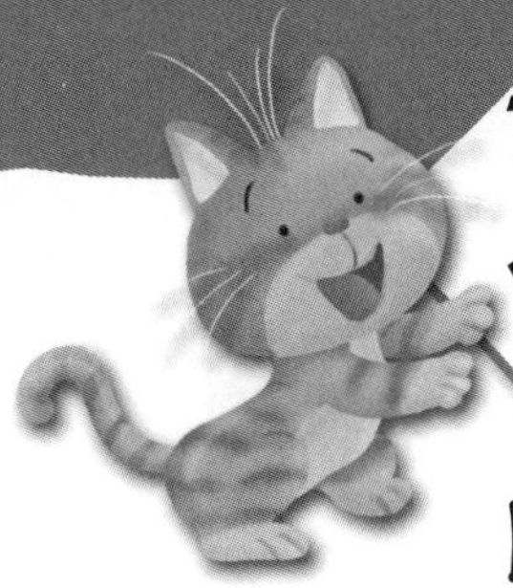

Test 10 Energy

Marks: /50

Topics:
- Heat and temperature
- Effect of heat

Name: ______________________ Class: __________ Date: ____________

Section A (15 x 2 = 30 marks)

For each question, four options are given. Choose the correct answer and write down your choice, 1, 2, 3 or 4, in the brackets provided.

1. Usha takes out a jam jar from a refrigerator. She finds that she cannot open the lid of the jar. To open the lid, she does the following:

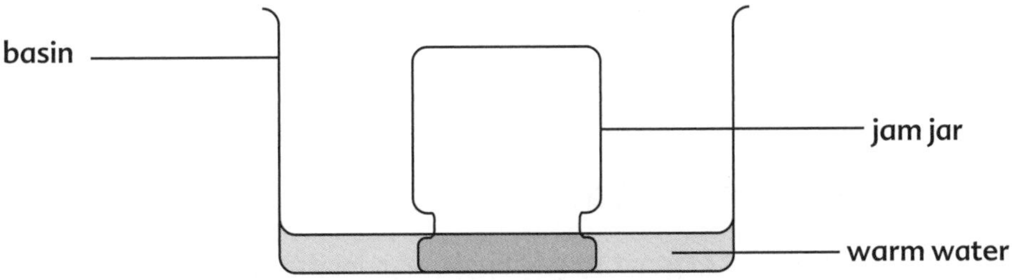

Which scientific knowledge is Usha applying?

(1) Heat travels from a hot region to a cold region.
(2) Matter usually expands on heating.
(3) Heat can cause matter to change its state.
(4) Liquid water flows under gravity. ( )

2. Nicholas took out a plastic spoon, X, and a metal spoon, Y. He melted a little wax on the handles of the two spoons. The wax then cooled and hardened on the handles. Next, Nicholas placed the two spoons into a beaker of hot water as shown below.

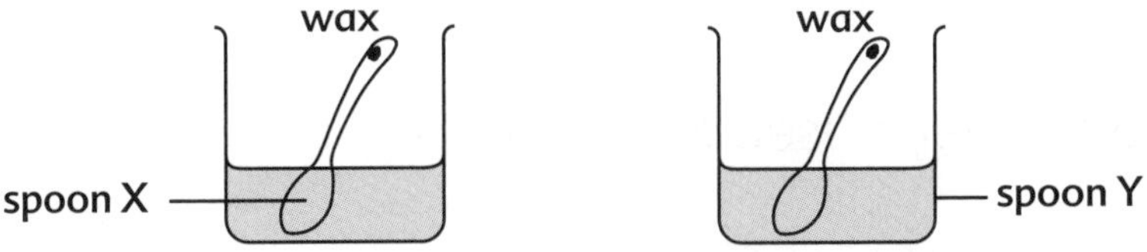

The wax on spoon (a) ____________ would melt first. This was because the material of this spoon was a better heat (b) ____________.

	(A)	(B)
(1)	X	insulator
(2)	Y	conductor
(3)	X	conductor
(4)	Y	insulator

( )

3. Igid performs the following experiment to find out which rod, X or Y, is a better heat conductor. She uses the same amount of wax on both rods. The rods are of different materials but the same length and diameter.

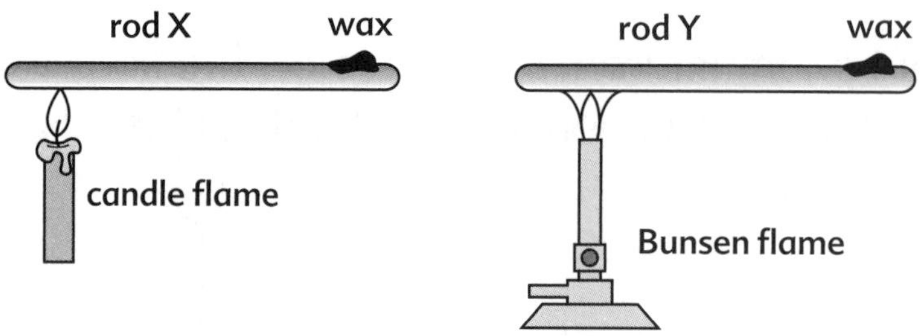

Igid's experiment is not fair. What should she do to make it fair?

(1) She should use the same materials for both rods.
(2) She should heat the ends of the two rods from the same flame.
(3) She should use different amounts of wax.
(4) She should use rods of different diameters. ( )

4. Are heat and temperature energy?

	Is heat a form of energy?	Is temperature a form of energy?
(1)	Yes	Yes
(2)	Yes	No
(3)	No	Yes
(4)	No	No

( )

5. What is a thermometer used to measure?

(1) Heat
(2) Temperature
(3) Light intensity
(4) Mass ( )

6. Gerald has the following things:

- A basin of water at room temperature
- Ice cubes
- An iron ball that has been placed in boiling water

Gerald takes out the iron ball from boiling water. He places the ice cubes and iron ball into the basin of water as shown:

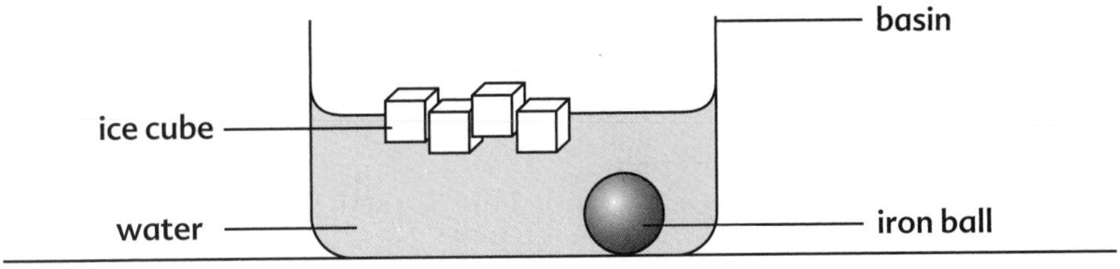

Which of the following will happen?

(A) The ice cubes will gain heat from the water and surrounding air.
(B) The iron ball will lose heat to the water and bottom of the basin.
(C) The water will lose heat to the ice cubes and surroundings.
(D) The water will lose heat to the iron ball.

(1) A, B and C only
(2) B, C and D only
(3) A, C and D only
(4) A, B, C and D ( )

7. Mark notices that his feet feel warmer on a rug than on a ceramic tile floor. This is because the rug ____________ than the tile.

(1) has a higher temperature
(2) is a better heat insulator
(3) is a better heat conductor
(4) contains more energy ( )

8. Four iron rods were heated to 100 °C. Which one of the rods has the least amount of heat?

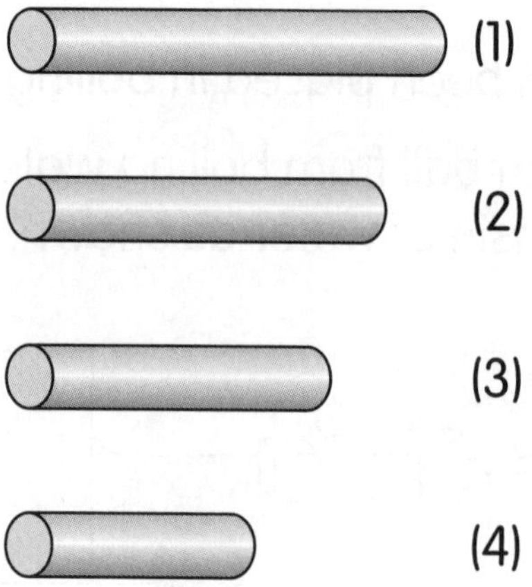

( )

9. Which of the following processes show heat being released?

(A) Water becoming ice in the freezer.
(B) Margarine becoming oil.
(C) Wet cloth becoming dry cloth.
(D) Hot milo becoming cold milo.

(1) A and D only
(2) A and B only
(3) B and C only
(4) C and D only

( )

10. Yahyar leaves a cup of hot coffee on a table.

How will the temperature of the coffee change?

(1)
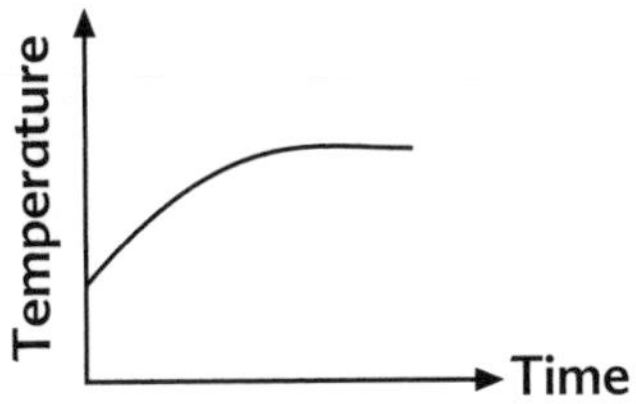

(2)
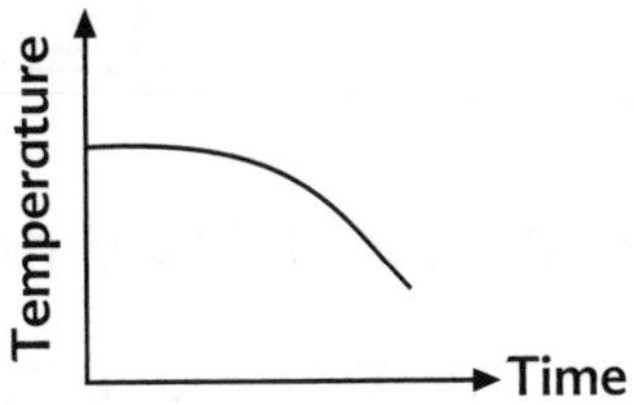

(3)
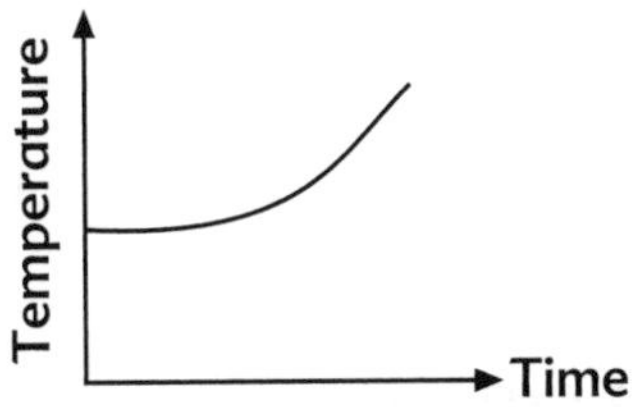

(4)
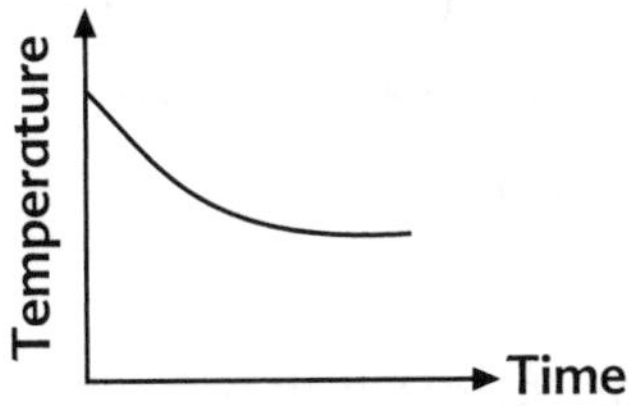

( )

11. (a) __________ is a unit of (b) __________.

	(A)	(B)
(1)	Heat	degrees Celsius
(2)	Temperature	heat
(3)	Degrees Celsius	temperature
(4)	Degrees Celsius	heat

( )

12. David sets up the following experiment to find out which liquid, A or B, will expand more when heated.

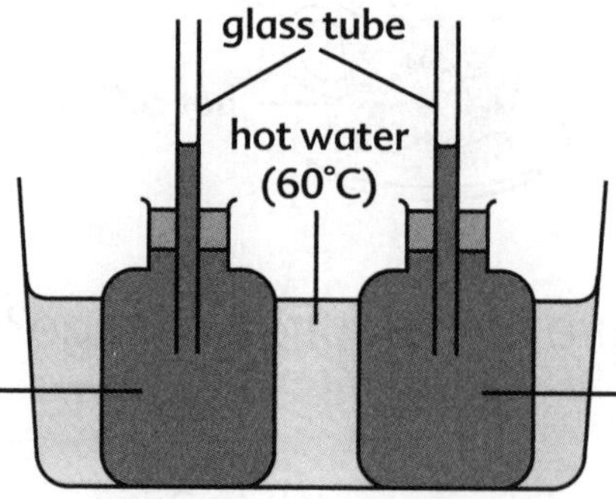

Which variable should David **not** keep constant?

(1) Starting temperature of Liquids A and B.
(2) Volume of Liquids A and B.
(3) Diameter of glass tubes.
(4) Type of liquid. ( )

13. The following shows the parts of a clinical thermometer.

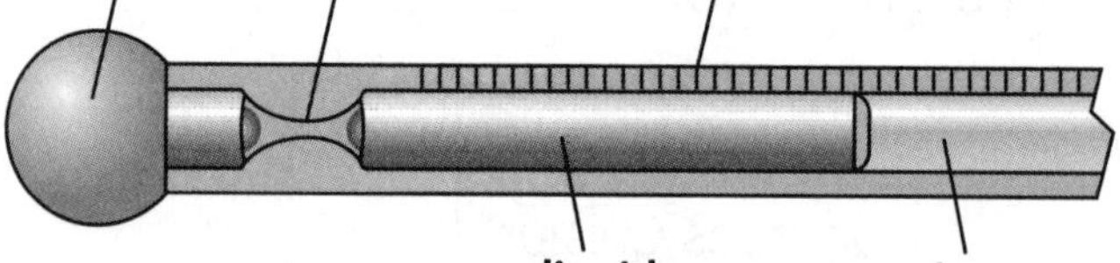

Which liquid does the thermometer use and why?

	Liquid	Reason
(1)	Water	It expands quickly when heated.
(2)	Water	It contracts quickly when heated.
(3)	Mercury	It expands quickly when heated.
(4)	Mercury	It contracts quickly when heated.

( )

Questions 14 and 15 refer to the following diagram.

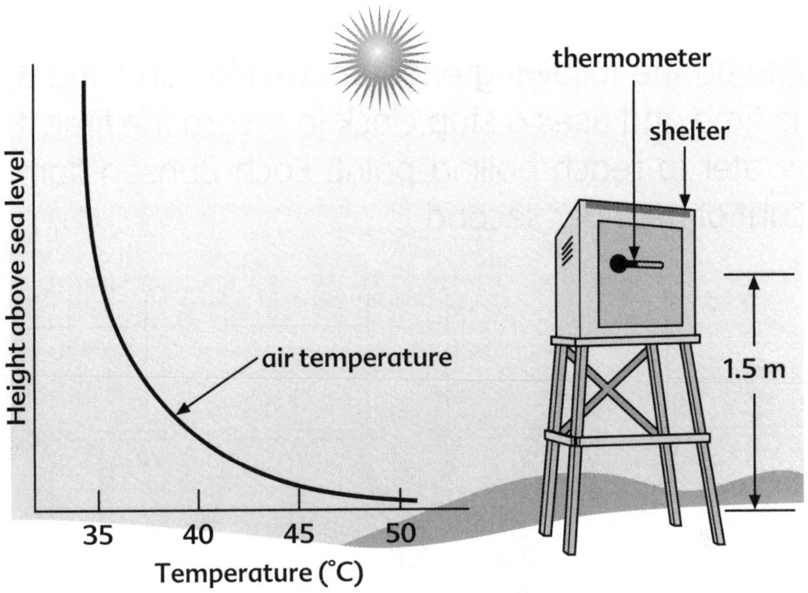

14. To get the readings to plot the above graph, Syed sets up a number of shelters at different positions on a mountain and measures the temperature regularly.

    Syed should keep the following variables the same, except the ________.

    (1) height of the shelters above ground
    (2) position of the shelters on the mountain
    (3) position of the thermometer in the shelter
    (4) materials the shelter is made of ( )

15. What can Syed infer from the above graph?

    (1) The higher you go up the mountain, the hotter it is.
    (2) The higher you go up the mountain, the colder it is.
    (3) It is cooler in the shelter.
    (4) The taller the shelter, the colder it is. ( )

Section B (20 marks)

Write your answers for each question in the blank spaces provided.

16. Benedict sets up the following experiment. He lights the Bunsen burners at the same time and uses a stop clock to record the time it takes for each beaker of water to reach boiling point. Each Bunsen flame gives off the same amount of heat per second.

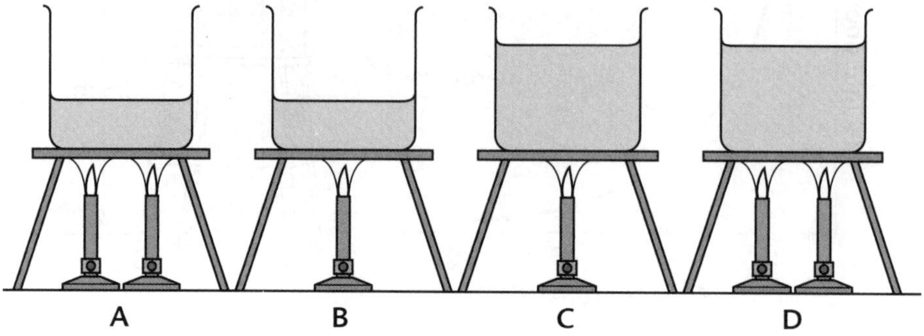

(a) How can Benedict tell when the water has reached its boiling point? [1]

____

(b) Benedict finds that B and D take the same length of time to reach boiling point. Fill in the bar chart below, to show the time taken for the water to boil in each of the four set-ups. [2]

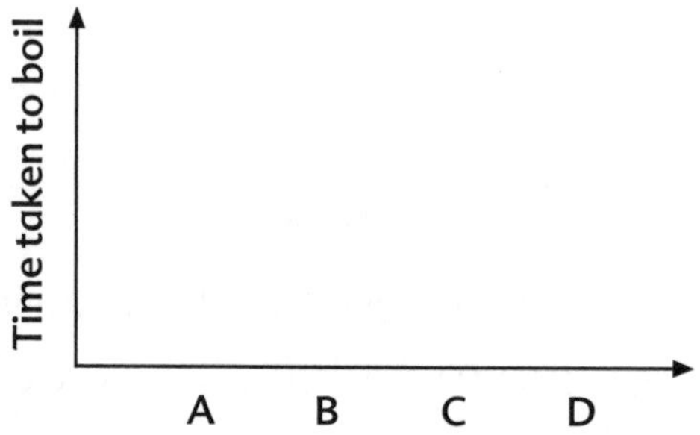

(c) When all the water has reached boiling point, which beaker will have the greatest amount of heat? [1]

____

17. Bernice sets up the following.

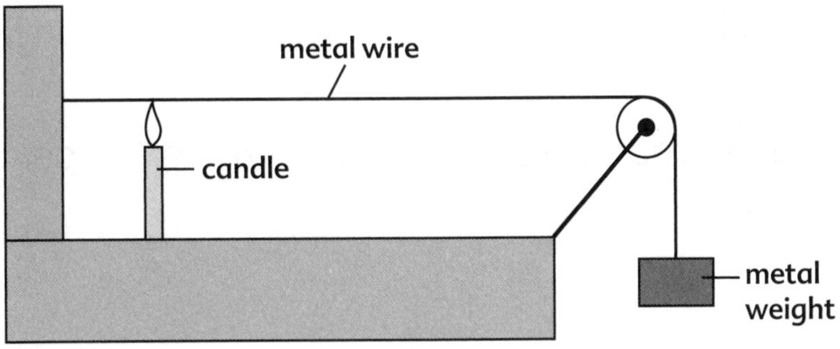

What will Bernice observe? Explain your answer. [3]

Observation: ______________________________

____

Reason: ______________________________

____

18. The diagram shows a flask and a beaker of hot water.

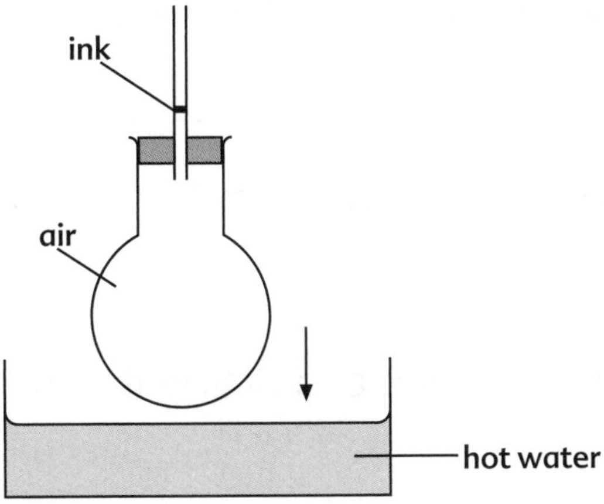

(a) What changes do you expect to see when the flask is lowered into the hot water? [1]

____

(b) Give an explanation for your answer. [3]

____

____

____

19. A thermostat is a special equipment used to control temperature. The thermostat in an oven is set for baking. It turns on the oven when the temperature is below 120 °C and turns off the oven when the temperature is above 140 °C.

Complete the line graph below to show how the temperature inside the oven changes over time. [4]

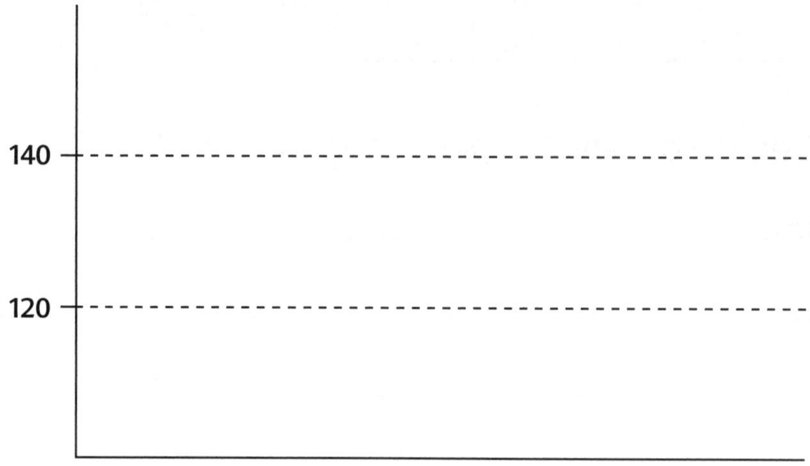

20. Explain:

(a) why gaps are found at regular intervals along MRT tracks. [1]

____

(b) what happens when water changes from 80 °C to 20 °C. [1]

____

(c) why the temperature range of a clinical thermometer is 35 °C to 42 °C. [1]

____

(d) the difference between heat and temperature. [1]

____

(e) what happens when an iron ball is heated. [1]

____

End of Paper

Marks: /100

Thematic Assessment 5

Energy

Name: ____________ Class: ________ Date: ____________

Section A (30 x 2 = 60 marks)

For each question, four options are given. Choose the correct answer and write down your choice, 1, 2, 3 or 4, in the brackets provided.

1. Which are forms of energy?

(A) Light
(B) Shadow
(C) Heat
(D) Temperature

(1) A and B only
(2) B and C only
(3) A and C only
(4) C and D only ( )

2. Which of the following explains why stars appear only at night?

(1) They cannot reflect light from the sun.
(2) They can reflect light from the moon only.
(3) They are not bright enough to be seen in the day.
(4) They only give off light in the night. ( )

3. Which of the following is our primary source of light and heat energy?

(1) Sun
(2) Stars
(3) Earth
(4) Moon ( )

4. In the following model of a solar heater, the plastic bottle and plastic hose are filled with water. The cardboard tray is left in direct sunlight. After some time, the thermometer reading rises.

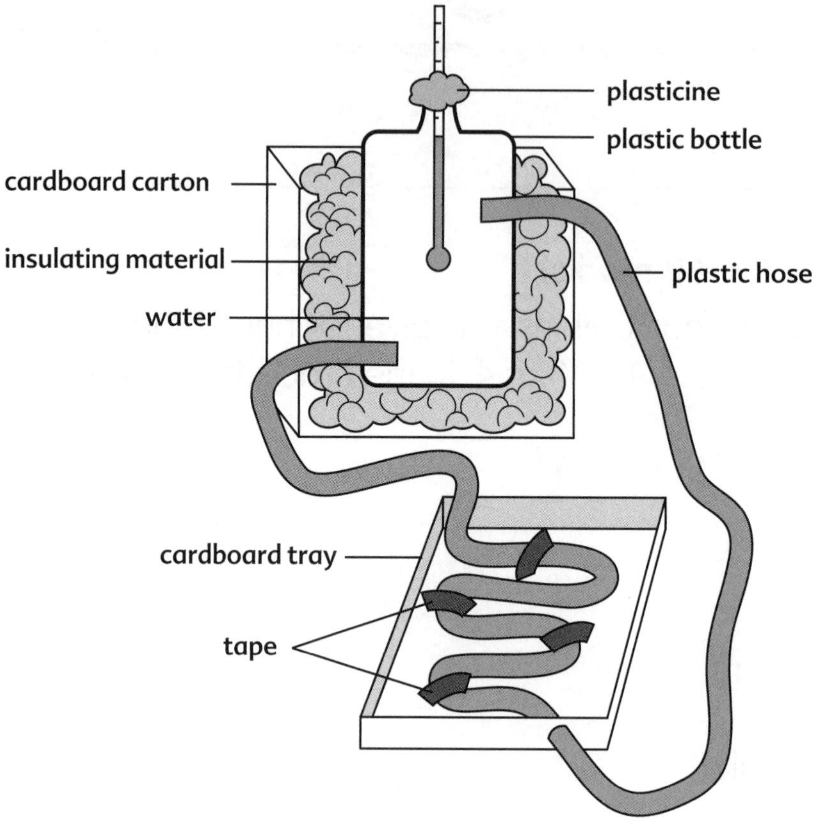

Why is the insulating material used?

(1) To prevent water from evaporating.
(2) To ensure no exchange of heat occurs between the water in the bottle and the surroundings.
(3) To prevent the plastic bottle from bursting due to heat expansion.
(4) To reflect heat from the sun into the plastic bottle. ( )

5. Study the diagram below carefully.

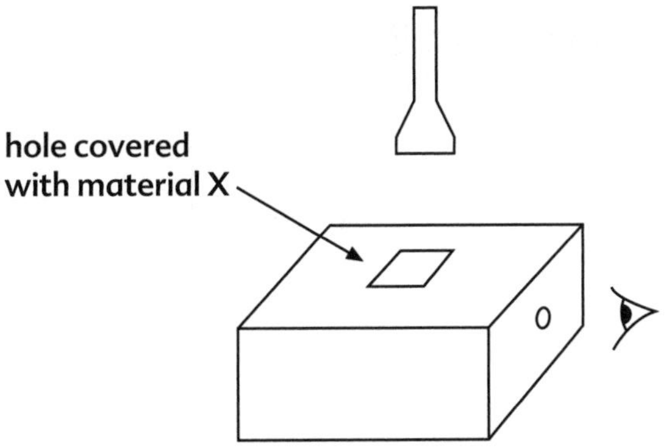

What should material X be in order for the eye to see the beam of light clearly?

(1) Clear plastic
(2) Coloured cardboard
(3) Styrofoam
(4) Aluminium foil ( )

6. Which of the following shows reflection of light?

(1)

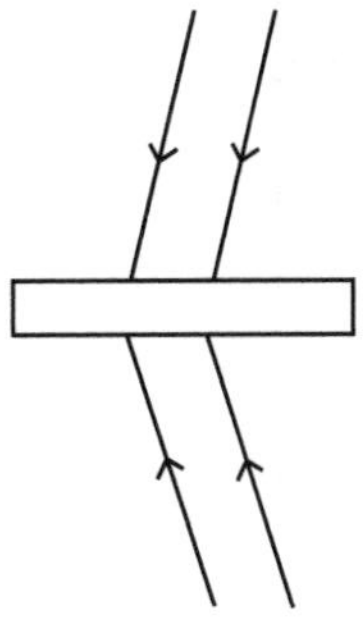

(2)

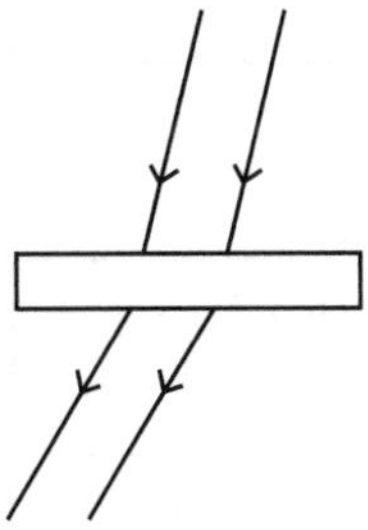

(3)

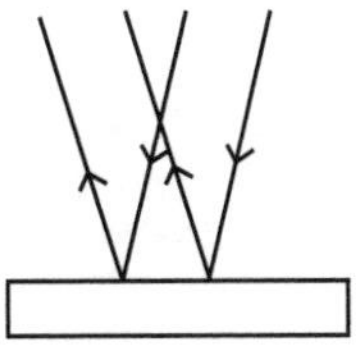

(4)

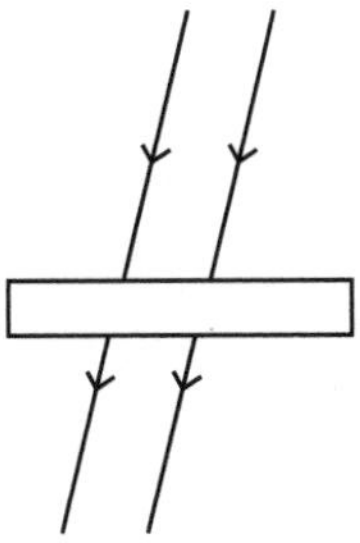

( )

7. Light from torch A shines onto the ball as shown below, to cast a shadow (shadow A) on screen A. Light from torch B shines onto the ball to cast a shadow (shadow B) on screen B.

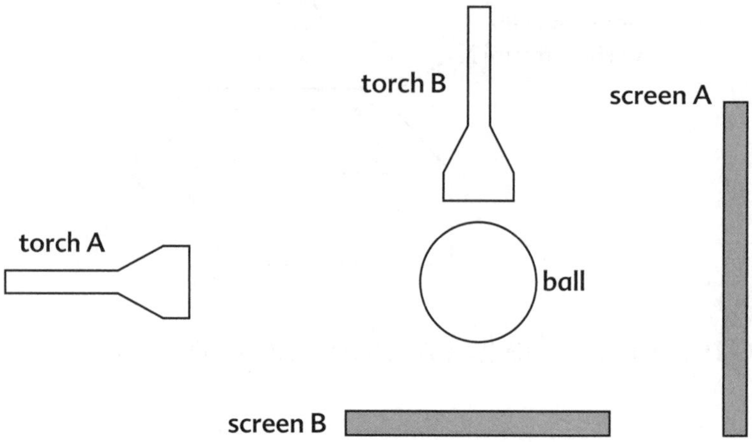

Which of the following correctly compares the sizes and shapes of the shadows?

	Size of shadows	Shape of shadows
(1)	Shadow A is larger than Shadow B.	Shadows A and B are of the same shape.
(2)	Shadow A is smaller than Shadow B.	Shadows A and B are of the same shape.
(3)	Shadow A is larger than Shadow B.	Shadows A and B are of different shapes.
(4)	Shadow A is smaller than Shadow B.	Shadows A and B are of different shapes.

( )

8. Study the following diagram.

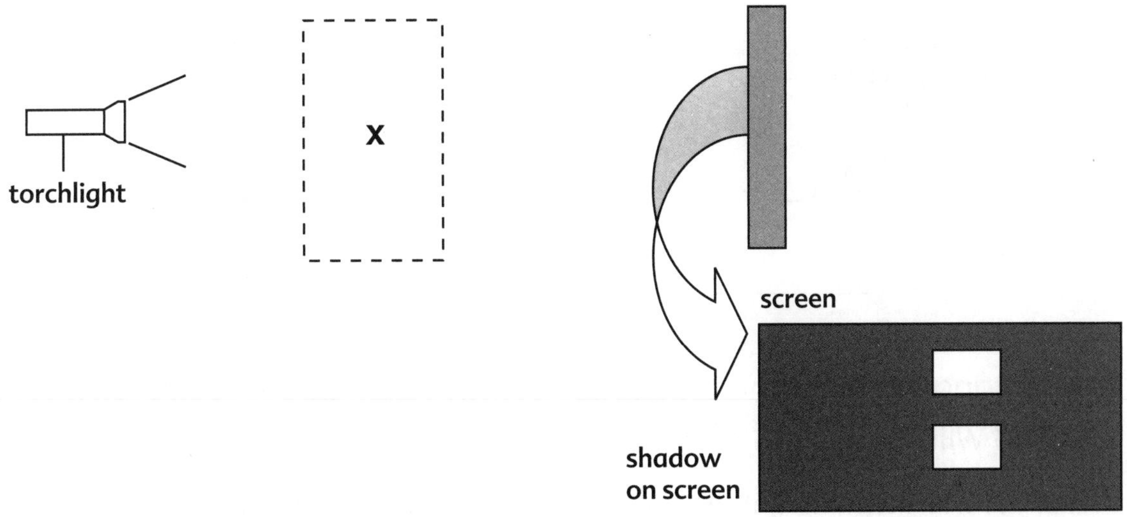

Which of the following should X be?

(1)

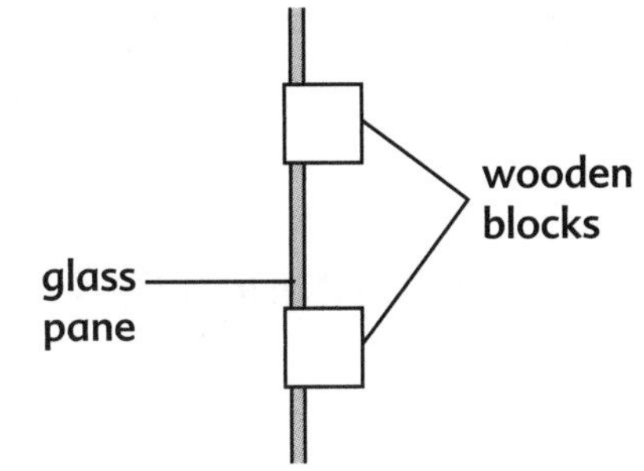

(2)

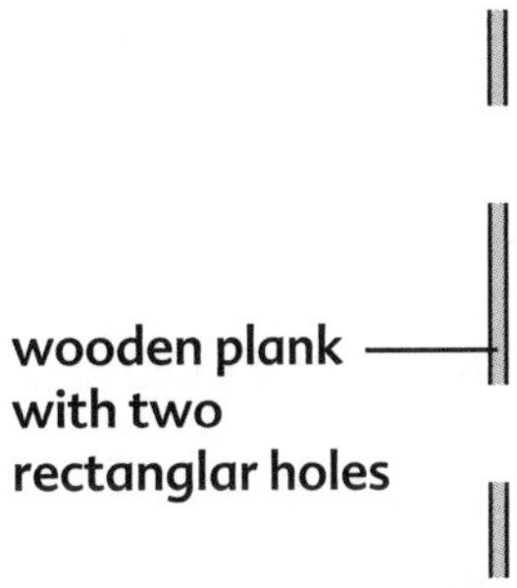

(3)

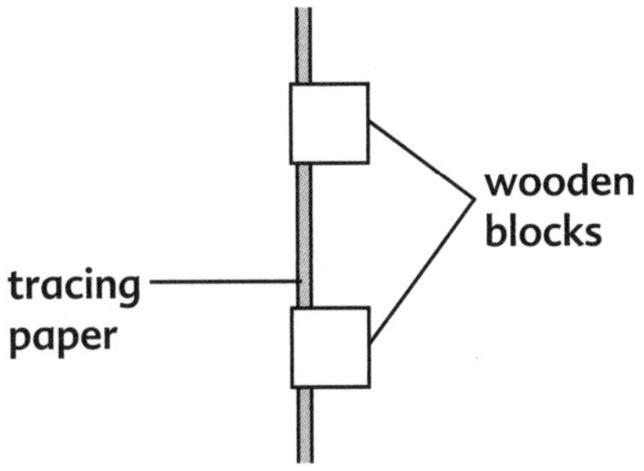

(4)

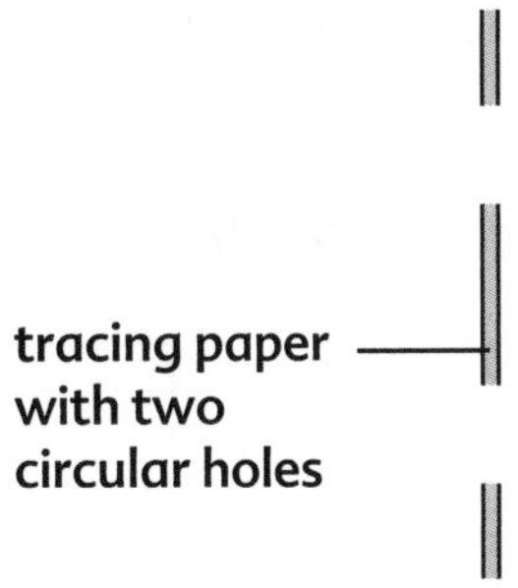

( )

9. Which of the following materials are **not** classified correctly?

	Transparent	Translucent	Opaque
(1)	Aluminium	Ceramic	Glass
(2)	Clear plastic	Frosted glass	Wood
(3)	Water	Tracing paper	Ceramic
(4)	Glass	Frosted glass	Aluminium

( )

10. The following experiment was set up to study shadow formation.

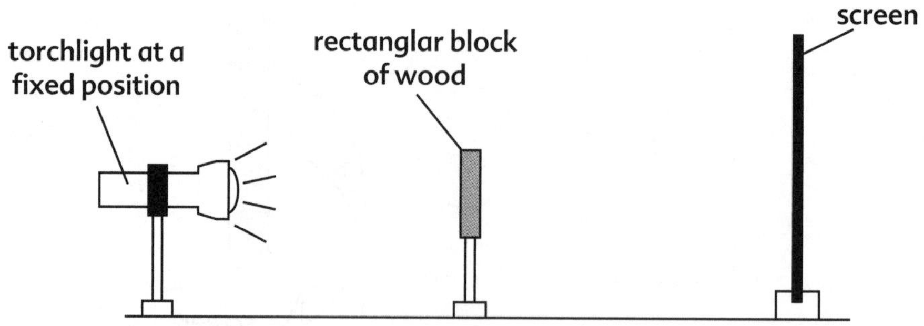

The rectangular wooden block has a round hole in the centre which is covered with a piece of black cloth.

Which of the following is the shadow formed on the screen?

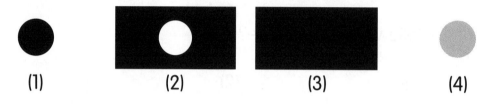

( )

11. What happens when an object allows light to pass through it?

(1) It will appear black.
(2) It will not be visible.
(3) It will reflect light after the light has passed through.
(4) The things behind it will be visible. ( )

12. What are X and Y likely to be?

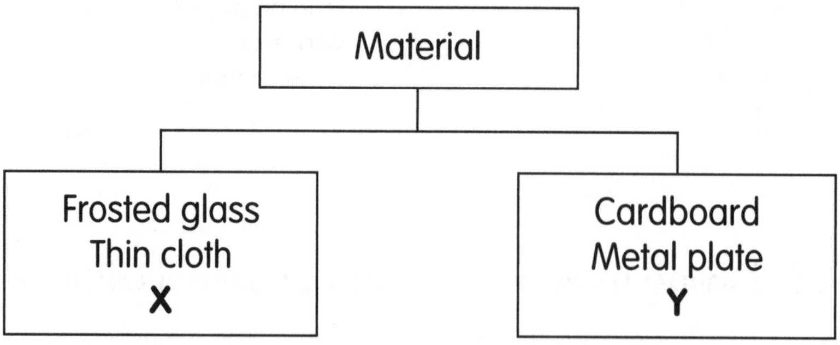

	X	Y
(1)	Woollen cloth	Porcelain plate
(2)	Clear plastic	Plywood
(3)	Tracing paper	Book
(4)	Carbon paper	Mirror

( )

13. The liquids below are classified into two groups.

Group A	Group B
Milk	Water
Red nail polish	Vinegar
Paint	Alcohol

What should Group A and Group B be?

	Group A	Group B
(1)	Transparent liquid	Opaque liquid
(2)	Translucent liquid	Transparent liquid
(3)	Transparent liquid	Translucent liquid
(4)	Opaque liquid	Transparent liquid

( )

14. Mei Ling has a porcelain mug.

She shines her torch on the mug to form different shadows. Which of the following is not a shadow formed by the mug?

(1) (2) (3) (4)

15. Which of the following gives out both heat and light?

(A) Hot plate
(B) Table lamp
(C) Laptop
(D) Gas stove

(1) A only
(2) B and C only
(3) C and D only
(4) B, C and D only

( )

16. Jenny has a metal strip made of two kinds of metals, A and B, which are tightly joined together.

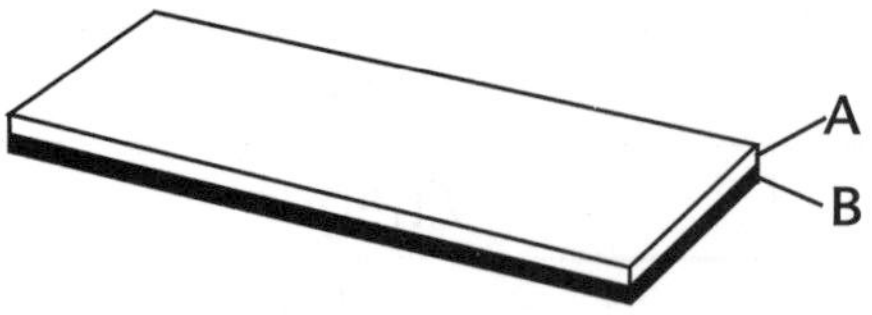

A expands more than B when heated. Which if the following shows the side view of the heated metal strip?

(1) 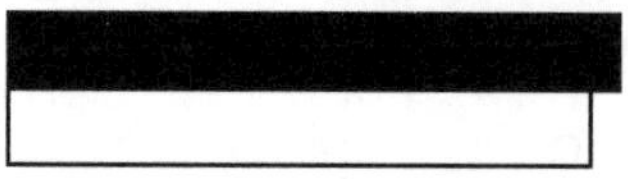

(2) 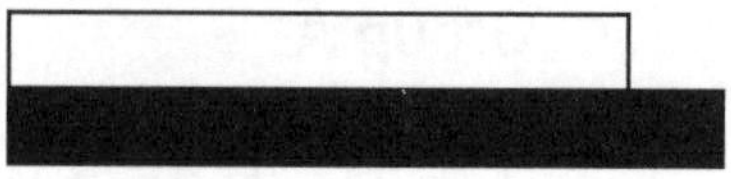

(3) 

(4) 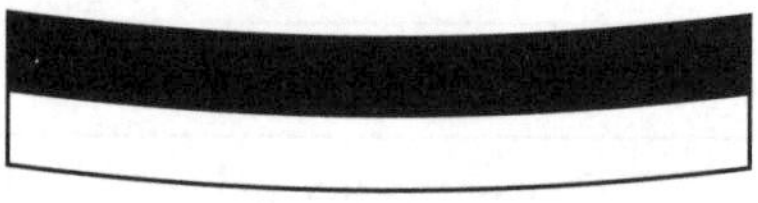

( )

17. The arrows in the following flowchart show changes in the state of water.

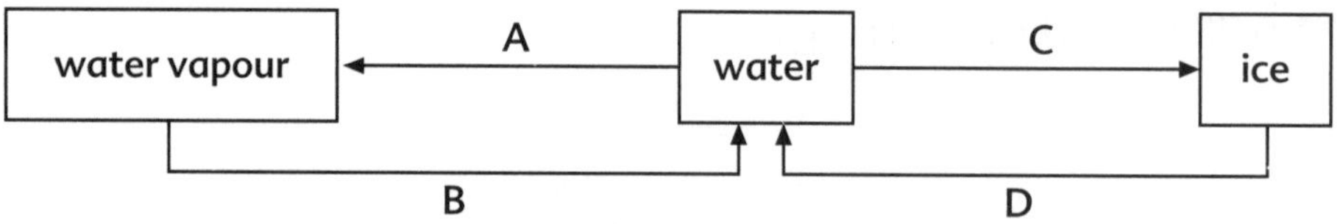

Which changes involve heat absorption by water?

(1) A and C
(2) A and D
(3) B and C
(4) C and D

( )

18. Tim put a metal spoon and some ice cubes into the following beaker of hot water.

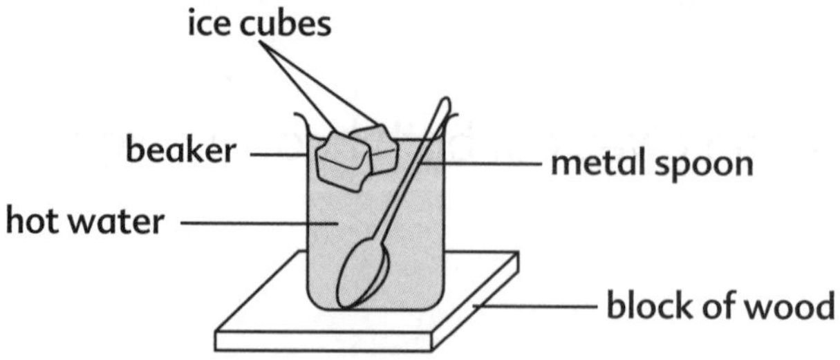

Which of the things will gain heat from the hot water?

(1) Ice cubes, beaker and metal spoon only.
(2) Beaker and surrounding air only.
(3) Ice cubes and block of wood only.
(4) Ice cubes, beaker, block of wood, metal spoon and surrounding air.

( )

19. A metal spoon is left in a bowl of hot soup.

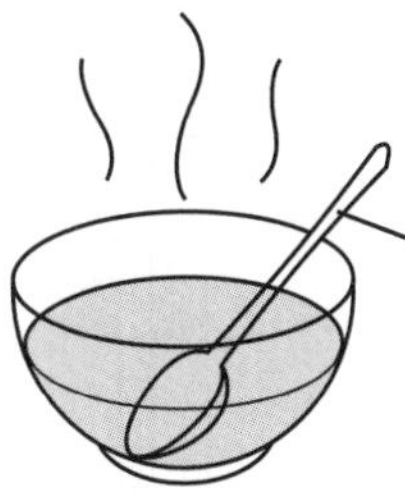

After some time, the handle of the spoon becomes hot because ____________.

(A) metals are poor conductors of heat
(B) steam from the soup heats up the spoon
(C) heat from the soup travelled up the spoon
(D) metals are always hot to the touch

(1) A only
(2) B and C only
(3) B, C and D only
(4) D only ( )

20. How do you loosen a tight metal cap of a wine bottle? The diagram shows a way.

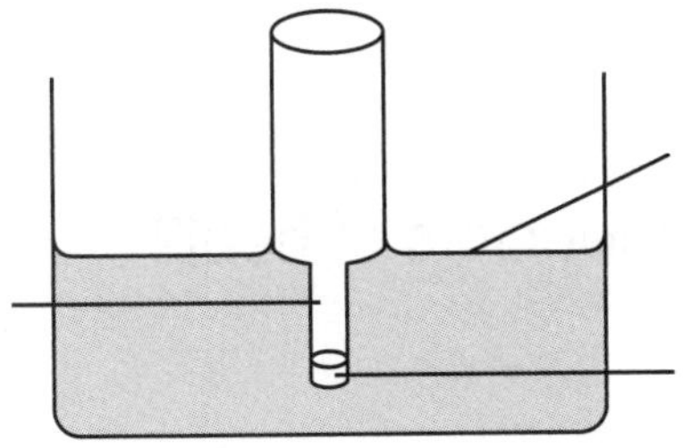

This method works because the ____________.

(1) metal cap conducts heat but the bottle neck does not
(2) metal cap expands more than the bottle neck
(3) hot water heats up the wine in the bottle, which pushes the metal cap out
(4) metal cap contracts more than the bottle neck ( )

21. Study the following diagram.

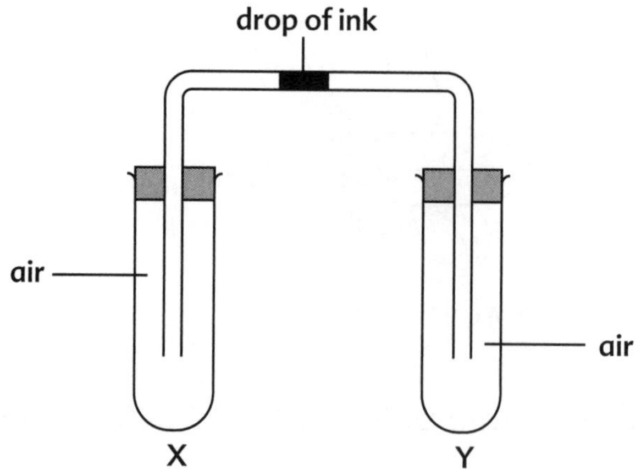

If test-tube X is heated by a Bunsen flame, the drop of ink will ______________.

(1) evaporate
(2) move towards X
(3) move towards Y
(4) remain where it is ( )

22. Look at the diagram of a kettle below.

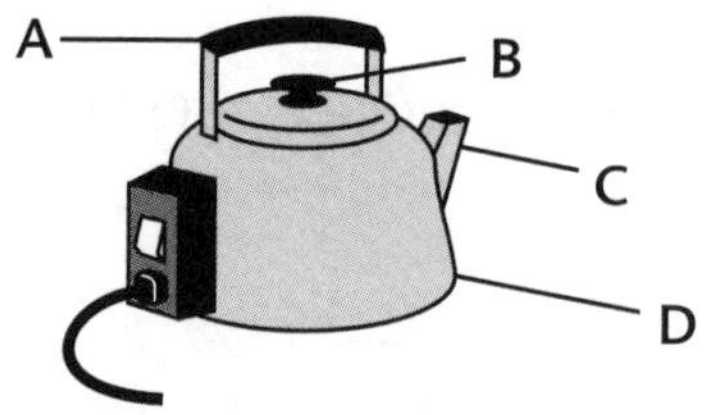

Which parts are poor conductors of heat?

(1) A and B
(2) B and C
(3) C and D
(4) A and D ( )

23. Study the diagram below carefully.

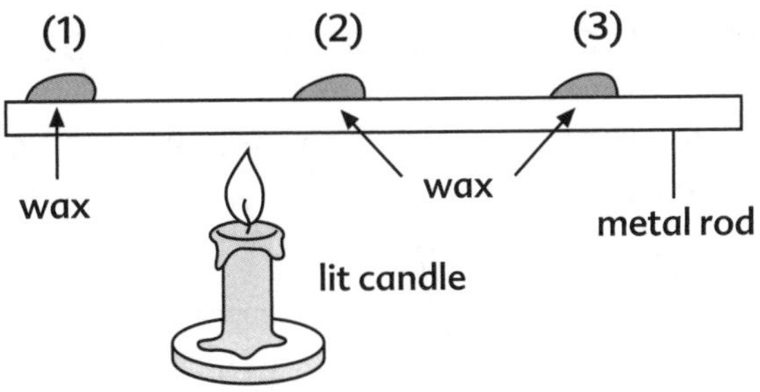

Which is the order in which the pieces of wax melt?

(1) 1 2 3
(2) 2 3 1
(3) 2 1 3
(4) 3 2 1 ( )

24. A glass of ice water is left on a table for ten minutes.

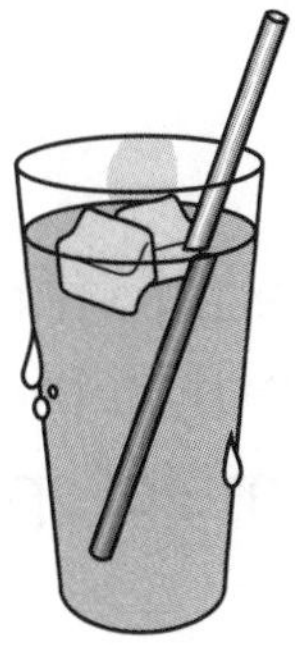

Which of the following about the ice is correct?

	Its temperature will ______.	It will ______ heat to/from its surroundings.
(1)	remain the same	gain
(2)	increase	gain
(3)	decrease	lose
(4)	remain the same	lose

( )

25. The cups below are identical except for the materials they are made from. They contain equal amounts of hot water. In which cup will the water take the longest time to cool to room temperature?

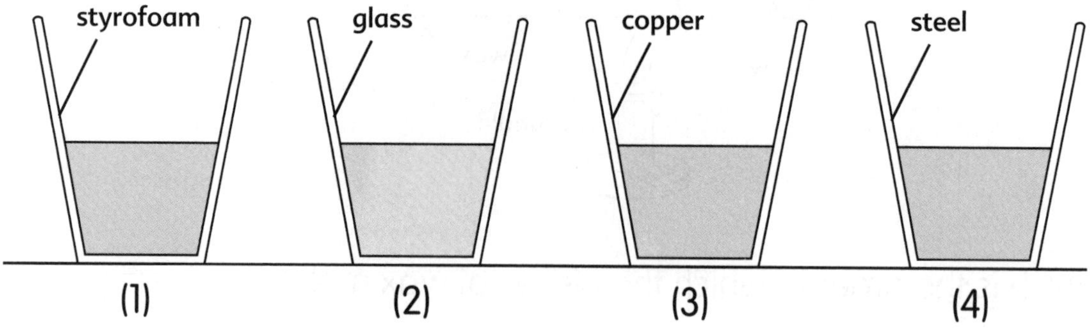

( )

26. A metal spoon is placed on ice as shown in the diagram below. After some time, the metal spoon feels cold. Which of the following is the likely reason?

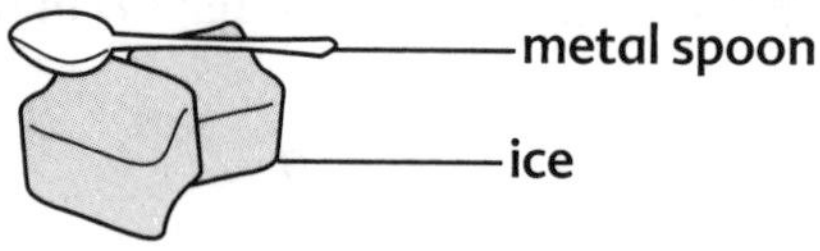

(1) The metal spoon has lost heat to the surrounding air.
(2) The metal spoon has lost heat to the ice.
(3) The ice has lost heat to the metal spoon.
(4) Metal always feels cold. ( )

27. Woollen gloves can keep our hands warm because they ____________.

(1) are good conductors of heat
(2) are poor conductors of heat
(3) are opaque and so can trap heat
(4) are made of non-magnetic materials ( )

28. Which one of the following is grouped correctly?

	Good conductor of heat	Poor conductor of heat
(1)	Aluminium	Iron
(2)	Silver	Gold
(3)	Copper	Wood
(4)	Plastic	Sponge

( )

29. Mrs Tan boiled some water and then allowed it to cool down to room temperature.

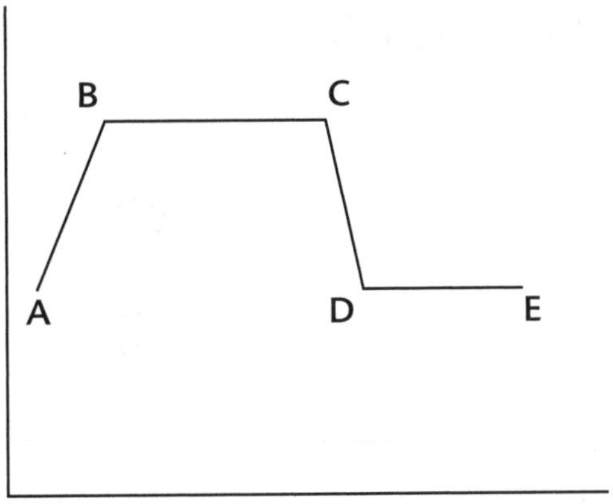

Which part of the graph above shows the water at the boiling stage?

(1) AB
(2) BC
(3) CD
(4) DE

( )

30. Study the diagram below carefully.

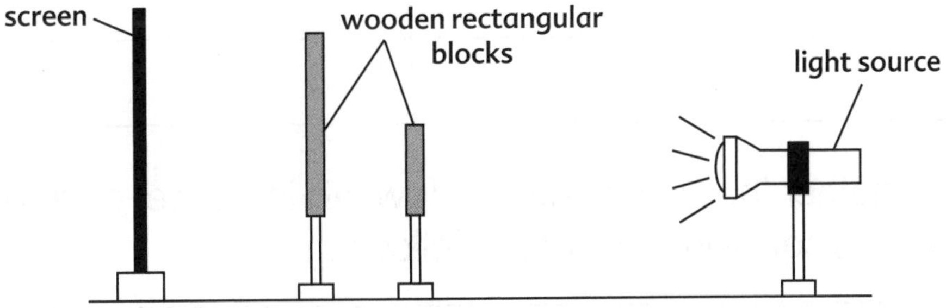

Which of the following correctly represents the shadow formed on the screen?

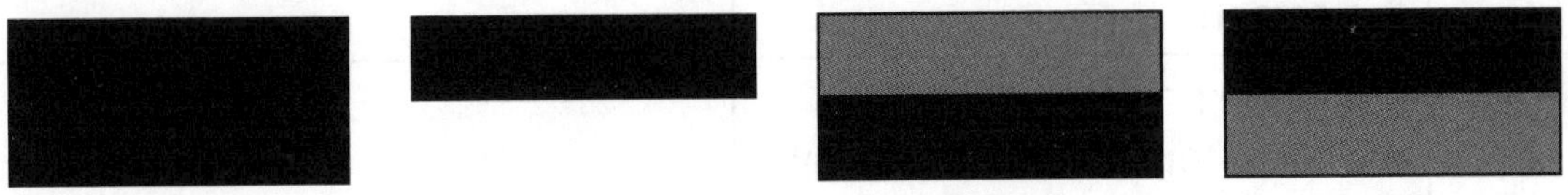

(1) (2) (3) (4)

( )

Section B (40 marks)

Write your answers for each question in the blank spaces provided.

31. Study the diagram below carefully.

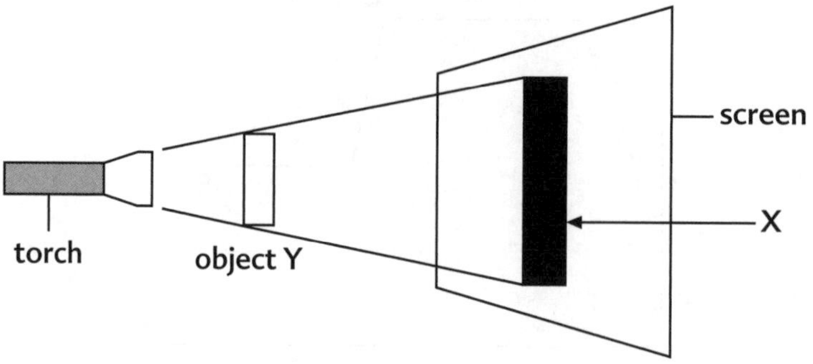

When object Y is placed in front of a torch, shadow X, which is completely black, is seen on the screen.

(a) (i) Which material is Y likely to be made of? Circle your answer. [1]

Clear plastic   Frosted glass   Aluminium

(ii) Explain your answer in (a)(i). [1]

____

____

(b) State whether the size of the shadow will increase, decrease or remain the same in each of the following. [3]

		The size of the shadow will ________.
(i)	The torch and screen remain still while Y is moved towards the screen.	
(ii)	Y and the screen remain still while the torch is moved away from Y.	
(iii)	The torch and Y remain still while the screen is moved away from Y.	

32. A cone is placed between four lights of equal heights and brightness. It has four shadows, as shown in the diagram below.

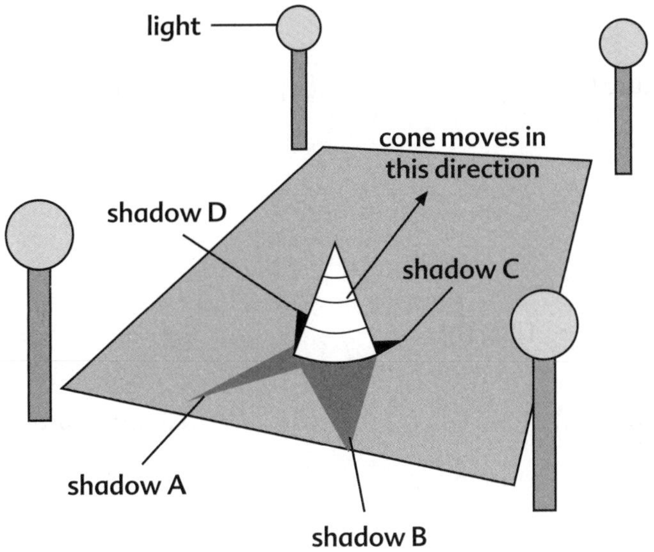

What will happen to each of the four shadows when the cone moves in the direction of the arrow? [2]

____

____

____

____

____

33. Four separate experiments, A, B, C and D, were conducted. The graphs below show how the temperature changed with time in each of the experiments.

(1)

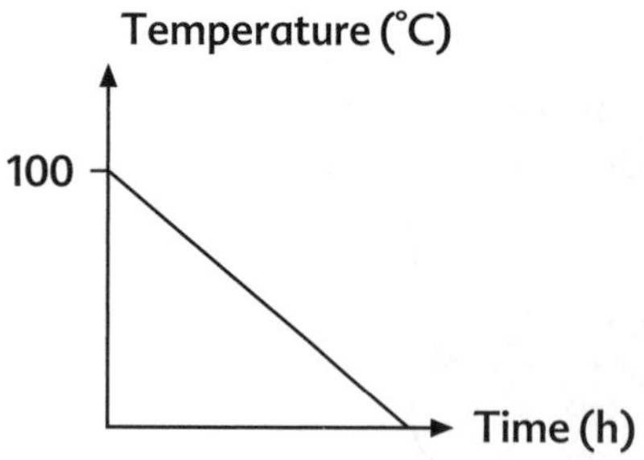

(2)

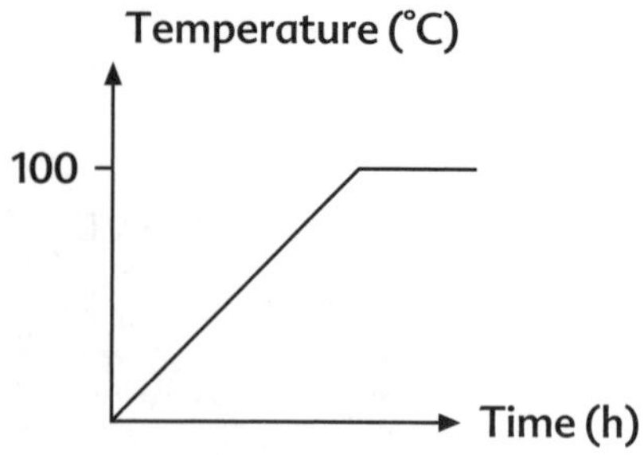

(3)

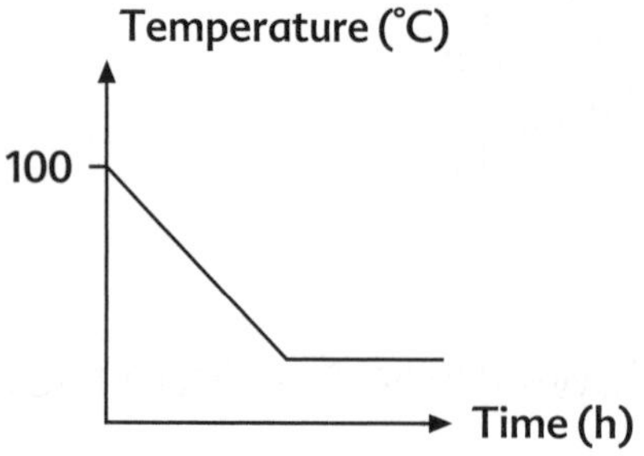

(4)

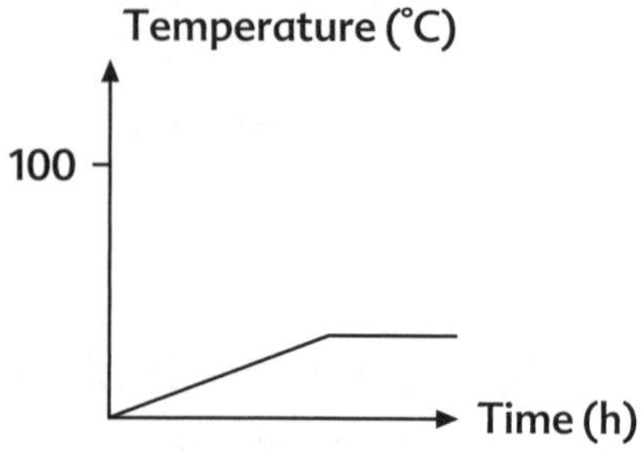

The table below gives a description of Experiments A, B, C and D. Match the graphs to their experiments by completing the table. [4]

	Experiment	Graph number
(A)	A tub of ice-cream is taken out of the freezer and placed on a table for a few hours.	
(B)	Mum cooks some soup. She transfers the boiling soup from the stove to the kitchen table and leaves it there for a few hours.	
(C)	Some soup is boiled on a stove. It is transferred to the freezer and left there until it is frozen.	
(D)	Ice water in a beaker is heated by a Bunsen flame until the water boils.	

34. Mr. Tan travels to work on a train everyday. In winter, he hears a loud click every time the train goes over the gaps in the rails. However, on hot summer days, he hears only faint clicks. Explain why. [3]

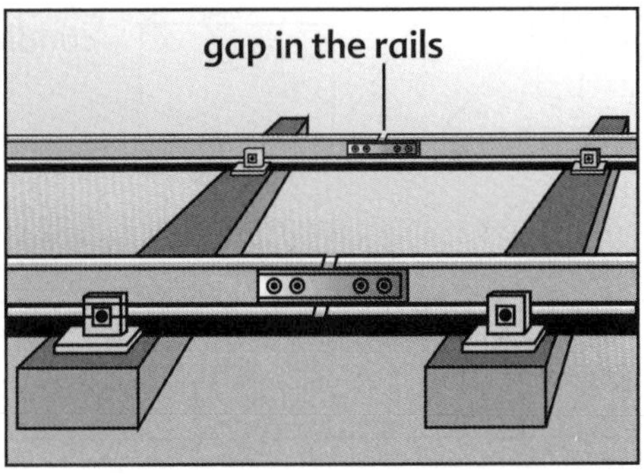

____

____

____

35. Ahmed uses thermometer P to measure the temperature of a bowl of dessert.

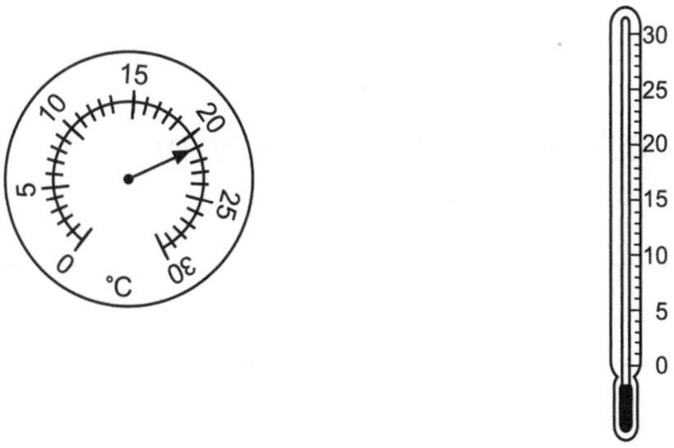

thermometer P thermometer Q

(a) What is the temperature of the dessert? ______________________ [1]

(b) Ahmed uses thermometer Q to measure the same bowl of dessert. On thermometer Q, shade the temperature that Ahmed would read. [1]

(c) Can thermometers P and Q be used to measure the temperature of boiling soup? Why? [2]

____

____

36. Mr. Lee sets up the following experiment.

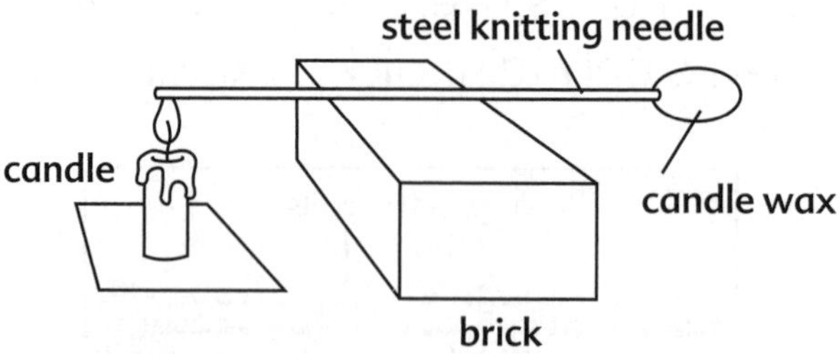

(a) What will happen to the candle wax after some time? [1]

____

(b) Mr. Lee asks Bruce, Cruise and Smith what the aim of the experiment is.

Bruce says: To show that different materials conduct heat at different rates.

Cruise says: To show that heat travels from a hotter region to a cooler region.

Smith says: To show that steel expands on heating.

Who is correct? [1]

____

(c) Explain why the other two boys are wrong. [2]

____

____

37. A block of metal was heated to 280 °C. It was then lowered into a beaker of water at room temperature (25 °C).

(a) What do you expect to observe when the hot metal touches the water? [1]

____

(b) Why does this happen? [2]

____

____

(c) Describe what happens between the hot metal and the water over the next ten minutes. [2]

____

____

(d) The temperature of the water is measured at the end of ten minutes. The reading on the thermometer will be 25 °C.
(Circle your answer.) TRUE / FALSE [1]

38. (a) Two metal cups were stacked together and became stuck.

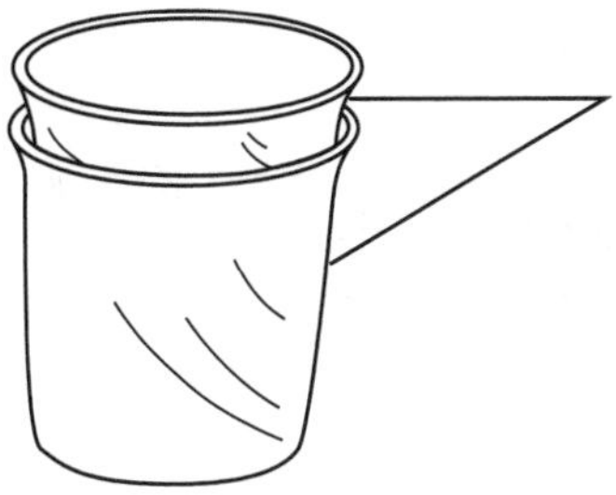

(i) What can be done to make it easier to separate the cups? Draw your answer in the space below. [2]

(ii) Explain how (a)(i) works. [2]

____

____

(b) (i) Using arrows, show the movement of heat, when an egg is cooked in a frying pan. [1]

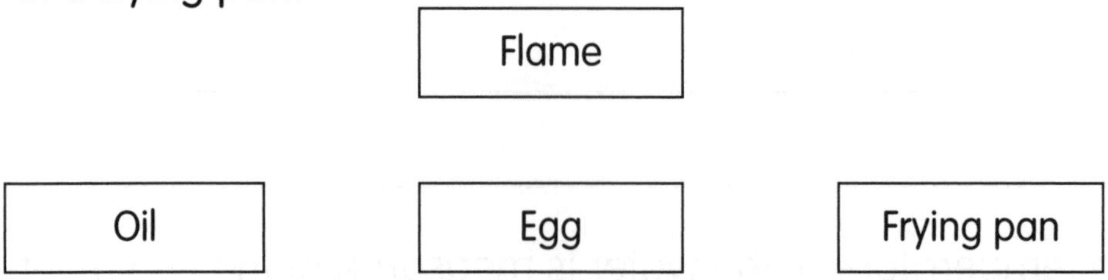

(ii) What happens to the temperature of the egg? [1]

____

39. Study the concept map given below.

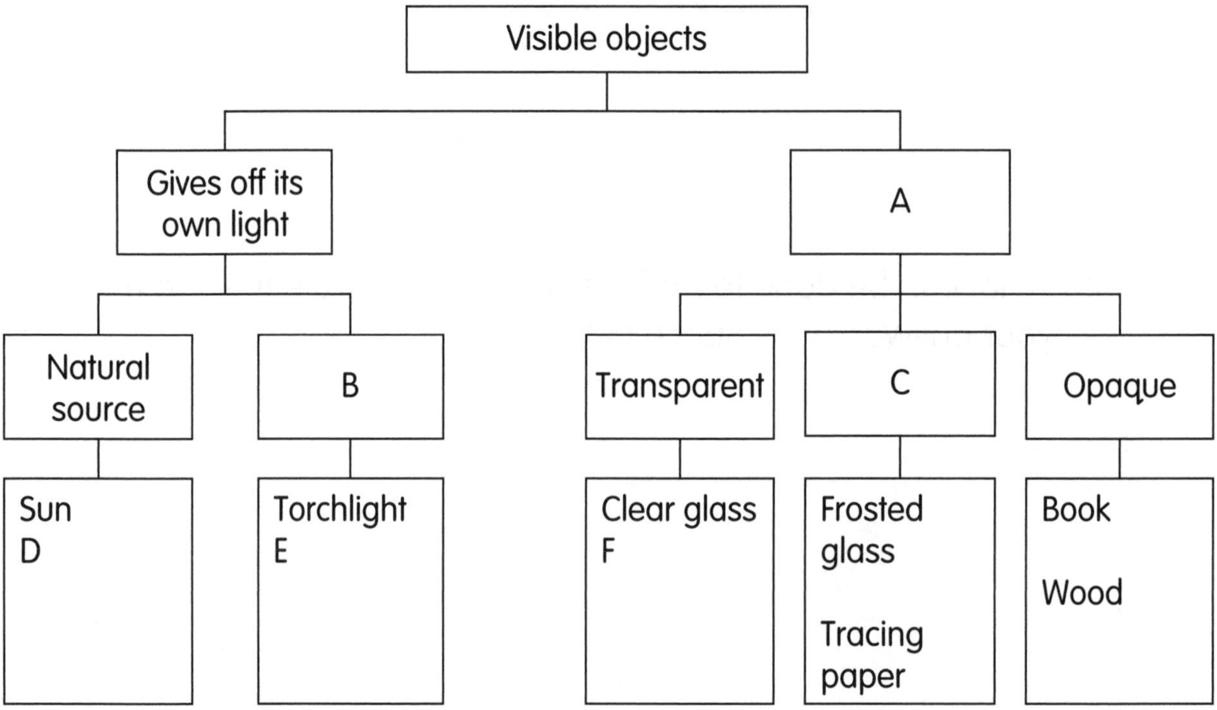

Give appropriate answers for:

A: ____________________ D: ____________________

B: ____________________ E: ____________________

C: ____________________ F: ____________________

End of Paper

Marks:

/100

Cross-thematic Assessment 1

- Diversity
- Cycles

Name: ______________________ Class: __________ Date: ______________

Section A (30 x 2 = 60 marks)

For each question, four options are given. Choose the correct answer and write down your choice, 1, 2, 3 or 4, in the brackets provided.

1. Which one of the following is grouped wrongly?

	Living thing	Non-living thing
(1)	Moss	Bottle
(2)	Fungi	Tin
(3)	Fern	Bacteria
(4)	Grass	Oil

( )

2. Which of the following serves to protect a fish?

(1) Gills
(2) Fins
(3) Scales
(4) Tail ( )

3. Which of the following statements about tadpoles is true?

(A) A tadpole looks like its parent.
(B) The tadpole is the stage after the egg.
(C) A tadpole lives in water.
(D) A tadpole breathes with its gills.

(1) A and B only
(2) C and D only
(3) A, B and D only
(4) B, C and D only ( )

4. Which of the following statements correctly explains why animals reproduce?

(A) To have more of their own kind.
(B) To ensure their own kind continues to be found on Earth.
(C) To have strength in numbers.
(D) To protect themselves from their enemies.

(1) A only
(2) B only
(3) A and B only
(4) A, B, C and D ( )

5. The table below shows the possible materials that could be used to make the objects listed.

	Made of plastic	Made of metal	Made of wood
Paper clip	Yes	Yes	No
Needle	No	Yes	No
X	Yes	Yes	Yes

Which of the following could be object X?

(1) Ruler
(2) Knife
(3) Kettle
(4) Pencil ( )

6. How is the young of a grasshopper different from the adult grasshopper?

(A) The young does not have wings. The adult has wings.
(B) They feed on different kinds of food.
(C) The young is smaller than the adult.
(D) They look different.

(1) A and C only
(2) B and D only
(3) A, B and D only
(4) B, C and D only ( )

7. Study the concept map below.

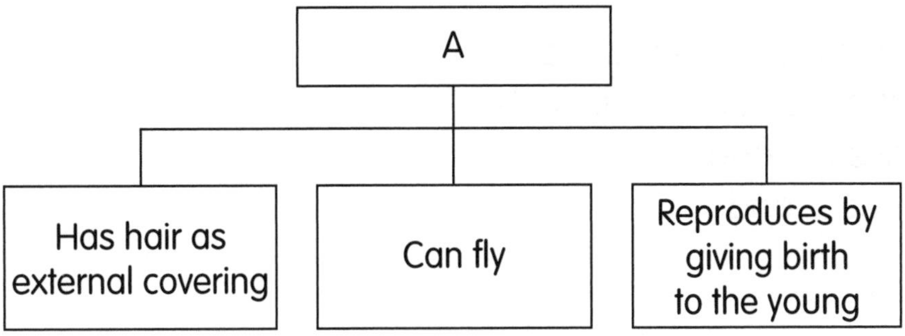

Y is a ____________.

(1) Monkey
(2) Bat
(3) Bird
(4) Penguin ( )

8. The diagram below shows the larva of a mosquito.

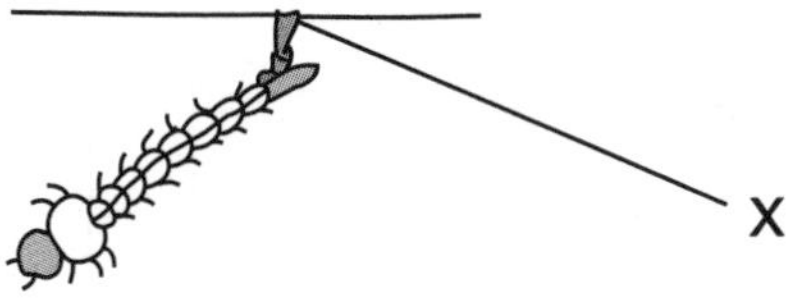

What is the purpose of X?

(1) Feeding
(2) Breathing
(3) Swimming
(4) Seeing ( )

9. Which of the following insects have the same number of stages in their life cycles as a mosquito?

(1) Butterfly and cockroach.
(2) Butterfly and housefly.
(3) Grasshopper and housefly.
(4) Beetle and grasshopper. ( )

10. Which of the following describes the similarities between a caterpillar and a mealworm?

(A) They moult as they grow bigger.
(B) They are the young of insects.
(C) They live on land.
(D) They need food.

(1) A and C only
(2) B and D only
(3) A, C and D only
(4) A, B, C and D ( )

11. The bar chart below shows the number of Aedes mosquitoes over the last four months.

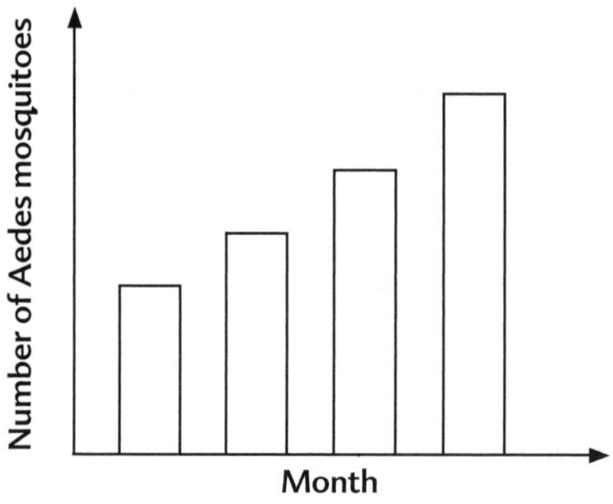

The bar chart shows that the Aedes mosquito is able to ____________.

(1) take in food
(2) reproduce
(3) grow
(4) respond to changes around it ( )

12. The diagram below shows a bicycle. It is made of different materials.

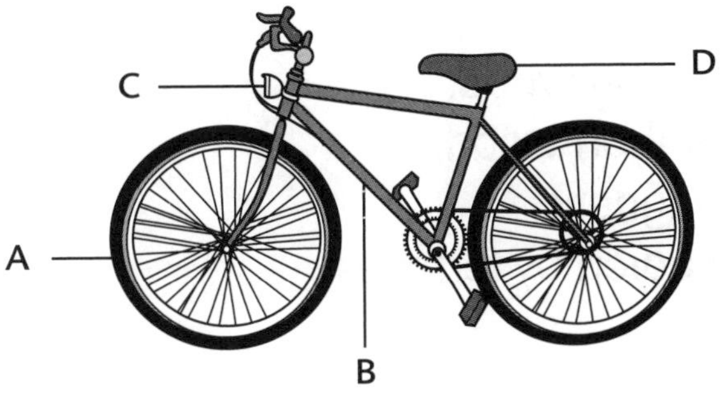

Which of the following is correct?

	Bicycle part	Material	Reason
(A)	Tyre	Rubber	It is flexible and can be stretched.
(B)	Body frame	Metal	It is strong and hard.
(C)	Lamp	Plastic	It allows light to pass through.
(D)	Seat	Foam	It is soft and comfortable.

(1) A and B only
(2) C and D only
(3) A, C and D only
(4) A, B, C and D ( )

13. Study the classification table below.

Group A	Group B	Group C
Magazines	Stapler pins	Glue
Newspapers	Thumb tacks	Paint
Brochures	Paper clips	Correction liquid

Which of the following objects are correctly placed?

	Group A	Group B	Group C
(1)	Greeting cards	Toothpicks	Ink
(2)	DVDs	Dental floss	Tooth paste
(3)	Books	Needles	Nail polish
(4)	Vanguard sheets	Erasers	Poster colour

( )

14. Which of the following correctly explains why bricks are considered better building materials than wood?

(A) Bricks are harder than wood.
(B) Bricks are heavier than wood.
(C) Bricks are non-magnetic.
(D) Bricks cannot be eaten by termites.

(1) A and D only
(2) C and D only
(3) A, B and C only
(4) A, B, C and D ( )

15. Which is the following are reasons why fungi are living things?

(A) Fungi can respond to changes in the surroundings.
(B) Fungi produce spores when they are mature.
(C) Fungi cannot make their own food.
(D) Fungi can grow.

(1) A and C only
(2) B and D only
(3) A, B and D only
(4) B, C and D only ( )

16. Mark has a cup which he likes very much. He has used the cup for a few months. He has dropped the cup many times and it does not break or change shape. Which of the following materials is the cup likely to be made of?

(1) Styrofoam
(2) Metal
(3) Porcelain
(4) Paper ( )

17.

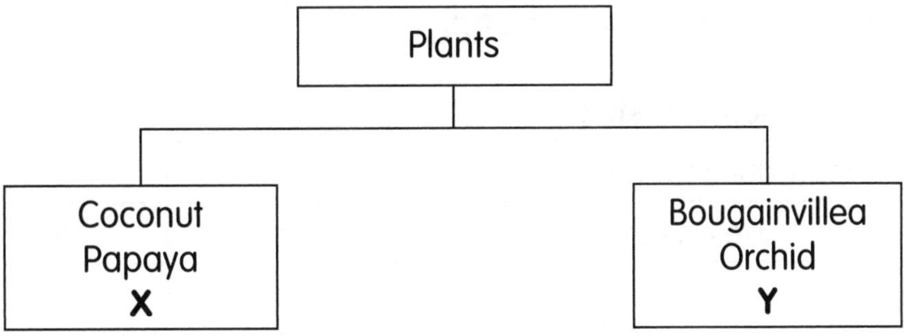

Which of the following are likely to be X and Y?

	X	Y
(1)	Durian	Rose
(2)	Water Lily	Hibiscus
(3)	Angsana	Mango
(4)	Heliconia	Rambutan

( )

18. Which of the following is a similarity between a whale and a shark?

(1) Breathes using gills.
(2) Lives in water.
(3) Lays eggs.
(4) Has scales as its outer covering. ( )

19. Which one of the following is **not** true about bacteria?

(1) Bacteria are microorganisms.
(2) Bacteria can live in the air, water and soil.
(3) Some bacteria are harmful while others are useful.
(4) Bacteria reproduce by spores found in spore sacs. ( )

20. Study the classification chart below carefully.

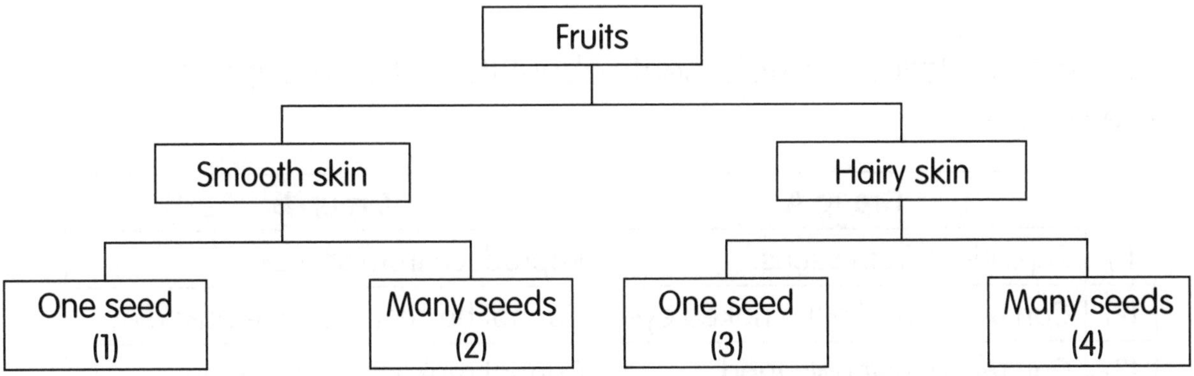

Where would you place tomato in the boxes above? ( )

21. Study the table given below carefully.

Characteristics	Plant A	Plant B
Reproduce from spores	Yes	No
Live on land	Yes	Yes

Where would Plants A and B fit in the classification chart below?

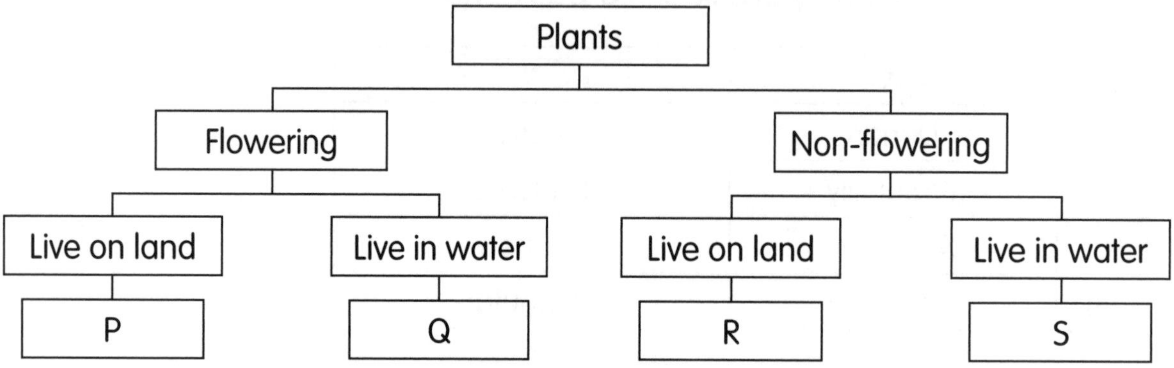

	Plant A	Plant B
(1)	P	Q
(2)	R	P
(3)	S	R
(4)	Q	S

( )

22. The diagram below shows two groups of living things.

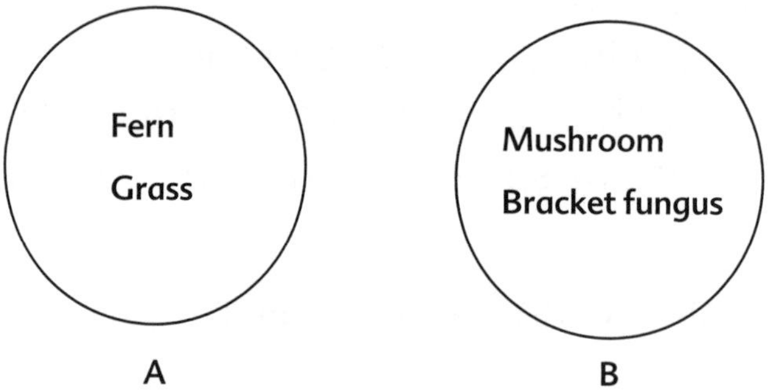

Which of the following statements about these two groups of living things are correct?

	Group A	Group B
(1)	Reproduce from seeds.	Reproduce from spores.
(2)	Can be seen with the naked eye.	Cannot be seen with the naked eye.
(3)	Can make their own food.	Cannot make their own food.
(4)	Are not edible.	Are edible.

( )

23. Which of the following statements correctly describes the following animals?

Cow	**Rabbit**	**Sheep**	**Hamster**

(A) They feed on plants only.
(B) They are food to other animals.
(C) They reproduce by giving birth to their young.
(D) They have the same outer coverings.

(1) A and B only
(2) C and D only
(3) A, B and C only
(4) A, B, C and D ( )

24. Study the diagram below carefully.

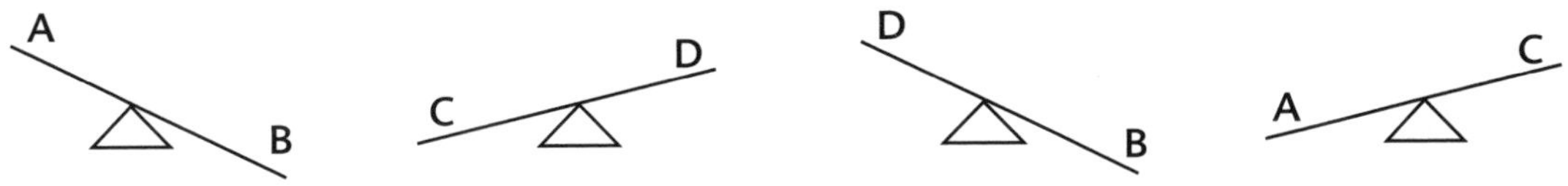

Which of the following arranges the objects' masses from the biggest to the smallest?

(1) C, D, B, A
(2) A, B, C, D
(3) D, C, A, B
(4) B, A, C, D ( )

25. In which state does matter have fixed volume?

(1) Solid only
(2) Solid and liquid only
(3) Liquid and gaseous only
(4) Solid, liquid and gaseous ( )

26. Steam and water vapour ____________.

(A) have mass
(B) do not have definite shapes
(C) have definite volumes
(D) occupy space

(1) A and D only
(2) B and C only
(3) A, B and D only
(4) B, C and D only ( )

27. Which of the following consists of two states of matter?

(1) Ping pong ball
(2) One dollar coin
(3) Wooden chopstick
(4) Alcohol ( )

28. Which of the following is **not** matter?

(1) Wind
(2) Heat
(3) Steam
(4) Butter ( )

29. Into which of the following containers can 150 cm^3 of air be pumped?

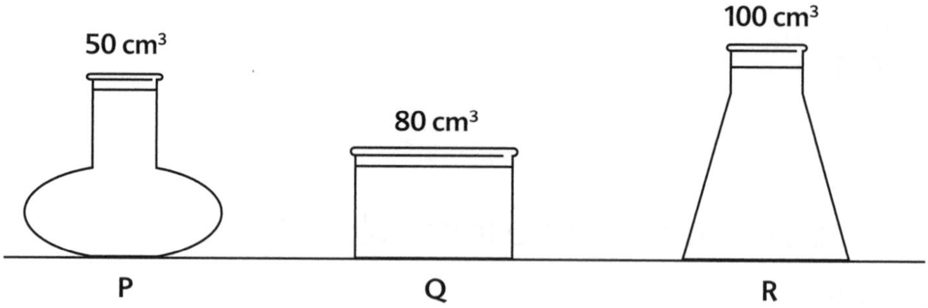

(1) Q only
(2) R only
(3) Q and R only
(4) P,Q and R ( )

30. Which of the following would change if 100 ml of water was poured from a beaker into a 150 ml round bottom flask?

(1) Space the water occupies.
(2) Shape of water.
(3) Volume of water.
(4) Mass of water. ( )

Section B (40 marks)

Write your answers for each question in the blank spaces provided.

31. The following is a list of the characteristics of living things.

(A) Need air, water and food.
(B) Grow
(C) Move by themselves.
(D) Respond to changes around them.
(E) Reproduce
(F) Die

Match the appropriate characteristic to each description in the table below. [7]

	Description	Characteristic
(1)	A mango tree bearing fruit.	
(2)	A bee flying round a flower.	
(3)	A boy removing his hand from a hot plate.	
(4)	A boy becoming a man.	
(5)	A sick man breathing through an oxygen mask.	
(6)	A plant wilting.	
(7)	A baby drinking milk.	

32. The flowchart below gives the characteristics of different animals.

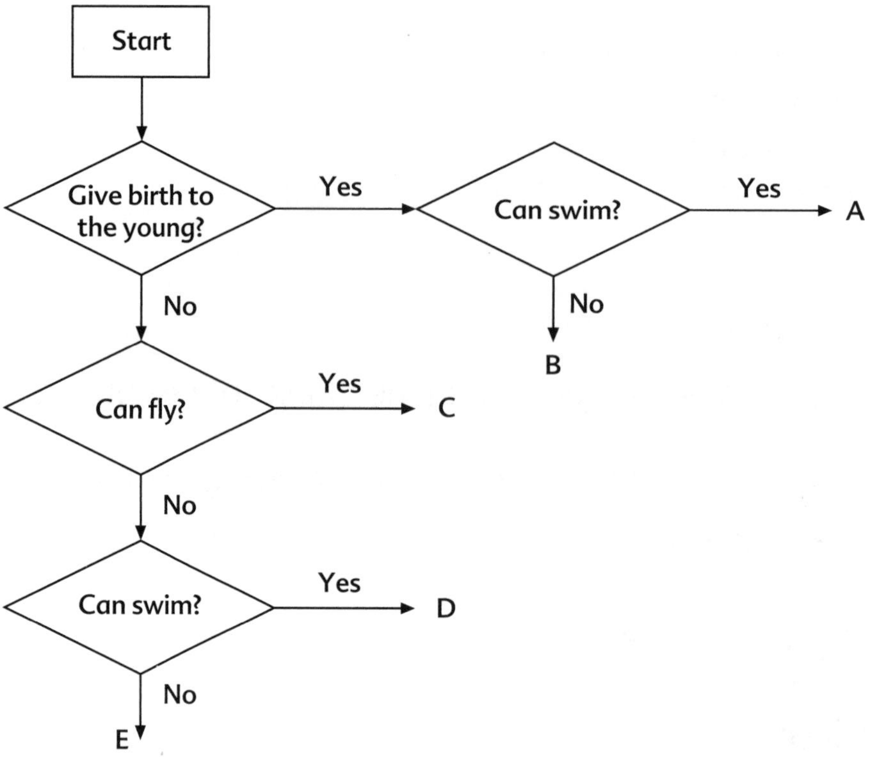

(a) Complete the table below by giving an example of an animal that has the characteristics stated in the flowchart. A has been done for you. [4]

A	B	C	D	E
Whale				

(b) What outer covering would animal C most probably have? [1]

____

(c) Where would you classify the following animals? [3]

(i) Mosquito: ______________________

(ii) Turtle: ______________________

(iii) Ostrich: ______________________

(d) Which group of animals do A and B belong to? [1]

____

33. Mrs Tan wants to investigate the strengths of four different sheets, A, B, C and D, which are identical except for the materials they are made of. She uses the experimental set-up shown below for each sheet.

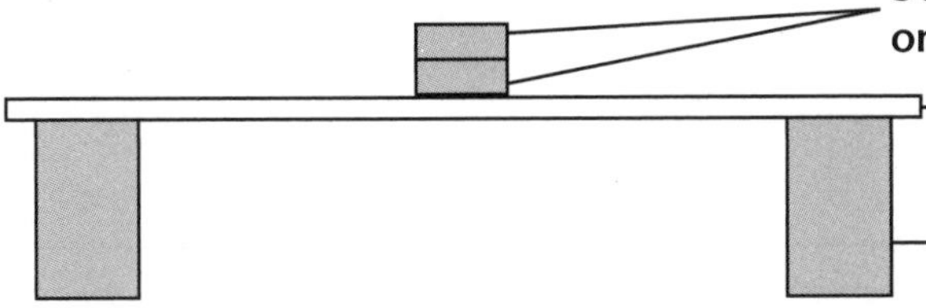

(a) Mrs Tan keeps stacking blocks on each sheet until it breaks or bends. She summarises her observations in the table below.

	Sheet A	Sheet B	Sheet C	Sheet D
Number of blocks that cause the sheet to break/bend	1	50	6	20

Which sheet is the strongest? Explain your answer. [2]

____

____

(b) The following lists four different materials according to their strengths, from the strongest to the least strong.

Steel > Plastic > Glass > Cardboard

Match each sheet to the material it is likely to be made of. [4]

Sheet A: ____________________

Sheet B: ____________________

Sheet C: ____________________

Sheet D: ____________________

34. Compare the tadpole to a fish using the graphic organiser below. [4]

Similarities

(a) ______________________________

(b) ______________________________

Tadpole   Fish

Differences

Tadpole	Fish
(a) ______________	______________
(b) ______________	______________

35. Study the classification chart below.

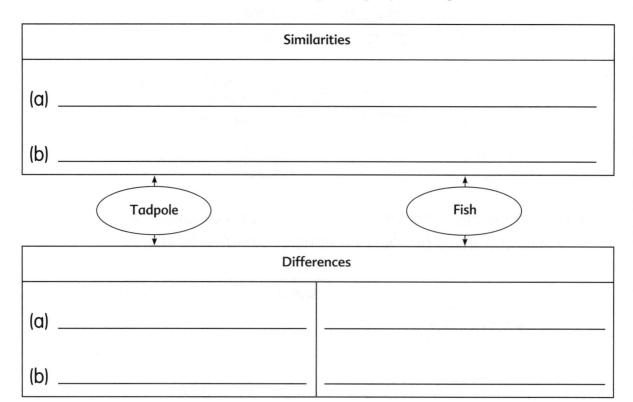

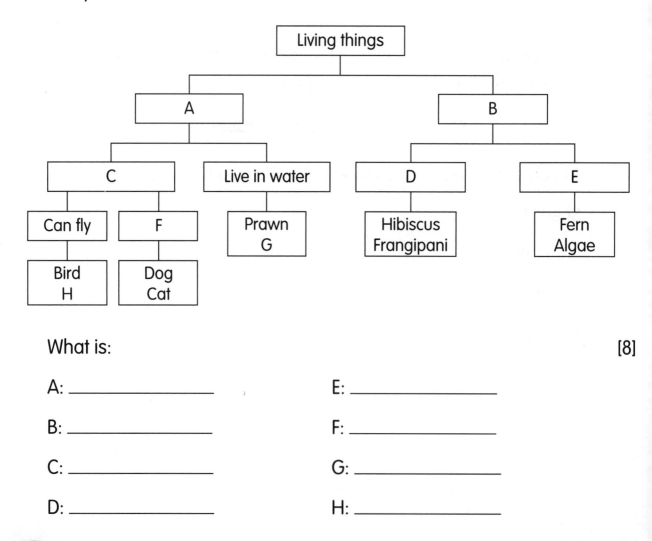

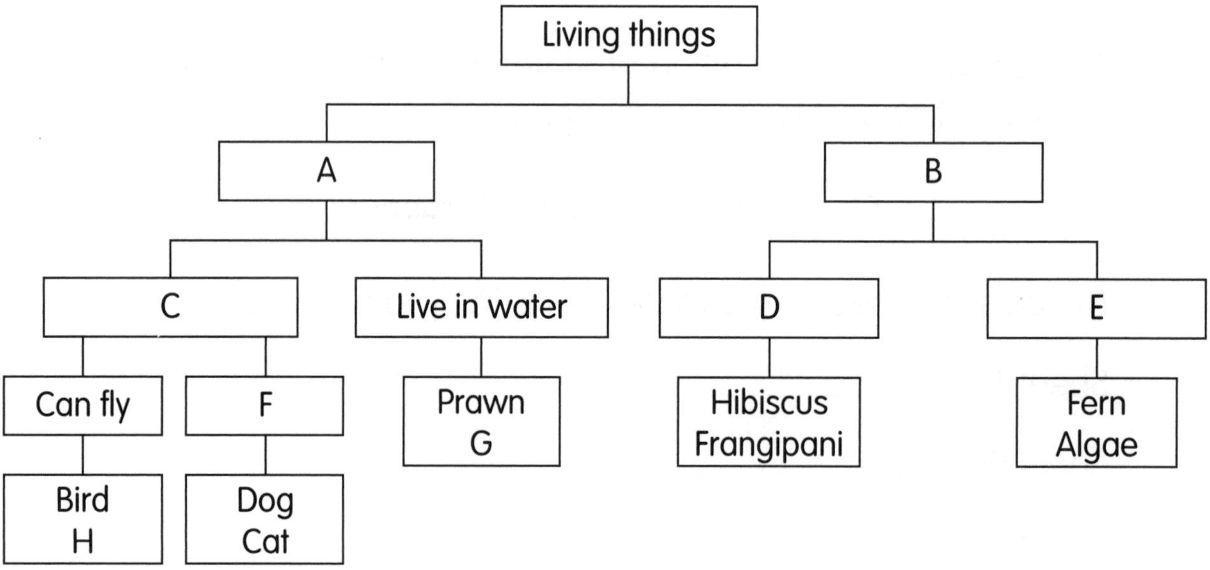

What is: [8]

A: ______________   E: ______________

B: ______________   F: ______________

C: ______________   G: ______________

D: ______________   H: ______________

36. The diagram below shows three syringes.

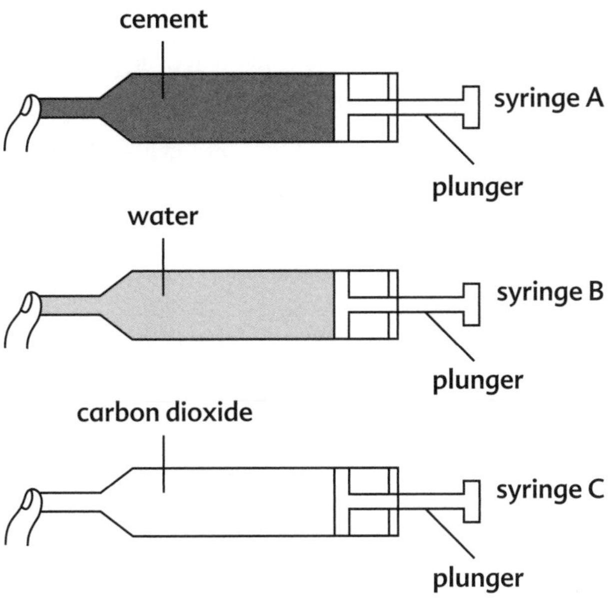

Complete the table below. [6]

	Can the plunger be pushed in?	Why?
Syringe A		
Syringe B		
Syringe C		

End of Paper

BLANK

Marks:

/100

Cross-thematic Assessment 2

- Systems
- Interactions
- Energy

Name: ______________________ Class: __________ Date: ______________

Section A (30 x 2 = 60 marks)

For each question, four options are given. Choose the correct answer and write down your choice, 1, 2, 3 or 4, in the brackets provided.

1. Which one of the following is not a system?

(1) Violin
(2) Piano
(3) Wooden flute
(4) Bell ( )

2. Which of the following substances are carried by blood?

(A) Oxygen
(B) Carbon dioxide
(C) Water
(D) Digested food

(1) A and D only
(2) B and C only
(3) A, B and D only
(4) A, B, C and D ( )

3. In which part of the digestive system is digestion not carried out?

(1) Mouth
(2) Stomach
(3) Small intestine
(4) Large intestine ( )

4. Which of the following has the functions stated?

	Function: Protects delicate organs and gives the body its shape
(1)	Circulatory system
(2)	Skeletal system
(3)	Respiratory system
(4)	Muscular system

( )

5. Which of the following is true about the skull?

(A) It protects the brain.
(B) It gives the head a shape.
(C) It is part of the skeletal system.
(D) It enables the body to move.

(1) A and B only
(2) C and D only
(3) A, B and C only
(4) A, B, C and D ( )

6. Which of the following statements is true about the muscles in our muscular system?

(A) They work with our skeletal system to allow us to move.
(B) They may or may not be attached to bones.
(C) They lie underneath our skin.
(D) They often work in pairs.

(1) A and C only
(2) B and D only
(3) A, B and D only
(4) A, B, C and D only ( )

7. The leaves of plants are able to use sunlight to make food because they have __________?
   (1) tiny openings called stomata
   (2) the green pigment called chlorophyll
   (3) veins which transport water
   (4) flat, broad surfaces ( )

8. Why do gardeners loosen the soil in pots or planting troughs?
   (1) To air the soil so that the roots can get enough oxygen.
   (2) To allow the roots to absorb more water.
   (3) To stimulate the roots to grow more roots.
   (4) To help the roots to absorb more mineral salts. ( )

9. The muscles in our __________ work all the time.
   (1) heart
   (2) leg
   (3) throat
   (4) arm ( )

10. Which of the following is true about blood vessels?
   (A) They are tube-like structures.
   (B) The blood in them moves continuously.
   (C) They carry blood rich in oxygen from the lungs to the heart.
   (D) They carry blood rich in carbon dioxide from all parts of the body to the lungs.

   (1) A and B only
   (2) C and D only
   (3) B, C and D only
   (4) A, B, C and D ( )

11. Alan sets up the following experiment.

Which one of the graphs below shows the change in temperature of the water over time?

(1)

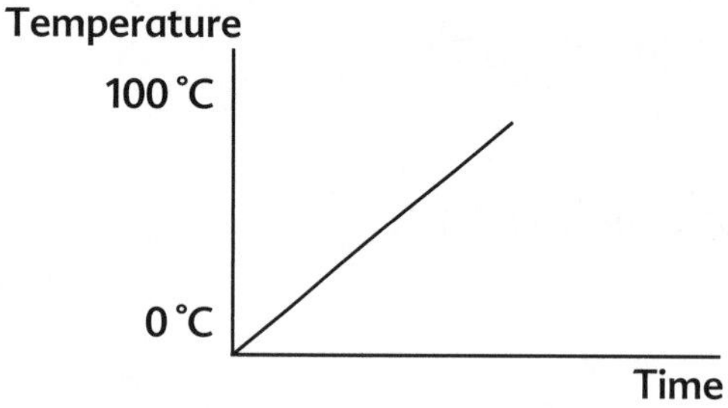

(2)

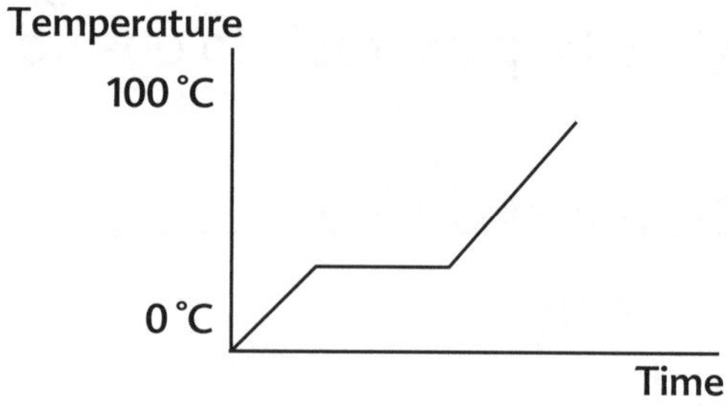

(3)

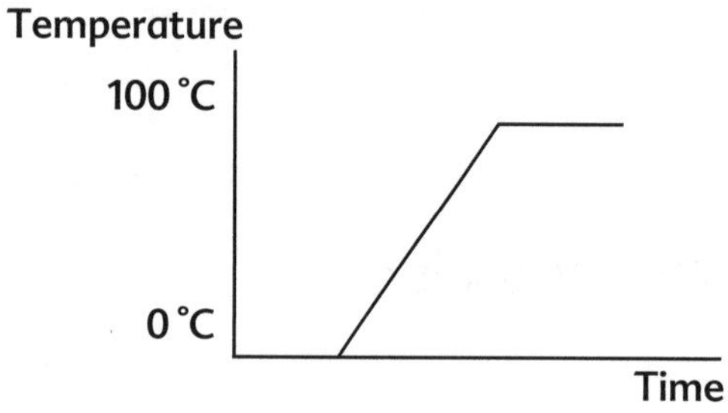

(4)

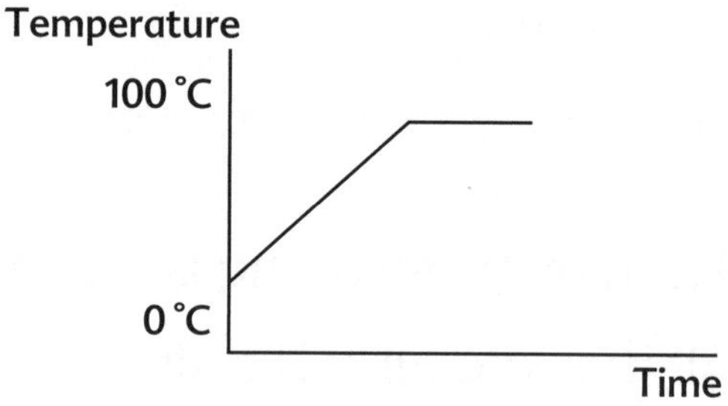

( )

12. In which of the following activities is heat lost?

(1) Barbecuing a piece of meat.
(2) Making ice cream from milk.
(3) Toasting bread.
(4) Making pop-corn. ( )

13. What happens when ice starts to melt into water?

(1) Heat is absorbed by the ice.
(2) Heat is given out by the ice.
(3) The temperature of the ice increases.
(4) The temperature of the ice decreases. ( )

14. Which of the following processes does not require heat to be supplied?

(A) The melting of wax.
(B) Forming a shadow.
(C) Steaming buns.
(D) The making of food by leaves.

(1) B only
(2) D only
(3) A and C only
(4) B and D only ( )

Use the classification table below to answer Questions 15 and 16.

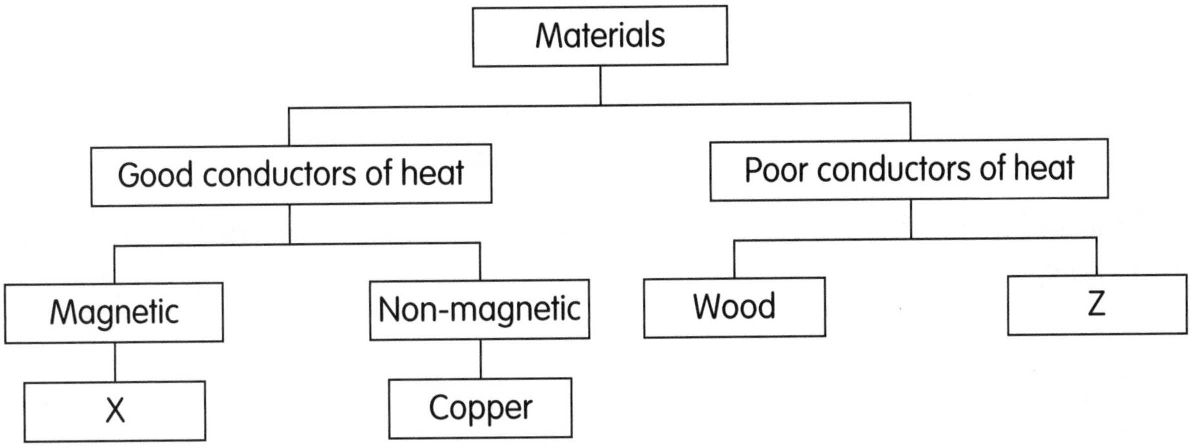

15. Which of the following is likely to be X?

(1) Plastic
(2) Steel
(3) Glass
(4) Wool ( )

16. Which of the following is likely to be Z?

(1) Zinc
(2) Nickel
(3) Aluminum
(4) Rubber ( )

17. Which of the following statements about heat and light is correct?

	Heat	Light
(1)	Cannot be seen	Can be seen
(2)	Cannot be felt	Can be felt
(3)	Is a form of energy	Is not a form of energy
(4)	Is not a form of energy	Is absorbed

( )

18. Study the diagram below carefully.

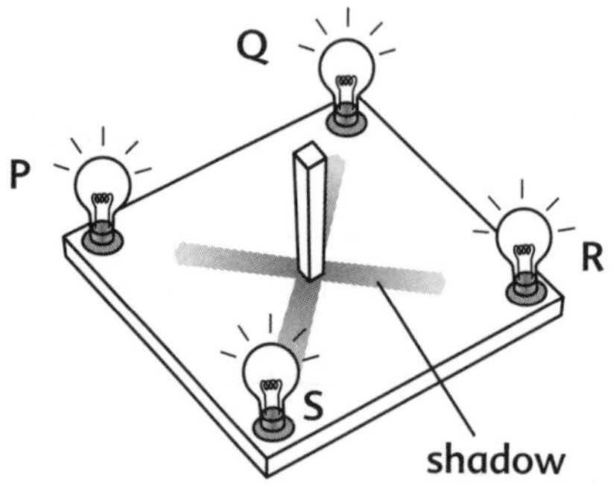

Which of the bulbs, P, Q, R or S must be switched on to get the shadows shown?

(1) P and Q only
(2) Q and R only
(3) R and S only
(4) P, Q, R and S

( )

19. Study the diagram below carefully.

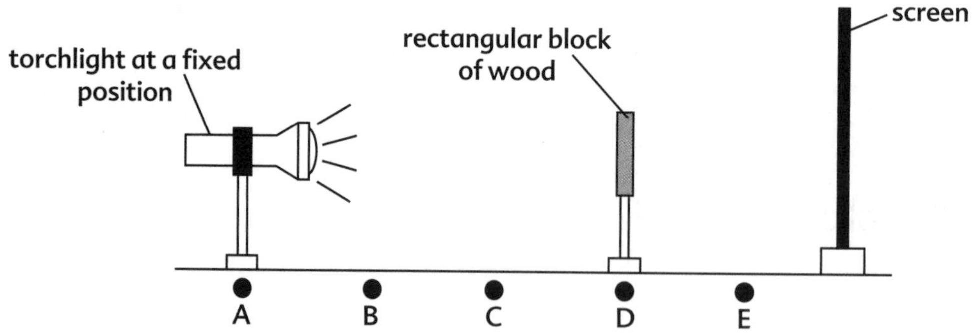

To obtain the largest shadow, which of the following positions must be used?

	Position of light source	Position of rectangular block
(1)	A	B
(2)	B	D
(3)	C	E
(4)	A	E

( )

20. Which of the following explains why cooking utensils are made of metal but the handles are made of plastic?

(1) Metal is hard while plastic is soft.
(2) Metal is heavy while plastic is light.
(3) Metal is durable while plastic is less durable.
(4) Metal is a good conductor of heat while plastic is a poor conductor of heat. ( )

21. Study the classification chart below carefully.

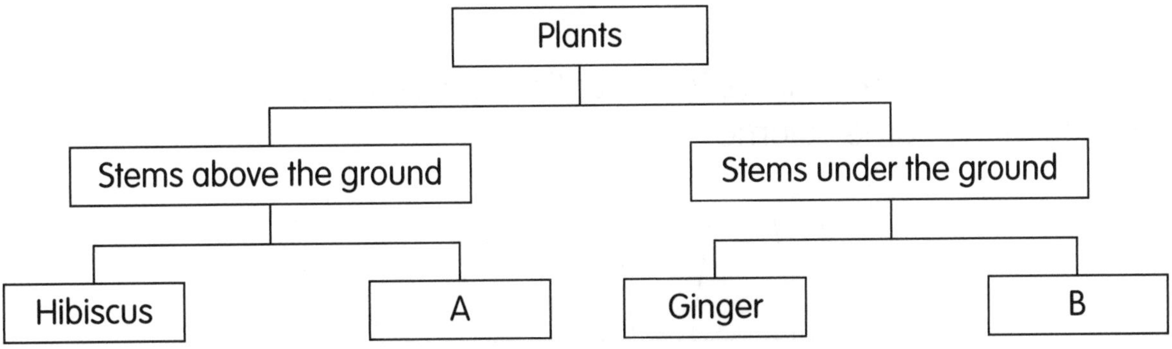

Which of the following are examples of A and B?

	A	B
(1)	Bougainvillea	Orchid
(2)	Rose	Potato
(3)	Onion	Rose
(4)	Ixora	Balsam

( )

22. Which of the following consists of objects that are all conductors of heat?

(1) Iron wire, thumb tacks, aluminium cup
(2) Plastic bottle, aluminium cup, rubber hose
(3) Wooden chopstick, paper towel, woollen scarf
(4) Pencil, iron lock, masking tape ( )

23. Which of the following will, when shone on with a torch, form a black shadow on the screen?

(1) Clear plastic sheet
(2) Frosted glass
(3) Ceramic tile
(4) Tracing paper ( )

24. The diagram below shows a wooden rod held vertically on a stand. From which position should light be shone such that the shadow formed is the shortest?

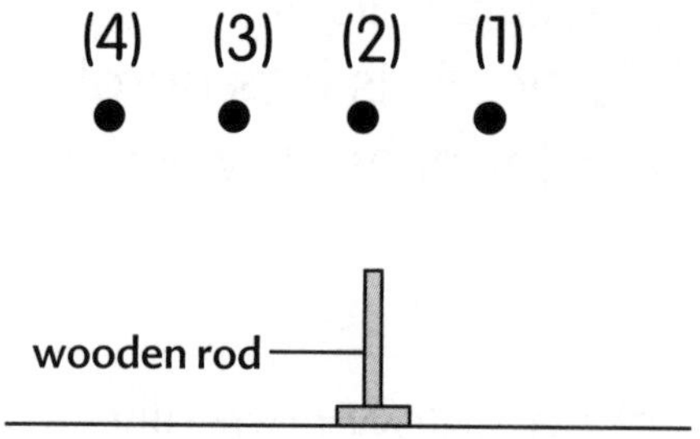

( )

25. The diagram below shows four identical glasses containing different liquids of the same volume.

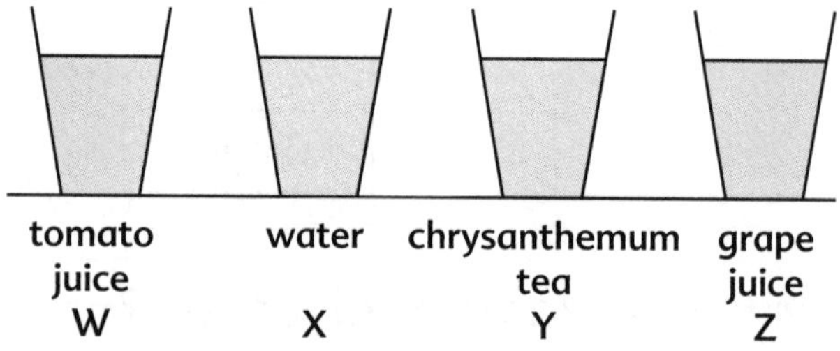

Arrange the glasses according to how much light they allow to pass through. The glass which allows the most light to pass through should be on the left.

(1) WXYZ
(2) XYZW
(3) YWXY
(4) ZYXW ( )

26. A bar magnet is lowered into a dish containing some iron filings as shown in the diagram below.

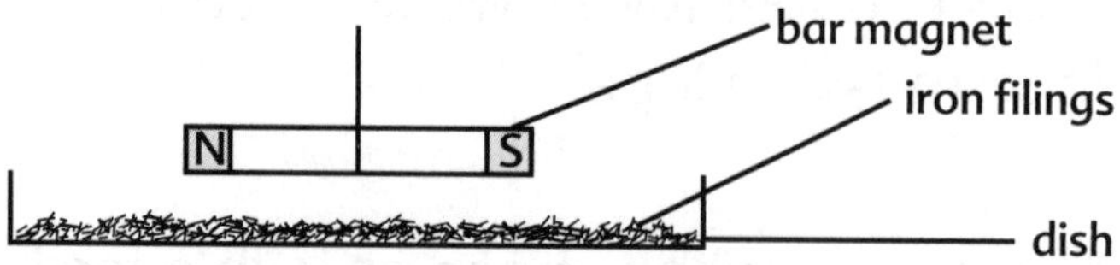

Which of the following is likely to be observed?

(1) The iron filings will be attracted to the centre of the magnet.
(2) The iron filings will be attracted to one end of the magnet.
(3) The iron filings will be attracted to both ends of the magnet.
(4) Nothing will happen. ( )

27. Which materials are classified correctly?

	Magnetic	Non-magnetic
(1)	Nickel	Iron
(2)	Iron	Aluminium
(3)	Aluminium	Copper
(4)	Copper	Steel

( )

28. Which of the following appliances have magnets in them?

(A) Gas cooker
(B) Washing machine
(C) Electric kettle
(D) Refrigerator

(1) A and C only
(2) B and D only
(3) A, B and D only
(4) A, B, C and D ( )

29. In which of the following situations will the magnets move away from each other?

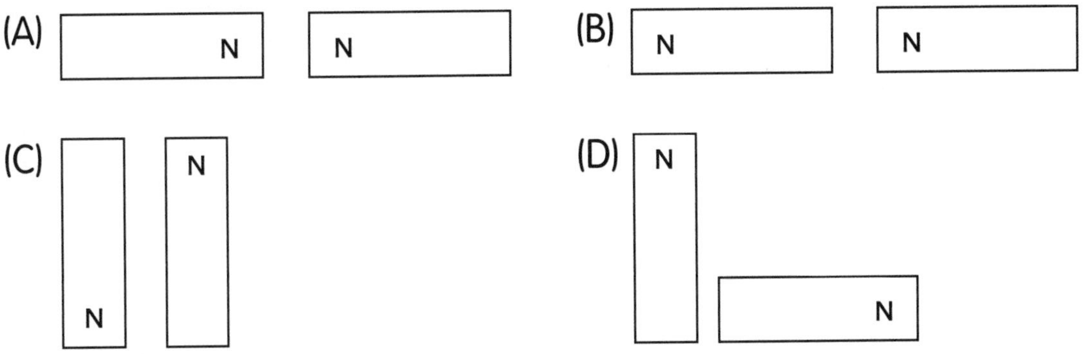

(1) A and D only
(2) B and C only
(3) A and C only
(4) B and D only ( )

30. A magnet is accidentally dropped and broke into pieces.

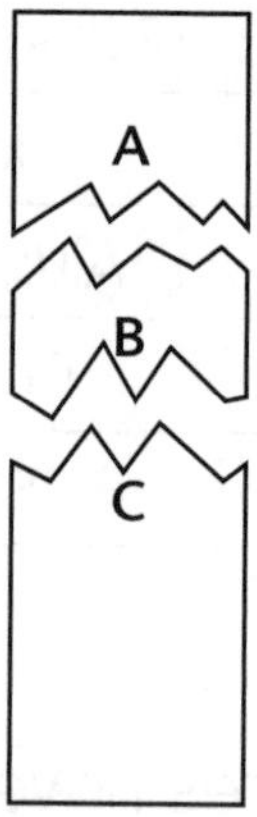

Which of the following is correct?

	A	B	C
(1)	N	S	N
(2)	S	N	S
(3)	S	S	S
(4)	N	N	S

( )

Section B (40 marks)

Write your answers for each question in the blank spaces provided.

31. Study the flowchart given below.

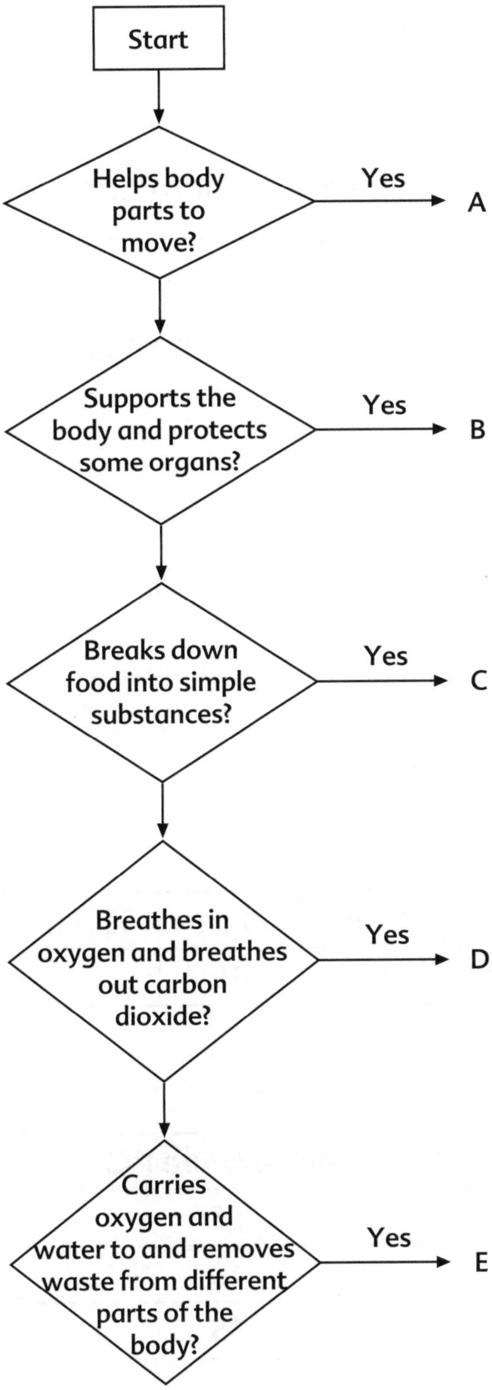

Which body systems do A, B, C, D and E represent? [5]

____

____

____

32. The following represents the different parts of the human digestive system.

Mouth → Gullet → Stomach → Small Intestine → Large Intestine → Anus

(a) What is the function of the gullet? [1]

____

(b) At which parts of the digestive system does digestion take place? [3]

____

(c) Describe what happens to food when it is in the mouth. [2]

____

____

(d) What activity takes place in the large intestine? [1]

____

33. Study the two tables given below.

Table 1

Time	8 am	10 am	12 pm	2 pm	4 pm
Length of shadow (cm)	90	45	0	45	90

Table 2

Time (min)	Temperature (°C)
0	25
3	40
6	55
9	75
12	95
15	100

(a) Suggest a suitable title each for Table 1 and Table 2. [2]

____

____

(b) Bar chart 1 represents the information in Table 1 while Bar chart 2 represents the information in Table 2.

(i) Fill in the boxes below to label the axes of Bar charts 1 and 2. [2]

(ii) Complete Bar charts 1 and 2 using the information from Tables 1 and 2. [5]

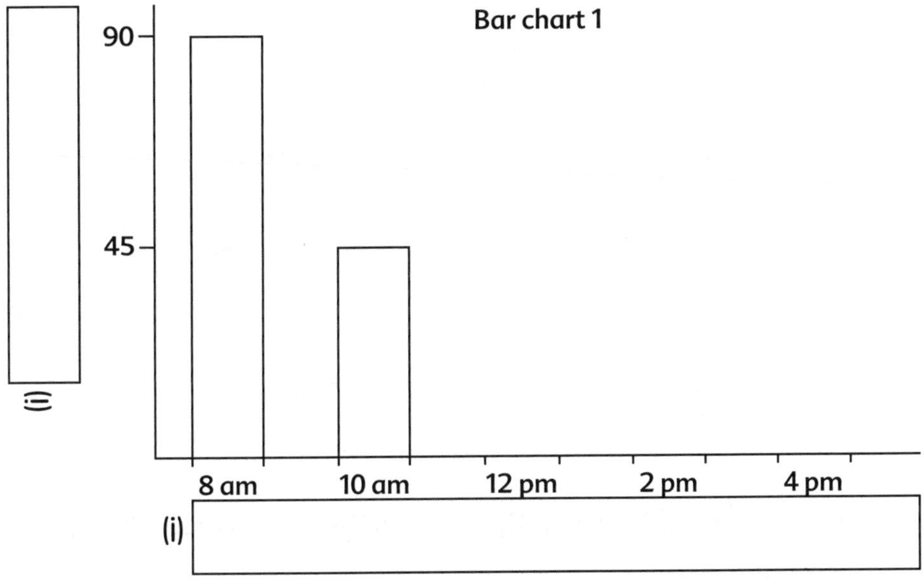

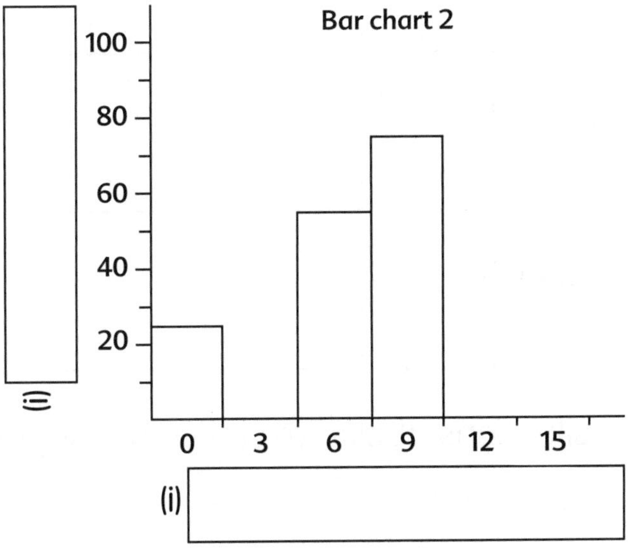

(c) Bar chart 2 actually shows the change in temperature of a beaker of water over 15 minutes.

(i) Has the water gained or lost energy during the 15 minutes? [1]

___

(ii) Explain your answer in (i). [1]

___

(iii) State one change that would occur if the water continues to be heated after 15 minutes. [1]

____

34. Study the following experimental set-up and answer the questions given.

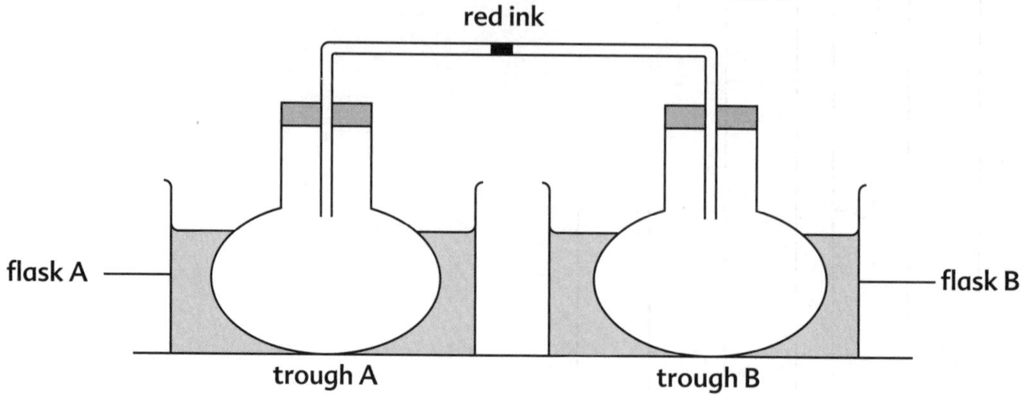

(a) What must you do to the water in trough A in order for the red ink to:

(i) move to the left [1]

____

(ii) move to the right [1]

____

(iii) remain where it is [1]

____

(b) In each of the situations above, explain what happens to the air in flask A. [3]

(i) In (a)(i) ____

(ii) In (a)(ii) ____

(iii) In (a)(iii) ____

(c) What will happen to the red ink if ice is added into trough B? [1]

____

35. The diagram below shows an experimental set-up to observe the shadows formed by different objects when lit from different directions.

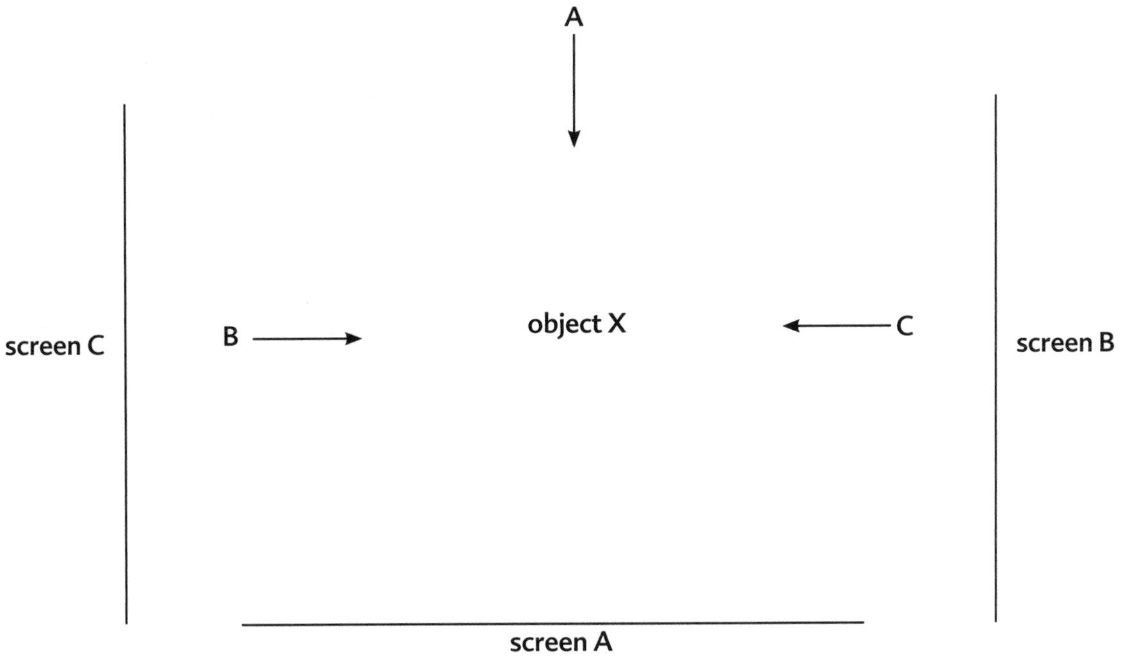

Object X is lit from directions A, B and C, one at a time. In the table below, draw the shadows that are formed on each of the screens, based on the shape of object X . [9]

Object X	Screen A	Screen B	Screen C

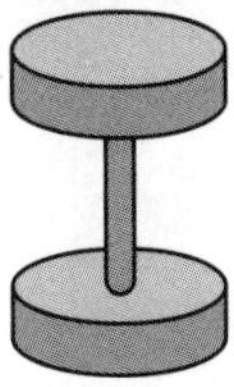			

End of Paper

BLANK

Cross-thematic Assessment 3

Marks: /100

- Diversity
- Cycles
- Systems
- Interactions
- Energy

Name: ______________________ Class: __________ Date: ______________

Section A (30 x 2 = 60 marks)

For each question, four options are given. Choose the correct answer and write down your choice, 1, 2, 3 or 4, in the brackets provided.

1. Which of the following states the similarities between a chicken and a snake?

   (A) They have the same body covering.
   (B) They eat the same kind of food.
   (C) They move in the same way.
   (D) They both lay eggs.

   (1) A and B only
   (2) C and D only
   (3) B and D only
   (4) D only ( )

2. Study the concept map below.

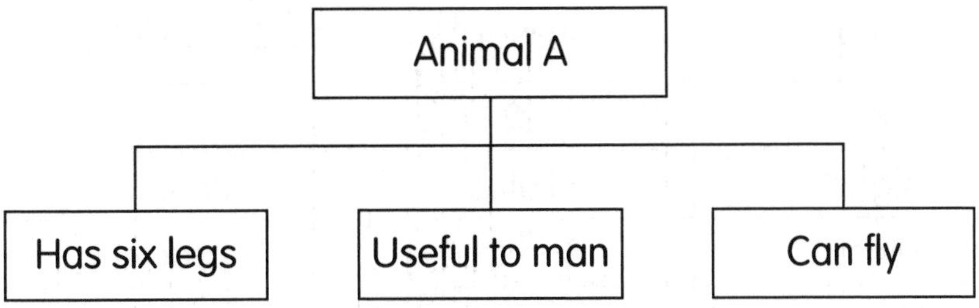

   Which of the following is most likely to be Animal A?

   (1) Grasshopper
   (2) Bee
   (3) Beetle
   (4) Butterfly ( )

3. Study the concept map below.

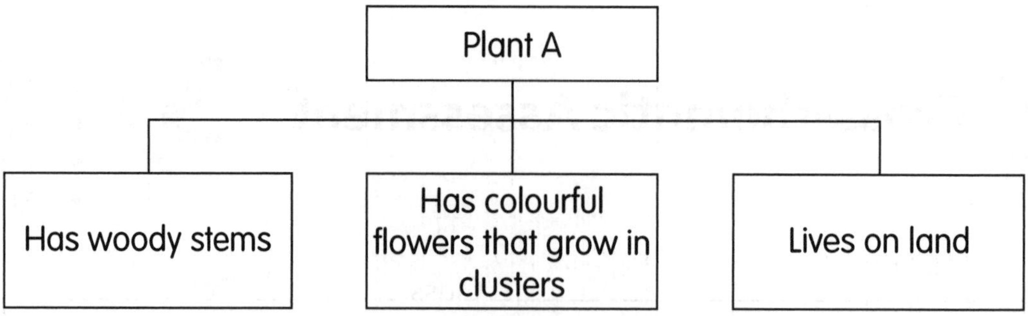

Which of the following is most likely to be Plant A?

(1) Sunflower
(2) Ixora
(3) Rose
(4) Morning glory ( )

4. Study the flowchart below.

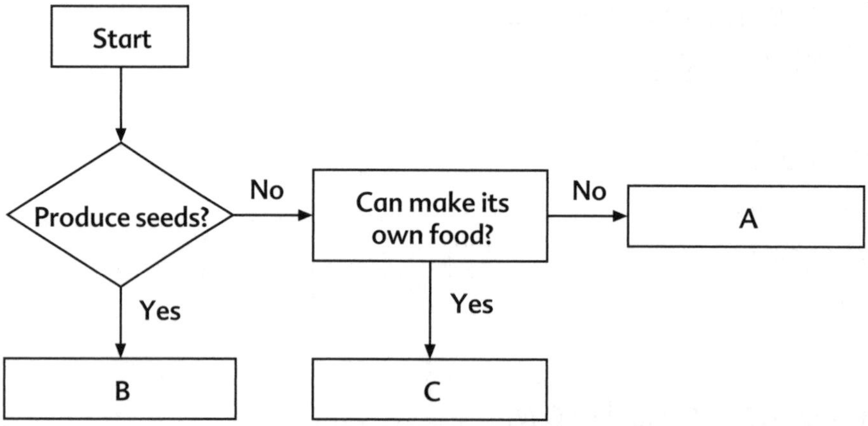

Which of the following best represents A, B and C above?

	A	B	C
(1)	Algae	Lotus	String bean
(2)	Moss	Bamboo	Bacteria
(3)	Mould	Tomato	Fern
(4)	Mushroom	Chilli	Potato

( )

5. Study the table given below carefully.

Animals	Has six legs	Has wings	Has shell as outer covering	Lives in the sea
Butterfly	✓	✓		
Pigeon		✓		
Prawn			✓	✓
Snail			✓	

Which animal has a shell as an outer covering but does not live in the sea?

(1) Butterfly
(2) Pigeon
(3) Prawn
(4) Snail ( )

6. Which of the following are characteristics of the mealworm beetle at its larval stage?

(A) It eats a lot.
(B) It has a pair of feelers.
(C) It moults.
(D) Its body is divided into three segments.

(1) A and C only
(2) B and D only
(3) A, C and D only
(4) A, B, C and D ( )

7. Which of the following is a similarity between a seed and a potato?

(A) Stores food.
(B) Can develop into new plants.
(C) Is protected by the fruit.
(D) Develops under the ground.

(1) A and B only
(2) C and D only
(3) A, B and D only
(4) B, C and D only ( )

8. The diagram below represents the circulatory system of a human. Which of the following is rich in oxygen?

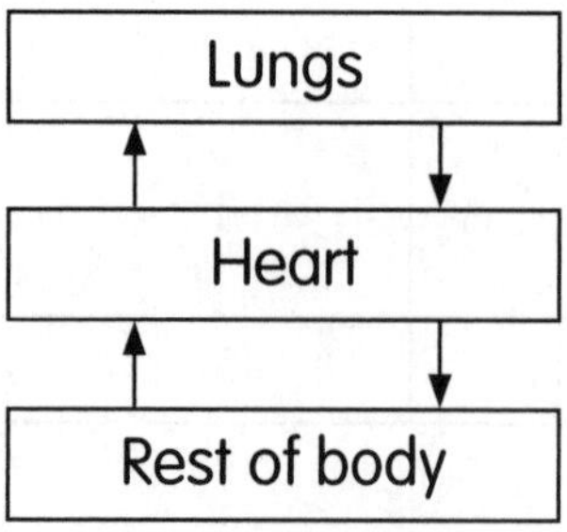

(1) Blood from the lungs to the heart.
(2) Blood from the heart to the lungs.
(3) Blood from the rest of the body to the heart.
(4) Blood from the heart to **ALL** parts of the body. ( )

9. Which of the following is true about all birds?

(A) They have two legs.
(B) They lay eggs.
(C) They have feathers.
(D) They have tails. ( )

(1) A and B only
(2) C and D only
(3) A, B and D only
(4) A, B, C and D ( )

10. Which of the following is not a system?

(1) Torch
(2) Toothpick
(3) Toothbrush
(4) Broom ( )

11. Which of the following has the function stated?

	Function: Carries food, oxygen and water to all parts of the body
(1)	Circulatory system
(2)	Skeletal system
(3)	Respiratory system
(4)	Muscular system

( )

12. A magnet can ____________.

(A) attract another magnet
(B) attract magnetic material
(C) repel magnetic material

(1) A and B only
(2) B and C only
(3) A and C only
(4) A, B and C ( )

13. Study the classification chart below carefully.

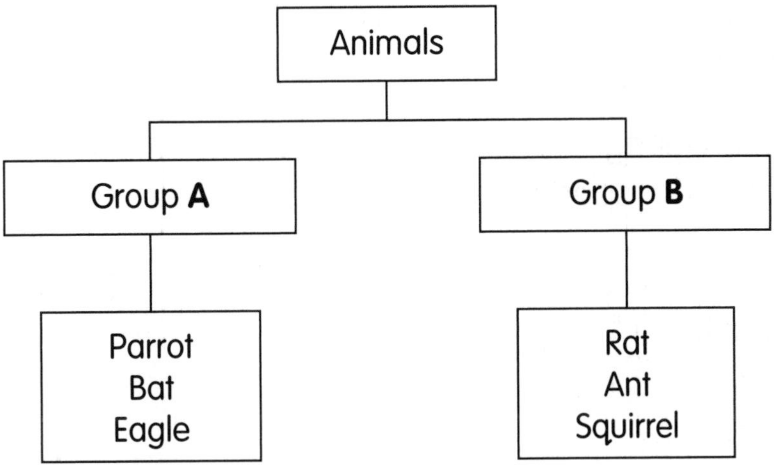

What is a suitable heading for the animals in Group A and B?

	A	B
(1)	Lay eggs	Give birth to the young
(2)	Can fly	Cannot fly
(3)	Two legs	Four legs
(4)	Feathers as outer covering	Hair as outer covering

( )

14. A cockroach and a beetle are similar in that they both ____________.

(A) have a three-stage life cycle
(B) have three body segments
(C) have six legs
(D) live on land

(1) A and C only
(2) B and D only
(3) B, C and D only
(4) A, B, C and D ( )

15. The bird's nest fern, moss and grass are similar because they ____________.

(A) live on land
(B) make their own food
(C) are non-flowering
(D) reproduce from spores

(1) A and B only
(2) B and D only
(3) A and C only
(4) B, C and D only ( )

16. A material has the following properties:

(A) It can be flexible or rigid.
(B) It can be transparent or opaque.
(C) It is light.

Which of the following materials has the properties described above?

(1) Rubber
(2) Plastic
(3) Cloth
(4) Styrofoam ( )

17. Joe sets up the following experiment.

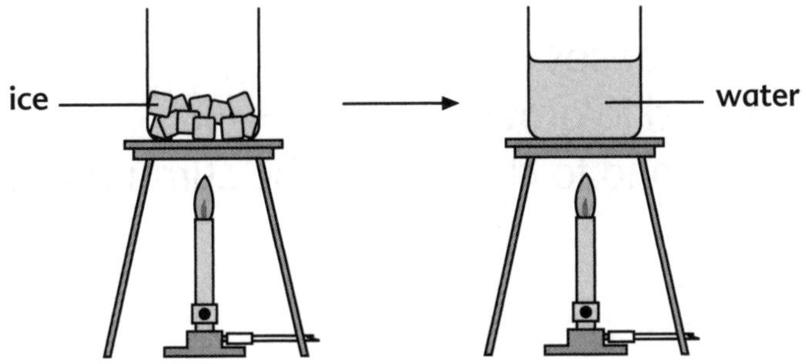

Which one of the graphs below shows the change in temperature of the water over time?

(1)
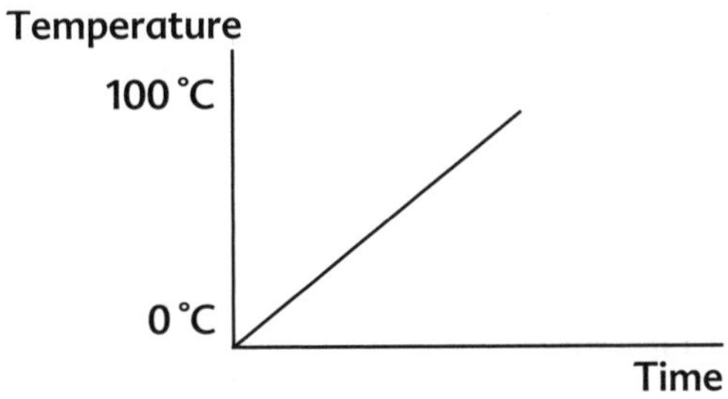

(2)
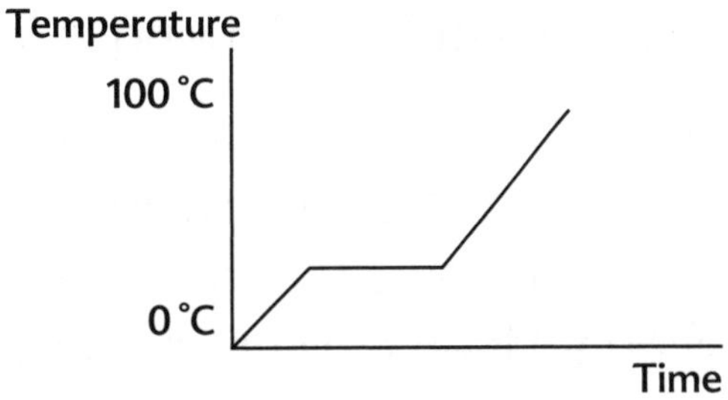

(3)
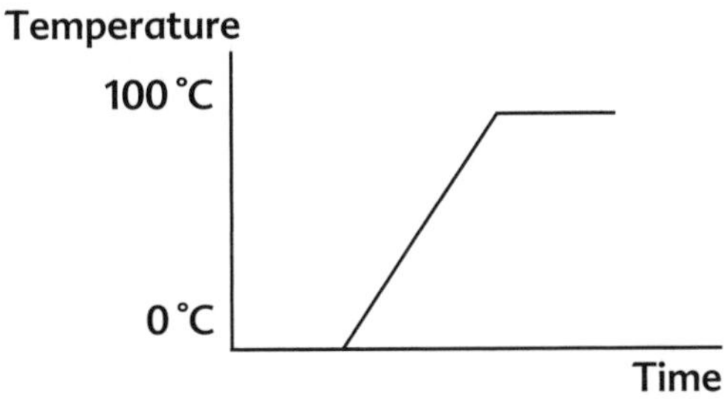

(4)
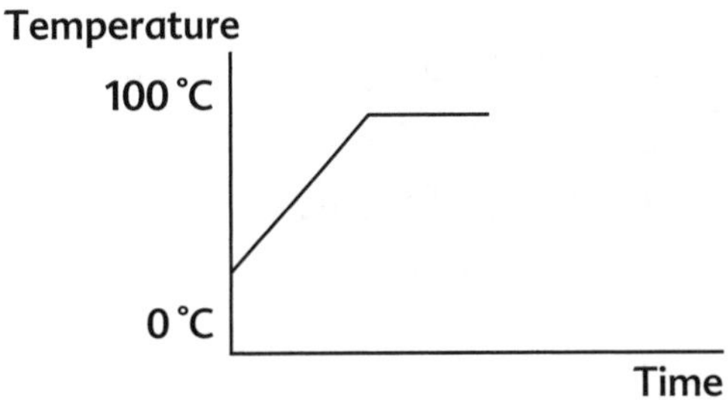

( )

18. Which of the following objects is both a conductor of heat and made of magnetic material?

(1) Aluminium strip
(2) Copper wire
(3) Iron rod
(4) Gold chain ( )

19. Which of the following are reasons why bacteria are living things?

(A) Bacteria reproduce.
(B) Bacteria cause diseases.
(C) Bacteria need food to grow.
(D) Bacteria can respond to changes in the surroundings.

(1) A and C only
(2) B and D only
(3) A, C and D only
(4) B, C and D only ( )

20. Which one of the following is true about fungi?

(A) Fungi reproduce from spores.
(B) All fungi are microorganisms.
(C) Fungi may be useful or harmful to man.
(D) Fungi feed only on animals, dead or alive.

(1) A and C only
(2) B and D only
(3) A, B and D only
(4) A, B, C and D ( )

21. Which of the following is a similarity between bacteria and fungi?

(1) Can be useful or harmful to humans.
(2) Reproduces by producing spores.
(3) Can make its own food.
(4) Is microscopic. ( )

22. Which of the following statements correctly describes the following animals?

Mosquito larva   Caterpillar   Mealworm   Maggot

(A) They are food to other animals.
(B) They are the young of insects.
(C) They hatch from eggs.
(D) They respond to changes in their surroundings.

(1) A and B only
(2) C and D only
(3) A, B and C only
(4) A, B, C and D   (   )

23. Study the diagram below carefully.

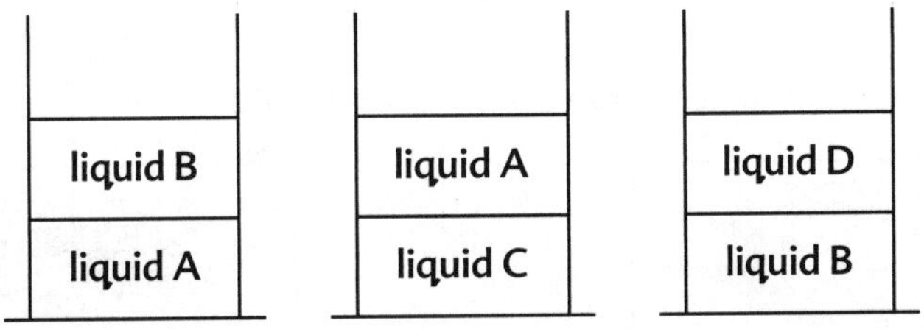

Which of the following arranges the liquids' masses from the greatest to the least?

(1) A, B, C, D
(2) D, B, A, C
(3) C, A, B, D
(4) C, D, A, B   (   )

24. Shadow is not matter because it does not have ________.

(1) mass
(2) a definite shape
(3) a definite colour
(4) a definite volume   (   )

25. Which of the following has all three states of matter?

(1)

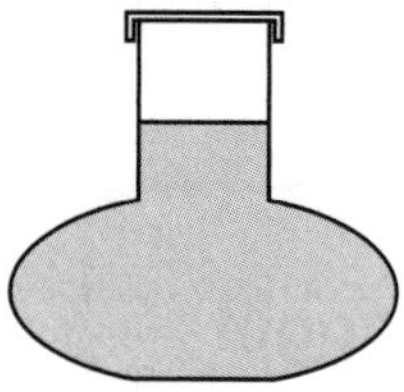

(2)

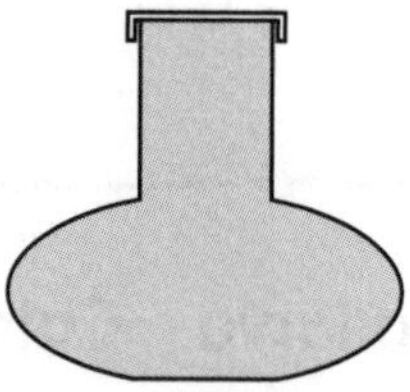

(3)

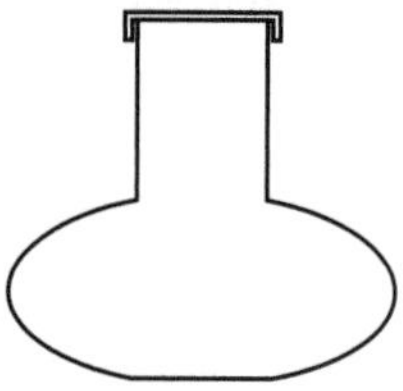

(4)

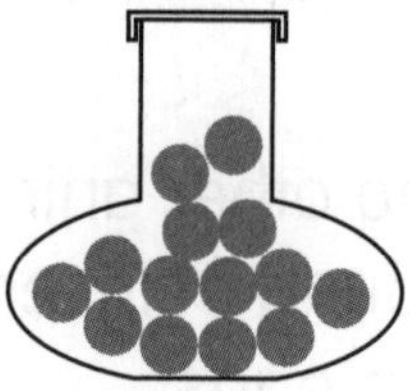

( )

26. Janet placed a piece of plastic sheet over a bar magnet. She placed a piece of thin steel plate over another similar bar magnet. She then dusted some iron filings over the plastic sheet and steel plate. The diagrams below show her observations.

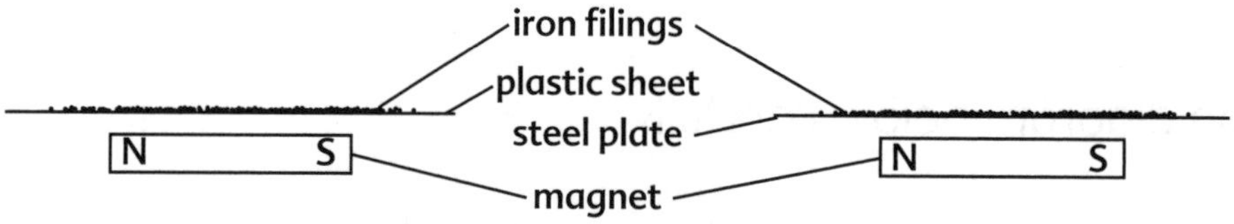

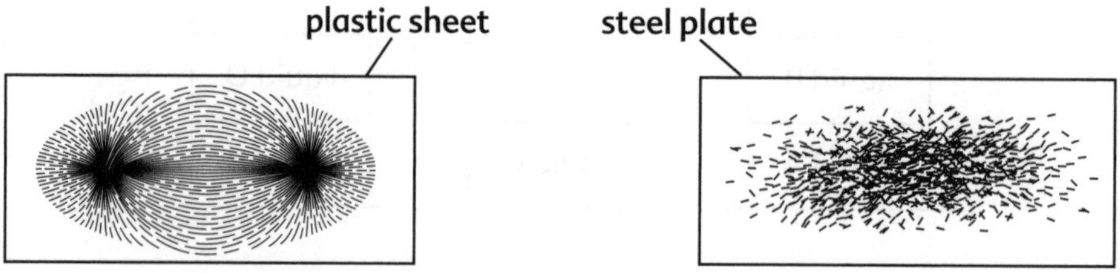

Which of the following statements is true?

(A) The force of a magnet can pass through plastic but not steel.
(B) Steel is a magnetic material while plastic is a non-magnetic material.
(C) A magnet is strongest at its poles.
(D) Iron filings are attracted to plastic but not steel.

(1) A only
(2) B and C only
(3) C and D only
(4) A, B and C only ( )

27. Which of the following involves a change of state?

(1) A piece of rubber band is stretched.
(2) Walnut chips are made from walnuts.
(3) Apple juice is made from apples.
(4) A piece of cardboard is shredded. ( )

28. Which of the following statements about magnets is true?

(A) A freely suspended magnet always comes to rest in a North-South direction.
(B) Unlike poles of a magnet repel each other.
(C) A magnet can be used to magnetise all metals.
(D) The pull of a magnet is strongest at its poles.

(1) A and B only
(2) C and D only
(3) A and D only
(4) B and C only ( )

29. Which of the following graphs shows the changes in the length of a shadow cast by an upright stick over a day?

(1)
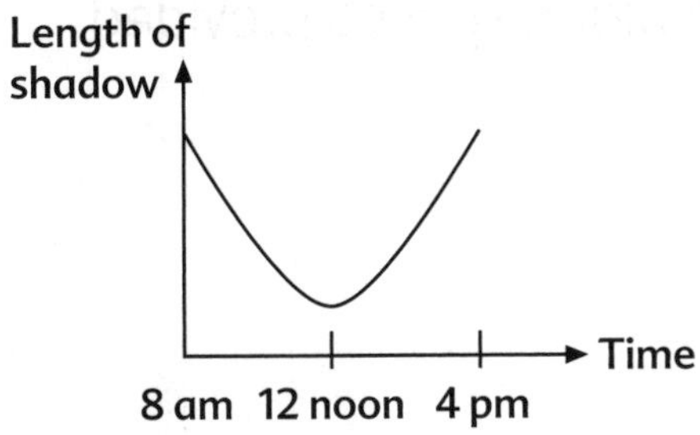

(2)
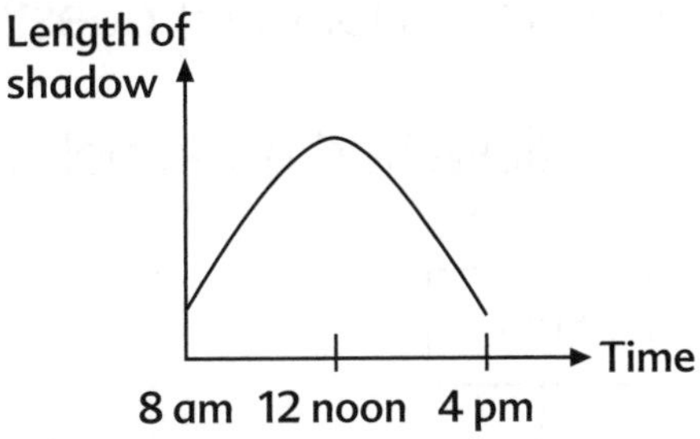

(3)
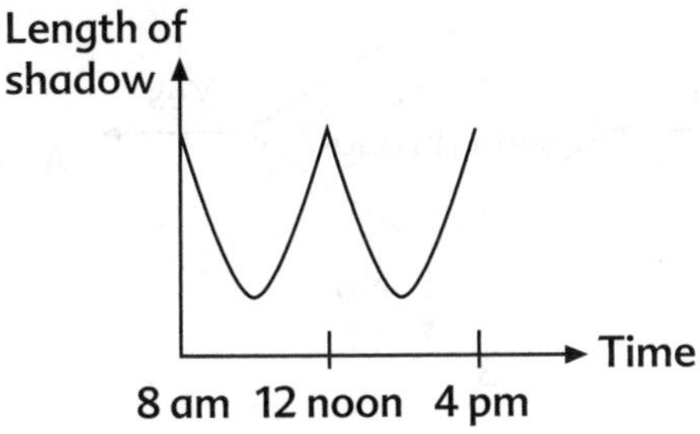

(4)
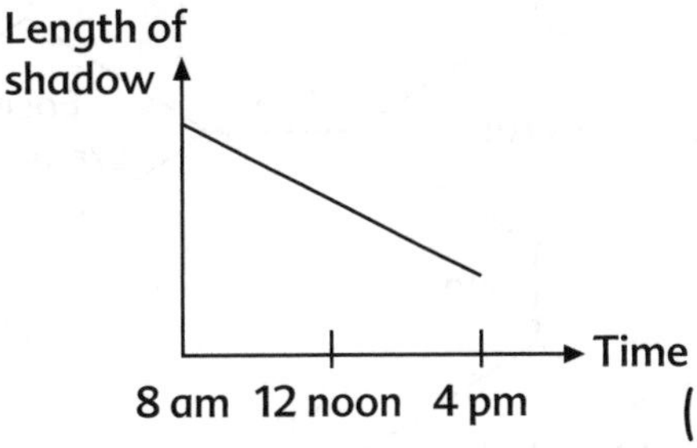

( )

30. The following shows a bottle thermometer strapped onto a baby bottle.

The bottle thermometer makes use of a ____________.

(1) light sensor
(2) timer
(3) touch sensor
(4) heat sensor ( )

Section B (40 marks)

Write your answers for each question in the blank spaces provided.

31. Study the flowchart given below.

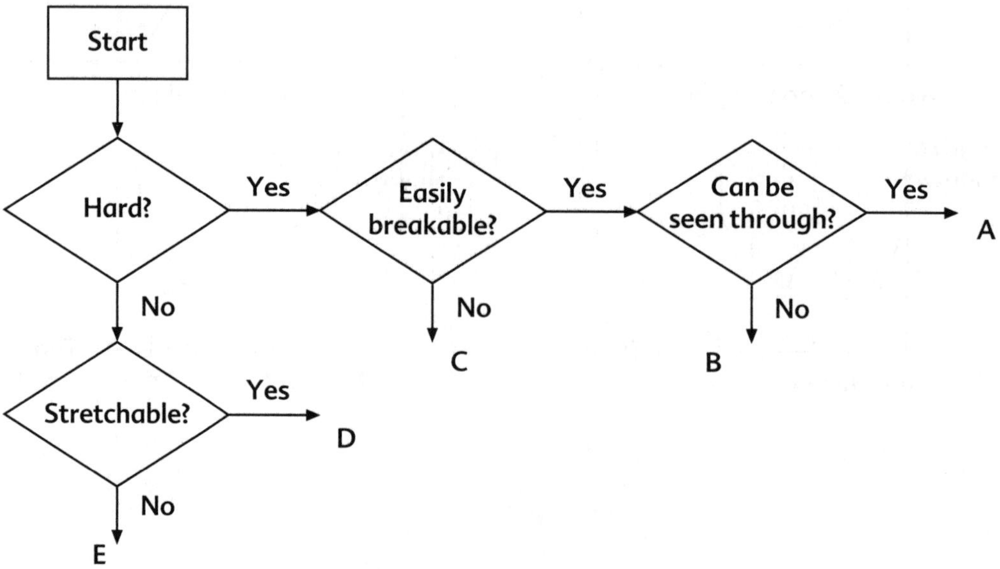

(a) For each of the following, give an example of an object that fits the properties described. [5]

A: ____________________ D: ____________________

B: ____________________ E: ____________________

C: ____________________

(b) Which two of the above objects will form a dark shadow when light is shone on them? [2]

____

32. The flowchart below describes the parts of a plant.

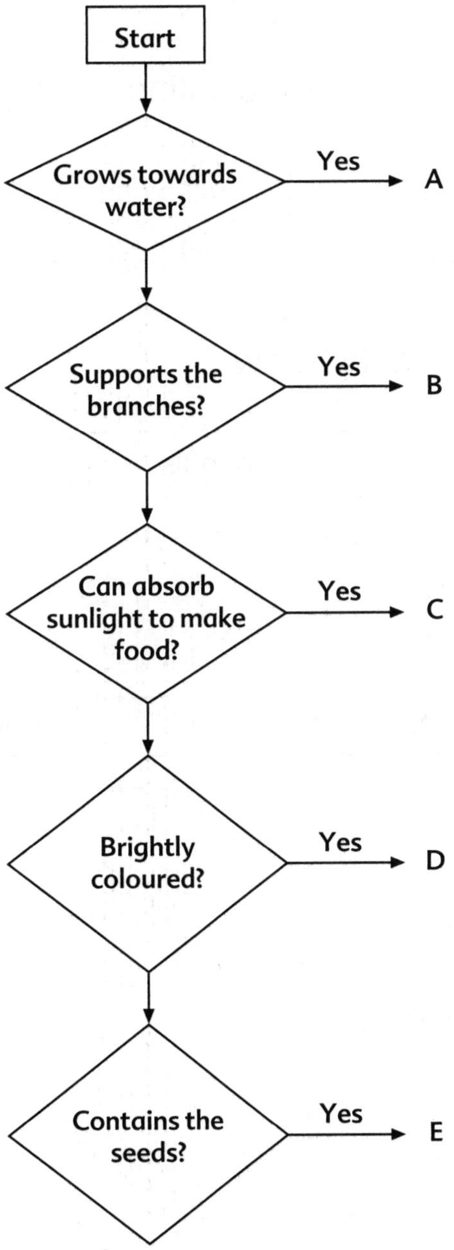

(a) Which part of the plant is represented by A, B, C, D and E? [5]

A: ____________ D: ____________

B: ____________ E: ____________

C: ____________

(b) State another function of the part labelled A. [1]

____

(c) Can the plant survive if the part labelled D is missing? What will happen to the plant? [2]

____

____

(d) Which part of the plant are you eating when you eat: [2]

(i) a potato ____________ (iii) ginger ____________

(ii) a tomato ____________ (iv) carrot ____________

33. Study the classification table below.

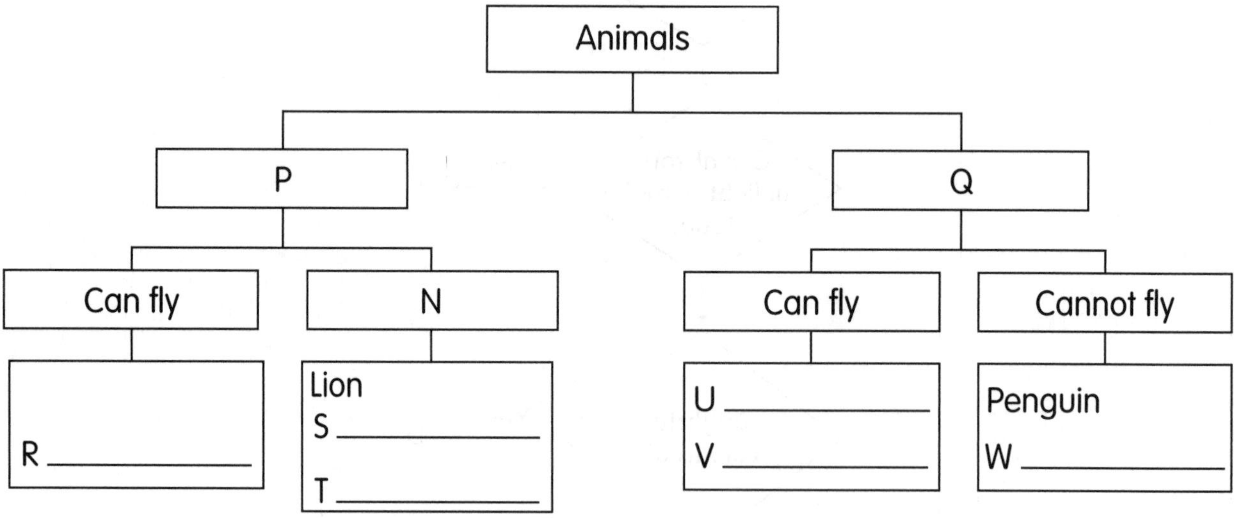

What should P, Q and N be? [2]

P: ____________

Q: ____________

N: ____________

Which animals may be represented by: [3]

R: ______________ U: ______________

S: ______________ V: ______________

T: ______________ W: ______________

34. Peter sets up an experiment as shown in the diagram below.

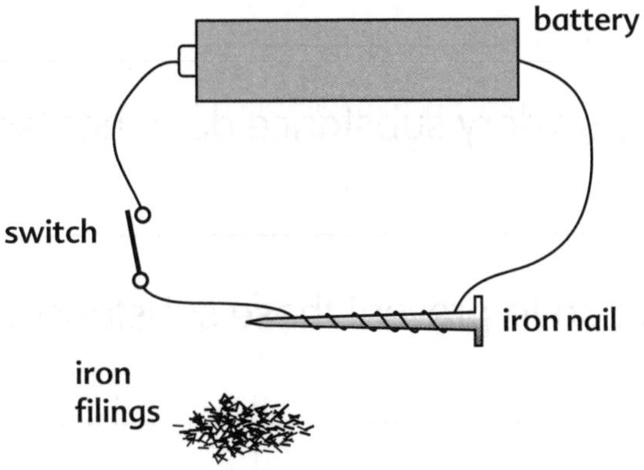

(a) (i) What will he observe when the switch is turned on? [1]

____

(ii) Why does this happen? [2]

____

____

(b) What will happen if the number of batteries is increased to two? Why? [2]

____

____

(c) What wil happen if the number of coils around the iron nail is reduced? Why? [2]

____

____

35. Jane finds that the leather shoes in her shoe cupboard are often covered with a layer of powdery substance. These are white to slightly greenish in colour. This usually happens when the weather is wet and the cupboard is not aired.

(a) What is this powdery substance? [1]

____

(b) Where did it come from? [1]

____

(c) What does this powdery substance do to her leather shoes? [1]

____

(d) What must Jane do to prevent these substances from growing? [1]

____

36. The diagram below shows our digestive system.

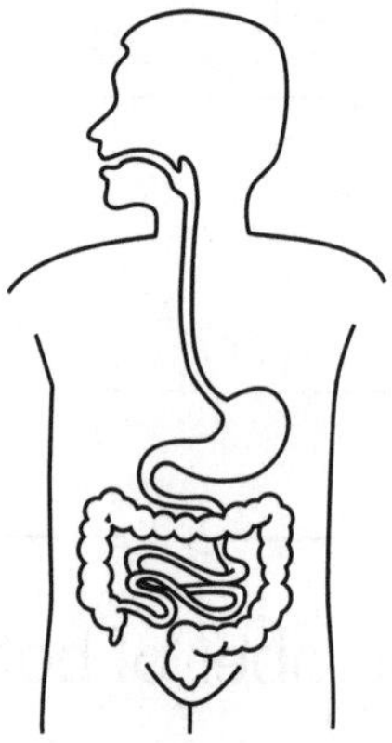

(a) Label the two parts of this system in which digestion does not occur. [2]

(b) What are the functions of the two parts in (a)? [2]

____

____

End of Paper

Marks:

/100

Cross-thematic Assessment 4

- Diversity
- Cycles
- Systems
- Interactions
- Energy

Name: ______________________ Class: __________ Date: ______________

Section A (30 x 2 = 60 marks)

For each question, four options are given. Choose the correct answer and write down your choice, 1, 2, 3 or 4, in the brackets provided.

1. What is the function of the roots of a plant?

   (1) To hold up the leaves and reach out for sunlight.
   (2) To absorb water and minerals.
   (3) To receive light energy and make food.
   (4) To reproduce. ( )

2. Which of the following carries out the function stated below?

	Function: Takes in oxygen and removes carbon dioxide
(1)	Circulatory system
(2)	Digestive system
(3)	Respiratory system
(4)	Muscular system

( )

3. Which of the following about the rib cage is true?

   (A) It protects the heart and the lungs.
   (B) It is connected to the backbone.
   (C) It is part of the skeletal system.
   (D) It is made up of curved bones.

   (1) A and B only
   (2) C and D only
   (3) A, B and C only
   (4) A, B, C and D ( )

4. A healthy boy was made to perform four different activities. His number of breaths per minute was recorded for each of the activities he performed.

Which of the following is incorrect?

	Activity	Breaths per minute
(1)	Sleeping	30
(2)	Walking	26
(3)	Skipping	40
(4)	Watching television	22

( )

5. Which of the following is a system?

(1) Fork
(2) Chopstick
(3) Cooking pot
(4) Bowl

( )

6. Which of the following about digestion is true?

(A) The gullet joins the mouth to the stomach.
(B) The stomach joins the gullet to the small intestine.
(C) Digestion begins in the mouth and ends in the small intestine.
(D) Digestion takes place only when there is food.

(1) A and B only
(2) C and D only
(3) A, B and D only
(4) A, B, C and D

( )

7. Study the classification chart below carefully.

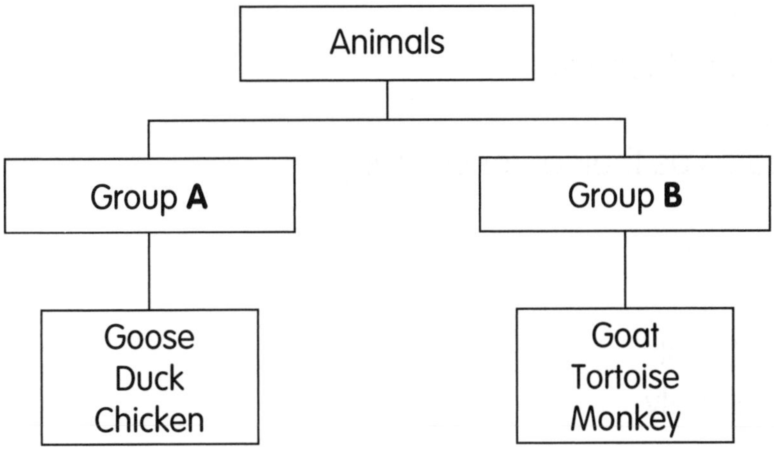

What are suitable headings for the animals in Groups A and B?

	A	**B**
(1)	Two legs	Four legs
(2)	Birds	Mammals
(3)	Lay eggs	Give birth
(4)	Feathers as outer covering	Hair as outer covering

( )

8. Which of the following will **not** change when we grow?

(A) Ability to roll our tongue.
(B) Colour of our eyes.
(C) Size of our palm.
(D) Length of our ears.

(1) A and B only
(2) C and D only
(3) A, B and D only
(4) B, C and D only ( )

9. A tadpole and a fish are alike because they ____________.

(A) live in water
(B) breathe with their gills
(C) lay eggs
(D) have scales as their outer covering

(1) A and B only
(2) C and D only
(3) A, C and D only
(4) A, B and D only ( )

10. The leaves of plants are able to make food because they have ________?

(1) stalks
(2) chlorophyll
(3) veins
(4) leaf blades ( )

11. Four seedlings were put into four different boxes A, B, C and D as shown in the diagrams below.

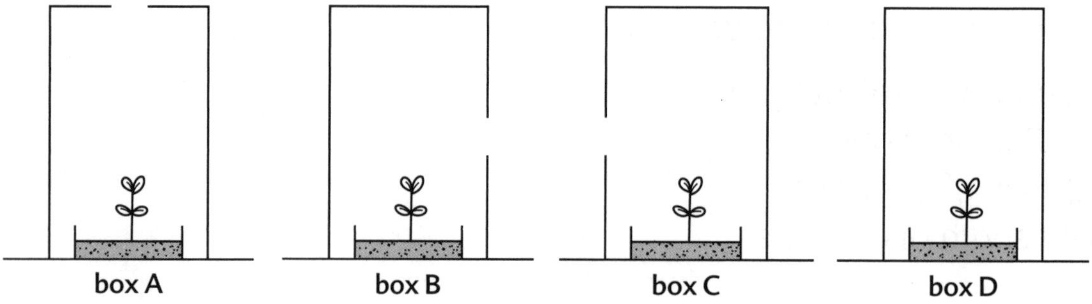

The diagrams below show the plants two weeks later. Match plants P, Q, R and S to the boxes they were grown in.

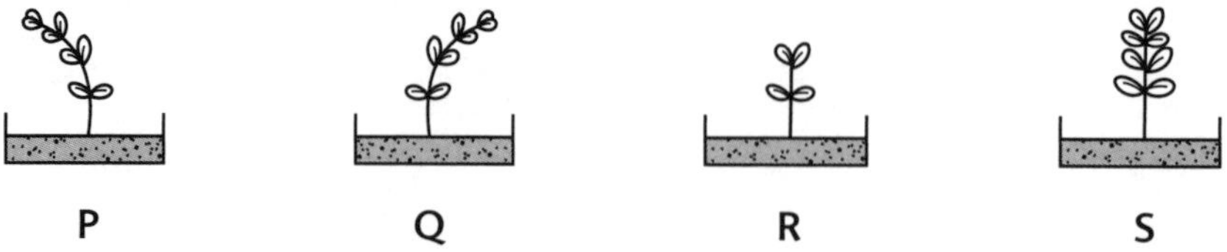

	Box A	Box B	Box C	Box D
(1)	P	S	R	Q
(2)	Q	P	S	R
(3)	S	Q	P	R
(4)	R	P	Q	S

( )

12. In what ways are the following animals similar?

Hamster	**Goat**	**Squirrel**	**Rabbit**

(A) They feed on plants only.
(B) They give birth to their young.
(C) They move by hopping.
(D) They have hair as their outer covering.

(1) A and B only
(2) C and D only
(3) A, B and D only
(4) A, B, C and D ( )

13. Which of the following statements is correct about the animals below?

Bee	**Ant**	**Pigeon**	**Frog**
Snake	**Elephant**	**Seal**	**Fish**

(A) The animals move in different ways.
(B) The animals come in different shapes and sizes.
(C) The animals can be found on land or in water.
(D) The animals have different outer coverings.

(1) A and B only
(2) C and D only
(3) A, C and D only
(4) A, B, C and D ( )

14. Which of the following materials has the properties described below?

(A) It can be flexible or rigid.
(B) It can be transparent or opaque.
(C) It is generally light.

(1) Rubber
(2) Plastic
(3) Wood
(4) Cloth ( )

15. Oil is lighter than water. Object X was found to float in oil and object Y to sink in water.

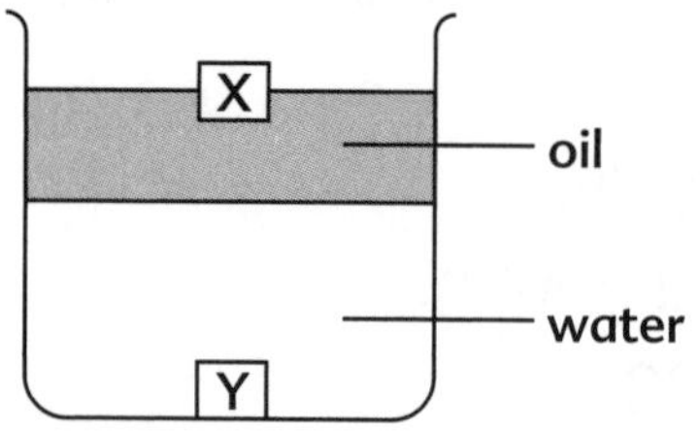

Which of the following is correct about objects X and Y?

	X	Y
(1)	Floats in water	Sinks in oil
(2)	Sinks in water	Floats in oil
(3)	Floats in water	Floats in oil
(4)	Sinks in water	Sinks in oil

( )

16. A tightly sealed container has 50 g of water at 25 °C. It is heated until all the water changes to steam.

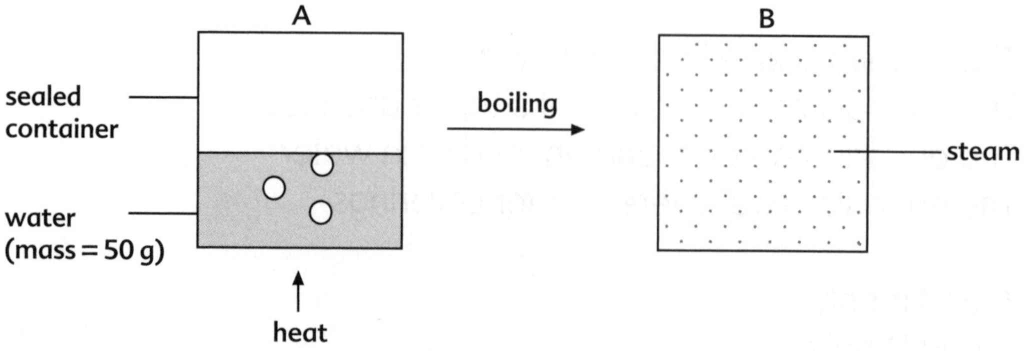

Which statement is **not** true?

(1) The mass of steam in B is 10 g.
(2) A change in state has occured between A and B.
(3) B has more energy than A.
(4) The temperature remains the same from A to B. ( )

17. The diagram below shows a toilet system.

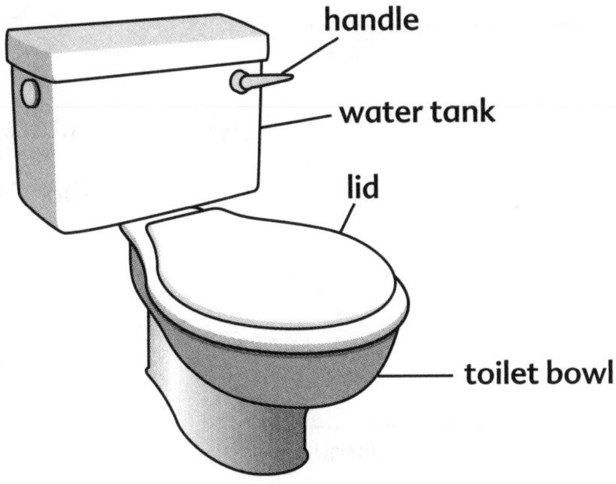

Which of the parts, when removed, will prevent the toilet system from functioning properly?

(A) Handle
(B) Water tank
(C) Lid
(D) Toilet bowl

(1) C only
(2) A and D only
(3) B and D only
(4) A, B and D only ( )

18. A piece of stone at 26 °C is placed into a beaker of water at the same temperature. Which of the following observations is correct?

(A) The temperature of the water remains unchanged.
(B) The level of the water in the beaker will rise.
(C) The stone will sink to the bottom of the beaker.
(D) The contents of the beaker will increase in mass.

(1) A and B only
(2) C and D only
(3) A, C and D only
(4) A, B, C and D ( )

19. Which of the graphs below correctly represents the change in temperature of water when ice cubes are added to water at 100 °C?

(1)

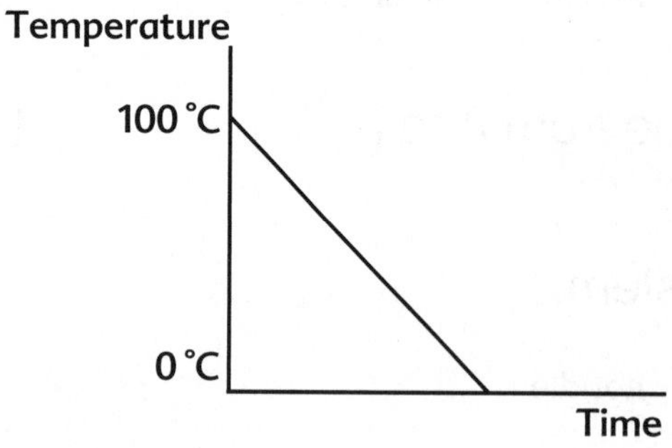

(2)

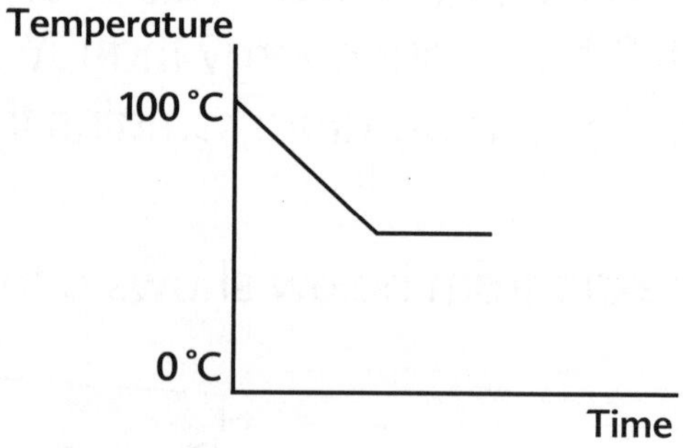

(3)

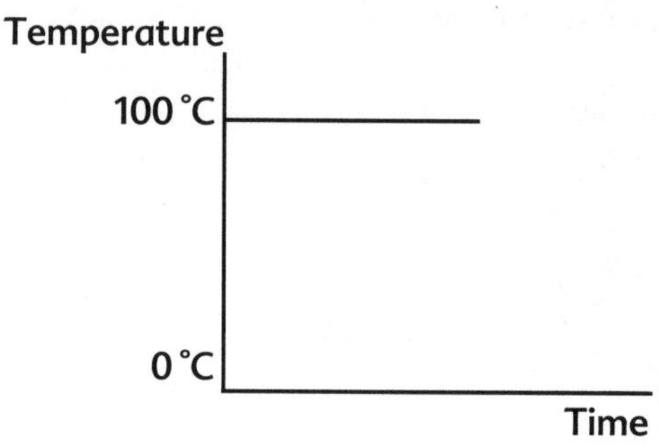

(4)

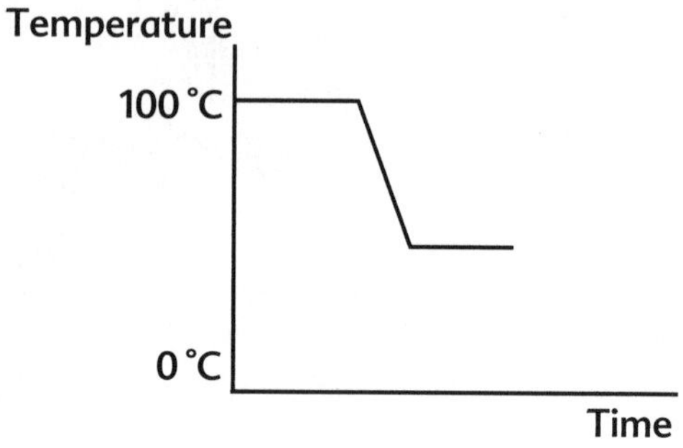

( )

20. Amos rubbed some of liquid X onto his arm. Liquid X felt cold. Very quickly, all the liquid X on Amos' arm disappeared. Which of the following takes place when the liquid leaves Amos' arm?

(1) Heat is absorbed by the liquid.
(2) The temperature of the liquid increases.
(3) Heat is given out by the liquid.
(4) The temperature of the liquid decreases. ( )

21. A solid cylinder was hold on a stand between two screens as shown in the diagram below.

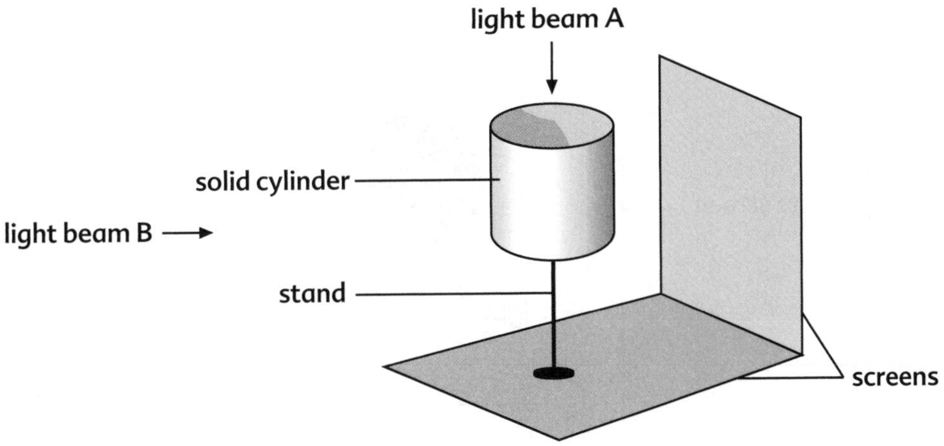

Light was shone on the cylinder from directions A and B, one at a time. Which of the following represents the shadows formed by shining light beams A and B on the object?

	Light Beam A	Light Beam B
(1)		
(2)		
(3)		
(4)		

( )

22. A cone and a clear blue plastic sheet were placed between a bulb and a white screen. The following is observed on the white screen.

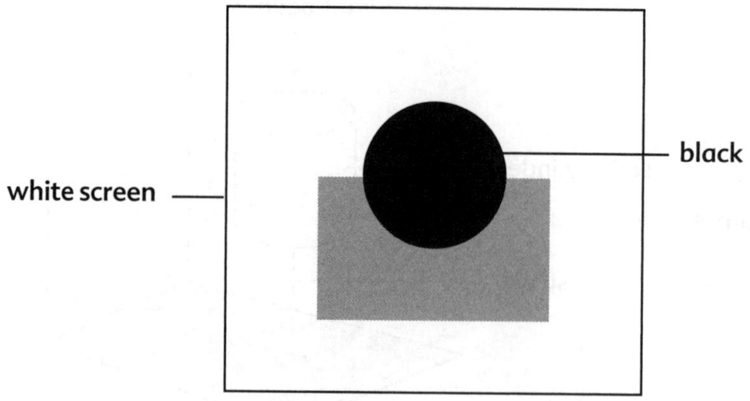

Which diagram shows the correct placement of the cone and blue plastic sheet?

(1)

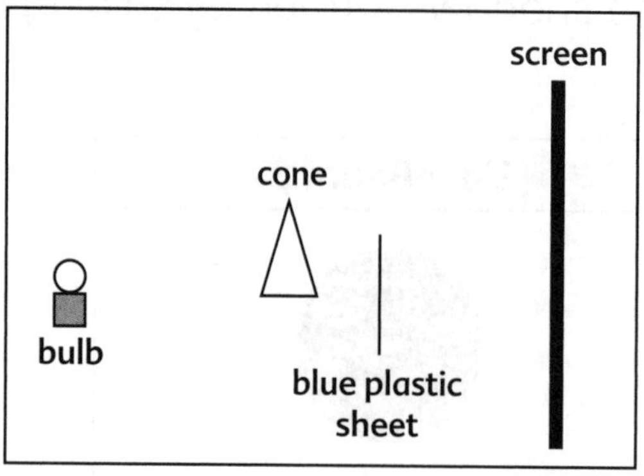

(2)

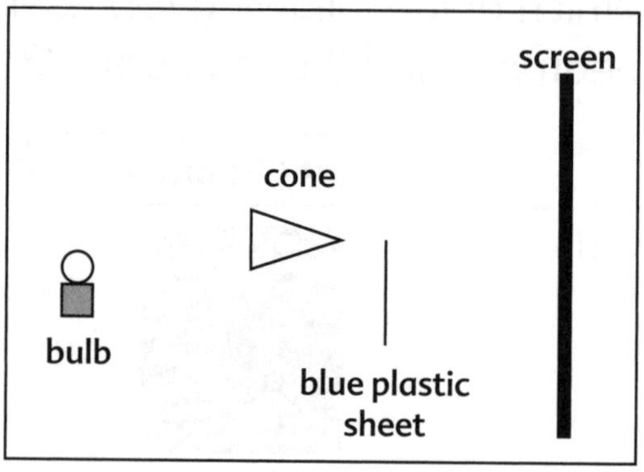

(3)

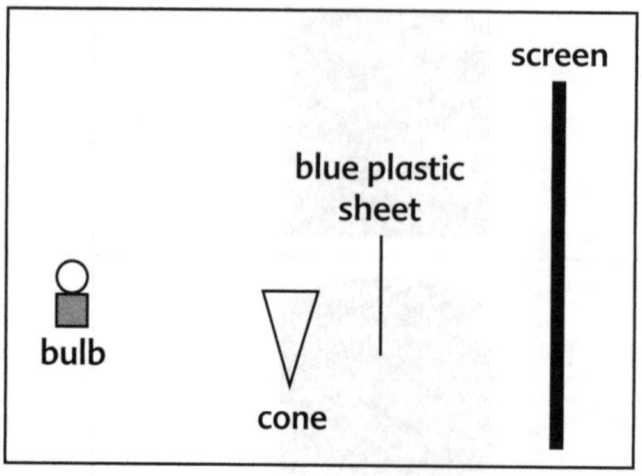

(4)

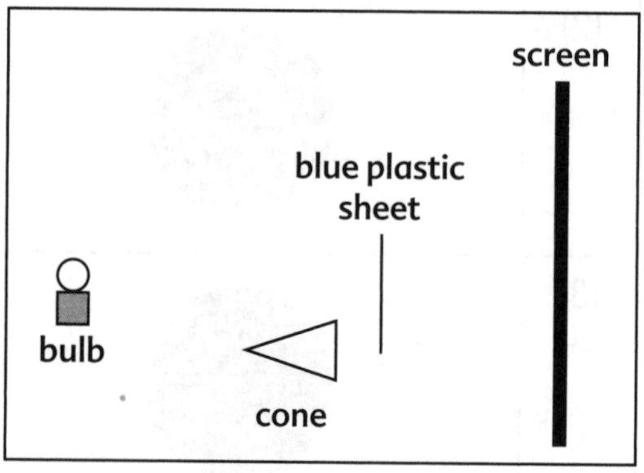

( )

23. Which of the following are similarities between a butterfly and a grasshopper?

(A) They have a four-stage life cycle.
(B) They can fly.
(C) They have three pairs of legs.
(D) They reproduce by laying eggs.

(1) A and B only
(2) C and D only
(3) B, C and D only
(4) A, B, C and D ( )

24. The diagram below shows two groups of living things.

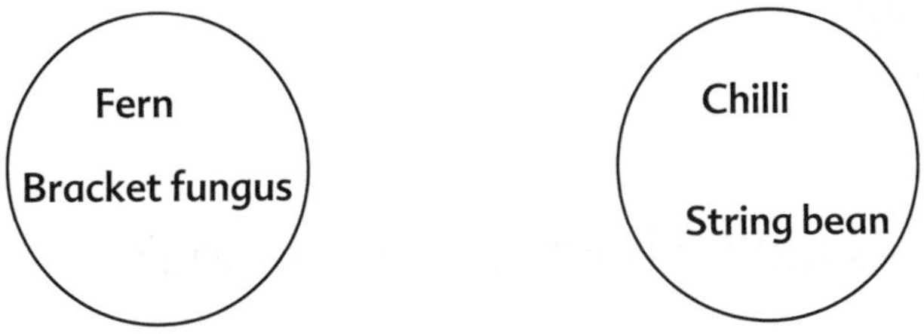

Which of the following pairs of statements about these two groups of plants is correct?

	Group A	Group B
(A)	Reproduce from spores.	Reproduce from seeds.
(B)	Cannot be seen with the naked eye.	Can be seen with the naked eye.
(C)	Cannot make their own food.	Can make their own food.
(D)	Produce flowers.	Do not produce flowers.

(1) A only
(2) A and D only
(3) B and C only
(4) A, B and D only ( )

25. Study the diagram below carefully.

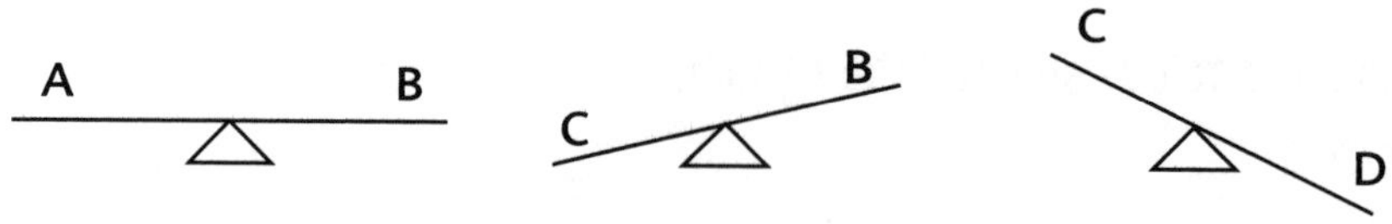

Which of the following is correct?

(A) A and B have the same mass.
(B) A has less mass than C.
(C) D has more mass than B.
(D) C has less mass than D.

(1) A and B only
(2) C and D only
(3) A, C and D only
(4) A, B, C and D ( )

26. At which state does matter have no fixed shape?

(1) Liquid only
(2) Solid and liquid only
(3) Liquid and gaseous only
(4) Solid, liquid and gaseous ( )

27. Which of the following would change if 10 g of plasticine is moulded into a dog and then is remoulded into a snake?

(1) Material
(2) Mass
(3) Shape
(4) Volume ( )

28. The bar chart below shows the number of eggs produced in a farm over the last four months.

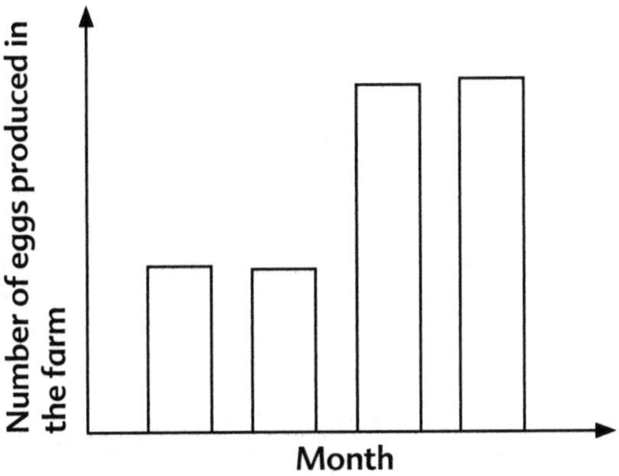

Which of the following is a likely explanation for the results shown in the graph?

(1) The chickens in the farm are laying more eggs than usual.
(2) More and more chickens are reaching the stage of producing eggs in their life cycle.
(3) The farmer has introduced more egg-laying chickens into his farm.
(4) The life cycle of the chickens has been shortened so that they can produce more eggs. ( )

29. When a magnetic material is placed near to (but not touching) a magnet, it acts as a shield to block the attractive force of the magnet.

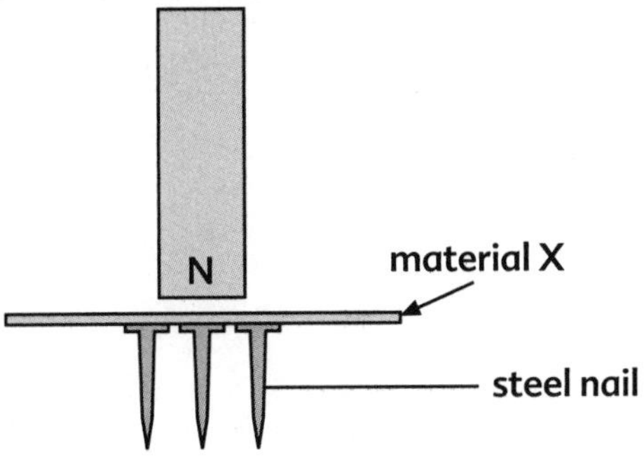

Which of the following can be material X?

(A) Paper
(B) Steel
(C) Glass
(D) Iron

(1) A and C only
(2) B and D only
(3) A, C and D only
(4) A, B, C and D ( )

30. Three bars, A, B and C, of equal shape and size, were found to have different properties.

A	B	C
- Attracted to Bar B - One of its sides repels a magnet	- Attracted to Bar A - Both sides are attracted to a magnet	- Has no reaction to Bar A or B - Has no reaction to a magnet

Which of the following correctly describes A, B and C?

	A	B	C
(1)	Magnet	Non-magnetic material	Magnetic material
(2)	Magnetic material	Non-magnetic material	Magnet
(3)	Non-magnetic material	Magnet	Magnetic material
(4)	Magnet	Magnetic material	Non-magnetic material

( )

Section B (40 marks)

Write your answers for each question in the blank spaces provided.

31. Study the classification chart below.

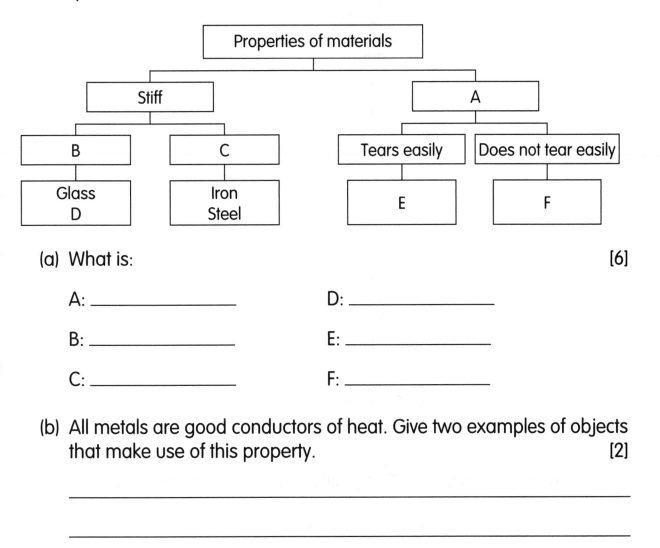

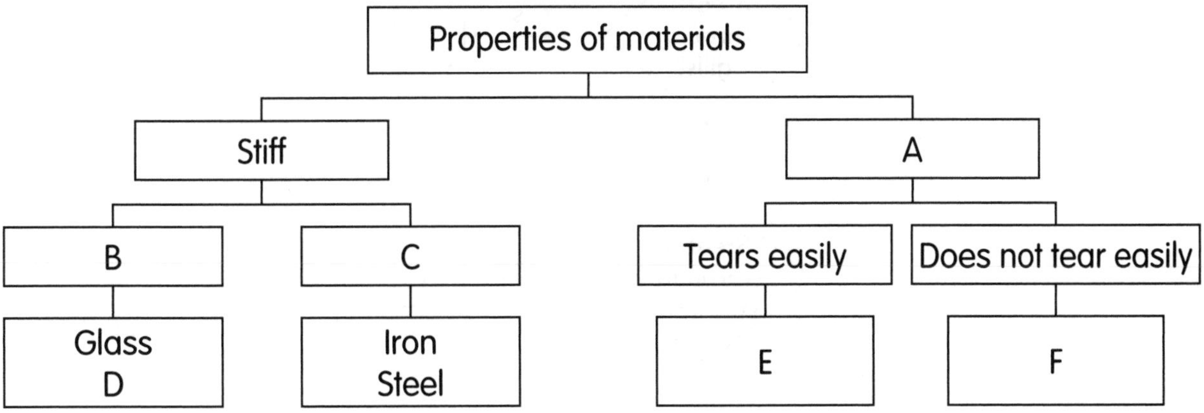

(a) What is: [6]

A: ____________ D: ____________

B: ____________ E: ____________

C: ____________ F: ____________

(b) All metals are good conductors of heat. Give two examples of objects that make use of this property. [2]

____

____

32. Study the flowchart given below.

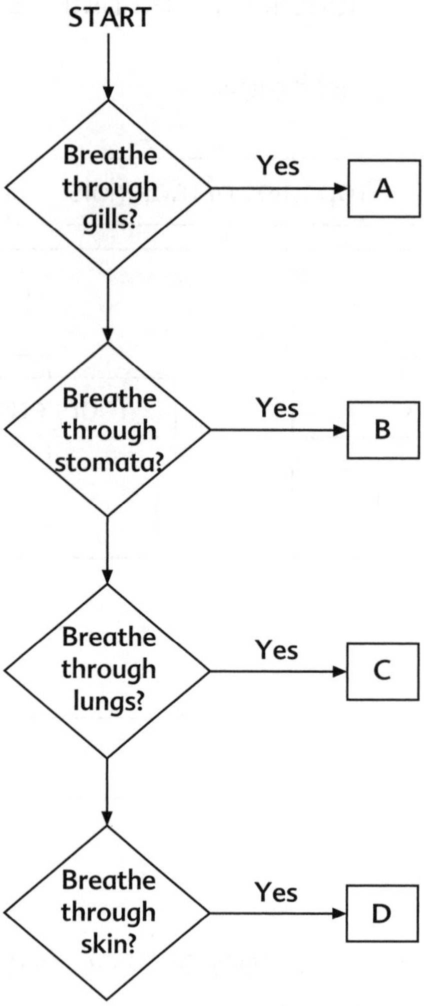

(a) Give an example of a living thing that may be represented by: [4]

A: ______________ C: ______________

B: ______________ D: ______________

(b) Is it correct to say that living things which breathe through their gills usually live in water and reproduce by laying eggs? Give reasons for your answer. [3]

____

____

33. Study the diagram below.

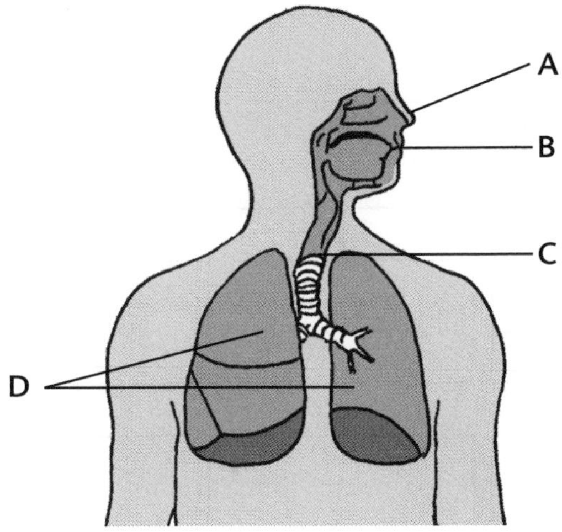

(a) What does each of the letters represent? [4]

A: ____________ C: ____________

B: ____________ D: ____________

(b) Write down the letter(s) that indicate(s) the part(s) [2]

(i) through which air enters the body. ____________

(ii) in which the exchange of gases occurs. ____________

34. (a) Fill in the boxes (i) and (ii) in the graphic organiser below. [2]

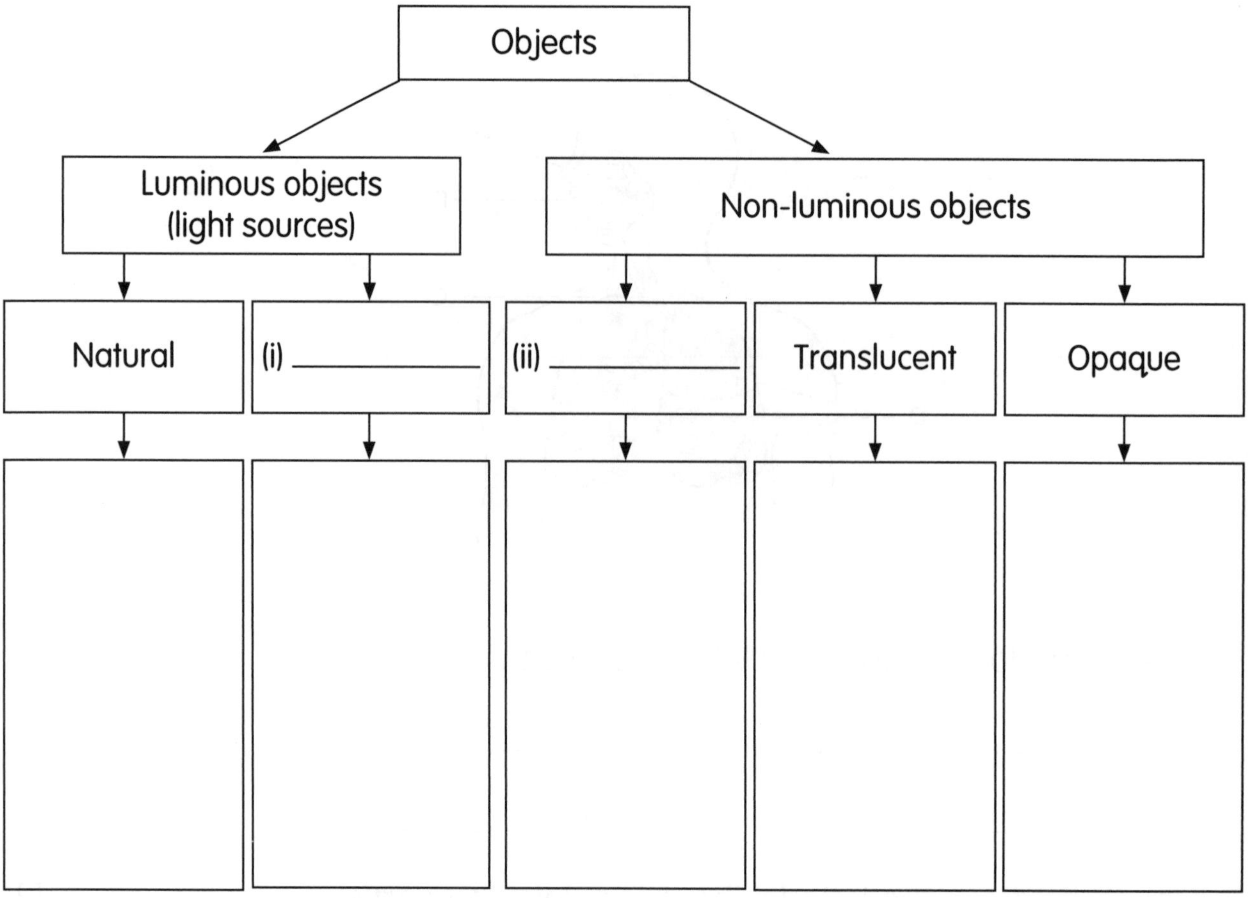

(b) Classify the items below using the graphic organiser above. [9]

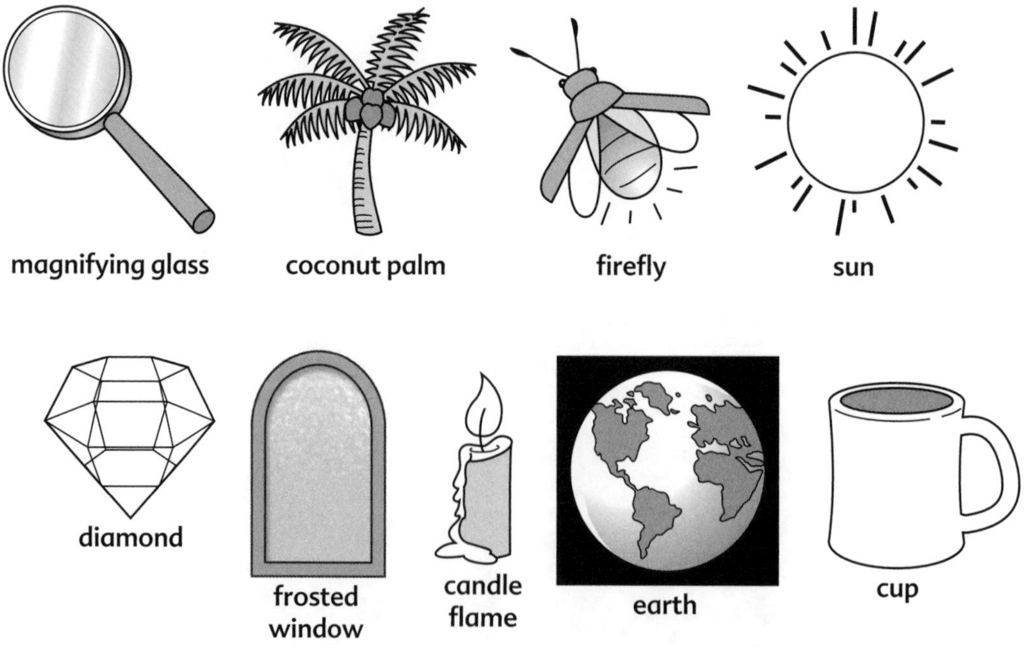

35. Compare the housefly and mosquito using the graphic organiser below. [4]

Similarities
(a) ______________________________
(b) ______________________________

Housefly | Mosquito

Differences	
(a) ______________	______________
(b) ______________	______________

36. Draw, in the dotted box, the shadow formed when the light from the bulb is shone on the object below. [2]

(a)

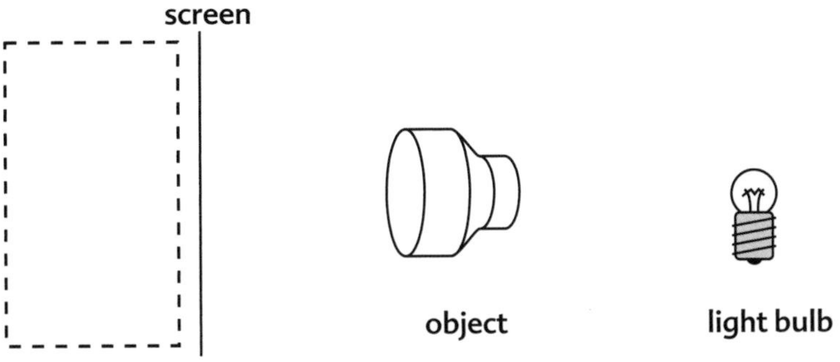

(b)

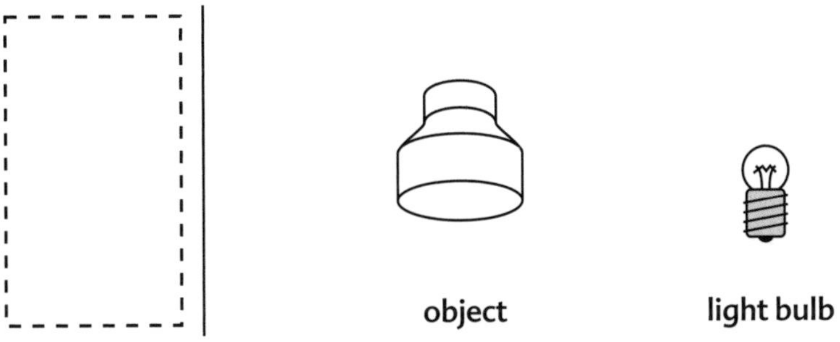

37. There are two things wrong with the shadow of the man in the following diagram. What are they? [2]

Answers

Test 1 – Diversity (Pages 1–10)

Section A (15 × 2 = 30 marks)

1.	(4)	6.	(2)	11.	(2)
2.	(3)	7.	(3)	12.	(2)
3.	(4)	8.	(2)	13.	(1)
4.	(3)	9.	(4)	14.	(3)
5.	(1)	10.	(1)	15.	(2)

Section B (20 marks)

[• 1 mark per point; ○ ½ mark per point]

16. (a) • True
    (b) • False
    (c) • False

17. Stationery

○ In the stationery holder	○ Outside the stationery holder
• eraser pencil stapler highlighter ruler correction tape	• activity book writing pad diary

(or any other sensible classification)

18.

	Which item does not belong with the group?	Why?
Group A	• Broccoli	• It is a flower while the rest are fruits.
Group B	• Rose plant	• It is a living thing while the rest are non-living.

19. (a) • Air/water/food/a clean environment (any 3)
    (b) • Punch holes in the lid <u>OR</u> replace the lid with a net. (or any other reasonable answer)

20. (a)

Objects	
Living	Non-living
○ Rat ○ Mosquito ○ Bird	○ Water bottle ○ Paper bag ○ Helicopter

(b)

Objects	
Able to fly	Unable to fly
○ Helicopter ○ Mosquito ○ Bird	○ Water bottle ○ Paper bag ○ Rat

Test 2 – Diversity (Pages 11–19)

Section A (15 × 2 = 30 marks)

1.	(4)	6.	(2)	11.	(2)
2.	(1)	7.	(4)	12.	(4)
3.	(1)	8.	(4)	13.	(2)
4.	(3)	9.	(1)	14.	(4)
5.	(1)	10.	(3)	15.	(1)

Section B (20 marks)

[• 1 mark per point; ○ ½ mark per point]

16. (a) • True
    (b) • False
    (c) • True

17.

Animals	
Lay eggs	Do not lay eggs
○ Frog ○ Pigeon ○ Python ○ Lizard	○ Cheetah ○ Giraffe ○ Elephant ○ Whale

18. (a)

Characteristic	Animal group
Live in water	• Fish
Give birth to young	• Mammal
Can fly	• Birds
Have six legs	• Insects

(b) • They lay eggs.

19. (a) • Birds
(b) • Feathers
(c) • Use 1: Keeps the animal warm
• Use 2: Allows the animal to fly

20.

Monkey	• Squirrel
Lizard	• Fish
Lobster	• Crab
Beetle	• Cockroach

Test 3 – Diversity (Pages 21–29)

Section A (15 × 2 = 30 marks)

1. (2)	6. (4)	11. (3)
2. (3)	7. (3)	12. (2)
3. (2)	8. (4)	13. (3)
4. (1)	9. (1)	14. (1)
5. (1)	10. (2)	15. (2)

Section B (20 marks)

[● 1 mark per point; ○ ½ mark per point]

16. (a) • False
(b) • False
(c) • True

17. (a)

0	10	30
• 11	• 25	• 49

(b) • Food

18. (a) • Fungi
(b) • Spores
(c) • From the substances they grow on.
(d) • As a source of food.

19. (a) • Group X: Objects made of one material
• Group Y: Objects made of more than one material

(b) (i) • Group X
(ii) • Group Y
(iii) • Group Y

20.

Properties	Object
Soft and absorbs water	• Towel
Flexible and elastic	• Rubber band
Stiff and hard	• Pin
Shiny and breaks when dropped	• Mirror

Thematic Assessment 1 – Diversity (Pages 31–48)

Section A (30 × 2 = 60 marks)

1. (4)	11. (3)	21. (4)
2. (3)	12. (4)	22. (2)
3. (2)	13. (4)	23. (1)
4. (1)	14. (2)	24. (2)
5. (3)	15. (4)	25. (1)
6. (3)	16. (1)	26. (2)
7. (2)	17. (3)	27. (2)
8. (1)	18. (2)	28. (3)
9. (1)	19. (3)	29. (4)
10. (3)	20. (4)	30. (3)

Section B (40 marks)

[● 1 mark per point; ○ ½ mark per point]

31. Need:
• air
• food
• water

Are able to:
• reproduce
• respond to stimuli
• move

32. (a) • Curl up its body tightly.
(b) • To protect itself.
(c) • The leaves of a rain tree close up in cloudy weather / at night.
(Or any other sensible answer.)

33. Similarities
- Do not move from place to place.
- Reproduce from spores.

Differences

○ Microscopic	○ Can be seen with the naked eye.
○ Cannot make their own food.	○ Can make their own food.

34. Similarities
- Breathe air
- Can swim
- Lay eggs

Differences

○ Soft outer covering	○ Hard outer covering
○ Eats insects	○ Eats sea creatures

35. • A: Living things
- B: Non-living things
- C: Plants
- D: Animals
- E: Heavy
- F: Flowering
- G: Non-flowering

36. (a) • Its body is not divided into three segments.
• It has eight legs instead of six.
(b) • It does not lay eggs but gives birth to its young.
• Its outer covering is not feathers but hair.
(c) • It does not lay eggs but gives birth to its young.
• It does not have scales as its outer covering.
(d) • It cannot make food.
• It does not have roots or leaves.

37. • A: Can be seen through
- B: Cannot be seen through
- C: Plastic
- D: Copper coin
- E: Clay pot
- F: Cork
- G: Iron nail

Test 4 – Cycles (Pages 49–58)

Section A (15 × 2 = 30 marks)

1.	(3)	6.	(1)	11.	(3)
2.	(1)	7.	(4)	12.	(3)
3.	(3)	8.	(1)	13.	(2)
4.	(4)	9.	(3)	14.	(4)
5.	(2)	10.	(1)	15.	(4)

Section B (20 marks)

[● 1 mark per point; ○ ½ mark per point]

16. (a) • True
(b) • False
(c) • True

17. ○ 3, 5, 1, 6, 4, 7, 8, 2 (½ mark per number)

18. (a) • Six stages
(b) • Five days
(c) • They last the same number of days.
(d) • 21 days

19. (a) (i) • The root.
(ii) • To absorb water and mineral salts.
(b) (i) • To give food to the developing seedling.
(c) • It shrinks and drops off from the plant.

20. (a) • To ensure continuity of their kind (more of their kind continue to be found on earth).
(b) • Air / water / warmth (any of these)
(c) • Three stages
(d) (i) • B
(ii) • Flowers

Test 5 – Cycles (Pages 59–67)

Section A (15 × 2 = 30 marks)

1.	(4)	6.	(3)	11.	(3)
2.	(1)	7.	(3)	12.	(2)
3.	(3)	8.	(4)	13.	(2)
4.	(1)	9.	(1)	14.	(4)
5.	(2)	10.	(2)	15.	(2)

Section B (20 marks)

[● 1 mark per point; ○ ½ mark per point]

16. (a) • True
(b) • False
(c) • True

17. (a)

State		
○ Solid	○ Liquid	○ Gas
Button	Wine	Oxygen
○ Flour	○ Honey	○ Carbon dioxide

18. (a) • Air
(b) (Any liquid)
• Water
• Juice
(c) (Any solid)
• Plasticine
• Block of wood
(d) • Substance Y

19. (a) • Shape
(b) • Solid
(c) • Plasticine

20. (a) • Bubbles can be seen.
• The water level in the glass decreases.
• The water level in the trough increases.
(b) • Water occupies space.
• Air occupies space.

Thematic Assessment 2 – Cycles (Pages 69–82)

Section A (30 × 2 = 60 marks)

1.	(3)	11.	(2)	21.	(4)
2.	(2)	12.	(2)	22.	(4)
3.	(1)	13.	(3)	23.	(1)
4.	(1)	14.	(1)	24.	(4)
5.	(1)	15.	(4)	25.	(2)
6.	(4)	16.	(2)	26.	(1)
7.	(4)	17.	(1)	27.	(1)
8.	(1)	18.	(1)	28.	(3)
9.	(1)	19.	(2)	29.	(1)
10.	(4)	20.	(3)	30.	(3)

Section B (40 marks)

[● 1 mark per point; ○ ½ mark per point]

31. (a) • The warmth necessary for the eggs to develop into chicks.
(b) • The Hen
(c)

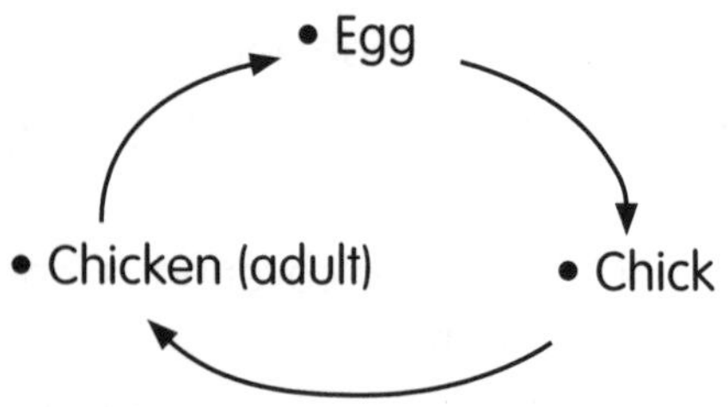

32. (a) Similarities
• Both are three-stage life cycles.
• Both cycles start with the egg stage.

Differences

○ The young (duckling) looks like the adult.	○ The young (tadpole) does not look like the adult.
○ The young and adult live in the same place (both live on land).	○ The young and adult live in different places (young in the water, adult on land).

(b) • The tail

33. (a) • Caterpillar
(b) • It eats/grows a lot.
• It moults.
(c) • The pupa is unable to move, the adult can.
• The pupa does not feed, while the adult does.
(d) (Any two)
• Mosquito
• Beetle
• Housefly
• Fruitfly

34. (a) • The maize seeds in dish A (with moist cotton wool) will germinate
• while those in dish B (with dry cotton wool) will remain unchanged.
(b) • Water is necessary for maize seeds to germinate.
(c) • Water
(d) (Any 2)
• The number of maize seeds.
• The type of dish (shape, size and material) used.
• The amount of cotton wool used.
• The location of the experiment (temperature, amount of light present).
(e) • To check if maize seeds could germinate if they were not provided with water.

35. (a) • A: Has definite volume and definite shape.
• B: Has definite volume and no definite shape.
• C: Has no definite volume and no definite shape.
(b) • A: Stone (any solid)
• B: Water (any liquid)
• C: Steam (any gas)
(c) (i) • Have mass
(ii) • Occupy space

36. (a) • Different shapes
• Different mass
• Made of different materials
(b) • Styrofoam slab, plastic container, glass ball
(c) • Put some water into the measuring cylinder and note the volume.
• Put the glass ball into the water in the measuring cylinder and note the new volume.
• The difference in volume is the volume of the glass ball.
(d) • No, because it will float on the water. OR
• Yes, if it is pushed down by the glass ball until it is totally submerged.

Test 6 – Systems (Pages 83–89)

Section A (15 × 2 = 30 marks)

1.	(2)	6.	(2)	11.	(3)
2.	(3)	7.	(4)	12.	(1)
3.	(2)	8.	(1)	13.	(3)
4.	(3)	9.	(2)	14.	(2)
5.	(4)	10.	(2)	15.	(4)

Section B (20 marks)

[● 1 mark per point; ○ ½ mark per point]

16. (a) • True
(b) • True
(c) • True

17. • 1. Dissolved oxygen (useful)
• 2. Dissolved carbon dioxide (not useful)
• 3. Digested food (useful)

18. • A: Circulatory System
• B: Respiratory System
• C: Muscular System
• D: Anus
• E: Ribs
• F: Other bones

19. (a) • The circulatory system moves nutrients, gases and wastes
• to and from different parts of the body.

(b) • The circulatory system is made up of different parts that work together to pump blood to all parts of the body.
• Our digestive system and our respiratory system also consist of parts that work together to carry out a specific function each.

20. (a) • It consists of different parts that function as a whole (as a system).

(b)

	Part	Function
(i)	• Screen	• To show information such as the song or volume.
(i)	• Headphone	• For listening to the music.
(iii)	• On/off button • (or play and stop buttons)	• To switch the player on or off. • (To play or stop the music)

Test 7 – Systems (Pages 91–97)

Section A (15 × 2 = 30 marks)

1.	(1)	6.	(3)	11.	(3)
2.	(1)	7.	(4)	12.	(2)
3.	(2)	8.	(4)	13.	(3)
4.	(4)	9.	(3)	14.	(2)
5.	(1)	10.	(2)	15.	(1)

Section B (20 marks)

[• 1 mark per point; ○ ½ mark per point]

16. (a) • False
(b) • True
(c) • False

17. (a) (½ mark each)
○ M: Mouth
○ N: Stomach
○ P: Large intestine
○ Q: Anus

(b) • Food is broken down into smaller pieces by the teeth
• and moistened by mixing with saliva.
• Some digestion takes place in "M".

(c) • Absorption of water.

18. • Root
• Seed
• Fruit
• Flower
• Leaf
• Stem

19.

Plant part	What will happen if it is missing?
Roots	• The plant cannot absorb water and mineral salts and it will not be able to anchor itself to the ground.
Leaves	• The plant will not be able to make food.
Flowers	• The plant cannot produce seeds
Fruits	• The seeds will not be protected
Seeds	• The plant will not complete its life cycle. No new plants will be formed.

Thematic Assessment 3 – Systems (Pages 99–117)

Section A (30 × 2 = 60 marks)

1.	(3)	11.	(2)	21.	(3)
2.	(2)	12.	(2)	22.	(4)
3.	(3)	13.	(2)	23.	(2)
4.	(2)	14.	(1)	24.	(1)
5.	(4)	15.	(4)	25.	(2)
6.	(1)	16.	(3)	26.	(2)
7.	(4)	17.	(4)	27.	(3)
8.	(2)	18.	(2)	28.	(3)
9.	(1)	19.	(4)	29.	(3)
10.	(3)	20.	(2)	30.	(3)

Section B (40 marks)

[• 1 mark per point; ○ ½ mark per point]

31. (a) • Yes, the taste is different.
(b) • Yes, the smell is different.
(c) • No, they feel the same, because they are of the same shape and size (colour cannot be felt, smelled, heard or tasted).

32. (a) • It is made up of different parts which together function as a whole.

(b) (½ mark each)

	Part	Function
(i)	○ Screen	○ To see the messages received.
(ii)	○ On/off button	○ To turn on/off the phone.
(iii)	○ Number pad (OR buttons / keys)	○ To key in phone numbers

(c) • Both have a screen to display the information keyed in or received.
• Both have keys (a number and alphabet pad) for keying in information.

(d) • The mobile phone is much smaller than a notebook. There is not enough space to have as many keys as in a notebook.

33. (a) • Circulatory
(c) • Muscular
(d) • Respiratory
(e) • Digestive

34. (a) • To ensure that any change in the volume of water is due to the plant and not because of evaporation (into the atmosphere).
(b) • Water was taken up by the two plants in A and C.
(c) • Container B.
• The plant in B behaved differently from the other two plants (it did not take up water). Therefore it should be the plastic plant. (Containers A and C contain the two real plants.)
(d) • Living things take up water but non-living things do not.
(e) • Yes.
• Because Ali's experiment should have included one more real plant in an identical container, but without water.

- After a week, if the plant died, he would know that Ahmad's first statement was right.

35. (a) • True
    (b) • False
    (c) • False
    (d) • True

36. (a) (i) • Leaf blade
        (ii) • Leaf stalk
        (iii) • Leaf vein
    (b) • Both have a leaf blade, stalk and veins.

Bird of Paradise	Hosta
○ Long	○ Rounded
○ Has one colour / completely green	○ Has two colours /green and yellow

37. (a) (i) • In the mouth.
        (ii) • To moisten/partially digest food.
    (b) (i) • 210 s
        (ii) • 120 s
    (c) • No more starch was present in the test tube.
        • It was changed by the saliva into something else (digested by saliva).
    (d) • 40 °C
        • It takes a shorter time for all the starch to be changed by the saliva at 40 °C than at 20 °C.

Test 8 – Interactions (Pages 119–125)

Section A (15 × 2 = 30 marks)

1.	(3)	6.	(3)	11.	(1)
2.	(1)	7.	(1)	12.	(4)
3.	(1)	8.	(3)	13.	(4)
4.	(2)	9.	(2)	14.	(2)
5.	(3)	10.	(2)	15.	(3)

Section B (20 marks)

[● 1 mark per point; ○ ½ mark per point]

16. (a) • True
    (b) • False
    (c) • True
17. (a) • Battery
        • Iron/steel rod (or any magnetic material)
        • Electrical wiring
    (b) • Electromagnet
    (c) • It is able to attract magnetic materials such as steel pins.
        • It repels the like pole of another magnet.
    (d) • Coil the electrical wiring more times around the rod.
        • Increase the electrical current (e.g. by using an addtional battery).
18. • Attach the iron nails in series (in a chain) to one pole of each magnet.

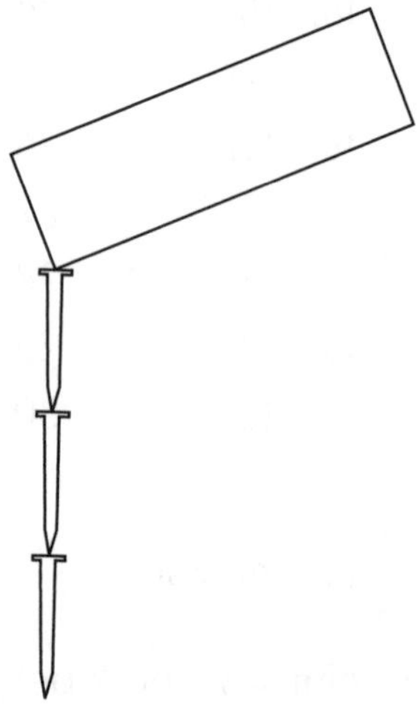

- The strongest magnet will be able to attract the most number of iron nails.
- The weakest magnet will attract the least.

19. • A: Metals
    • B: Non-magnetic
    • C: Steel
    • D: Iron/nickel
    • E: Gold
    • F: Silver

Thematic Assessment 4 – Interactions (Pages 127–142)

Section A (30 × 2 = 60 marks)

1.	(3)	11.	(4)	21.	(4)
2.	(3)	12.	(3)	22.	(3)
3.	(2)	13.	(1)	23.	(3)
4.	(3)	14.	(3)	24.	(3)
5.	(4)	15.	(4)	25.	(1)
6.	(1)	16.	(3)	26.	(1)
7.	(4)	17.	(3)	27.	(3)
8.	(2)	18.	(2)	28.	(2)
9.	(4)	19.	(1)	29.	(4)
10.	(3)	20.	(3)	30.	(3)

Section B (40 marks)

[● 1 mark per point; ○ ½ mark per point]

31. (a) ● Place a magnet against the walls of the bottle. (The nails will be attracted to the magnet.)
● Slowly move the magnet upwards until the nails are out of the oil.
(b) ● The ability to be attracted by magnets.
(c) ● Yes, the force of a magnet can pass through different liquids.
(d) ● No, copper cannot be attracted by a magnet.
● It is non-magnetic.

32. (a) ● The poles facing each other for magnets 2 and 1, and magnets 2 and 3, are like poles.
● Since like poles repel,
● magnet 1 pushes magnet 2 up, while magnet 2 pushes magnet 3 up.
(b) ● Turn magnet 2 around.

33. (a) ● Attach iron nails/paper clips in a chain to one pole of each magnet.

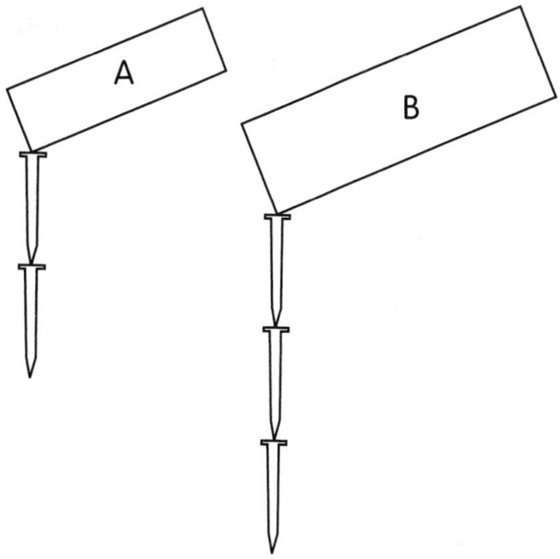

● The stronger magnet will be able to attract more iron nails/paper clips.
(b) ● The size (length) of the iron nails/paper clips.
● The weight of the iron nails/paper clips.

34. (a)

Magnetic	Non-magnetic
○ Butter knife (steel) ○ Steel needles ○ Nickel clips ○ Nickel coins ○ Steel nail clipper	○ Plastic fork ○ Small pieces of copper wires ○ Aluminium cans ○ Gold ring ○ Silver pendant

(b) ● Bring a magnet near each of the objects.
● The magnetic objects will be attracted by the magnet.

35. (a) ● Bring the bar magnet M near each of the bars P, Q and R.
● M will repel the magnet at one end,
● attract the magnetic material at both ends, and
● have no effect on the non-magnetic material.
(b) ● Use magnet M to stroke bar P several times.
● Stroke in one direction only.
● Use only one pole of magnet M.

36. (a) (One mark per point; total four. Two marks for axis labels)

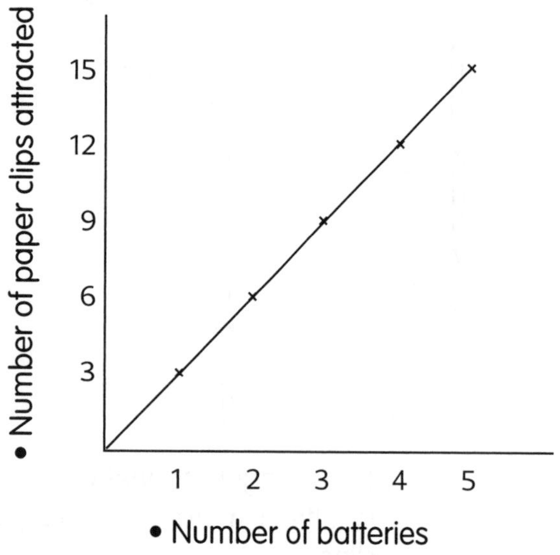

(b) • More paper clips can be attracted by the temporary magnet if more batteries are used (a stronger current is used).

(c)

Number of strokes	Number of paper clips attracted
10	• 1
20	• 3
40	• 8
80	• 12

Test 9 – Energy (Pages 143–155)

Section A (15 × 2 = 30 marks)

1.	(2)	6.	(2)	11.	(4)
2.	(3)	7.	(4)	12.	(3)
3.	(2)	8.	(3)	13.	(4)
4.	(2)	9.	(2)	14.	(2)
5.	(2)	10.	(4)	15.	(2)

Section B (20 marks)

[• 1 mark per point; ○ ½ mark per point]

16. (a) • False
(b) • True
(c) • False

17.

Transparent	Translucent	Opaque
• spectacles, clear glass, bulb	• frosted glass, tracing paper	• storybook, computer mouse, wooden drawer, photograph, school bag, worksheet, mobile phone

18. • A: A can of coke (any cylindrical object) with light shining on the top <u>OR</u> a cardboard circle (any opaque object with a circular outline).

• B: A metal ring with a hole in the centre <u>OR</u> doughnut (any opaque circle with a hole in the middle).

• C: A smaller circle of cardboard pasted on a larger circle of tracing paper (any opaque material rimmed with any translucent material).

• (1 mark for object between light and screen, object faces light)

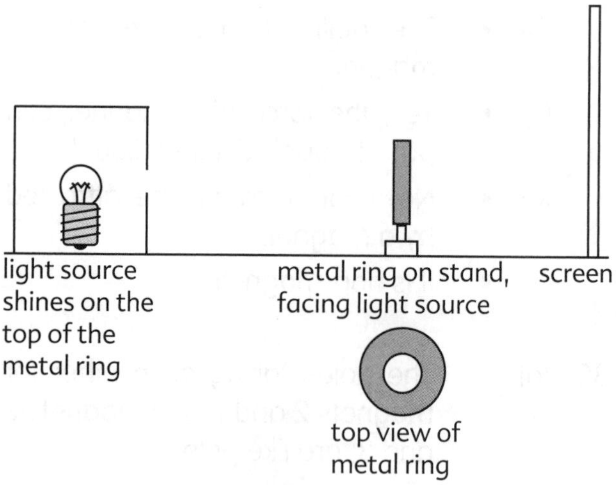

19. (a) (i) •

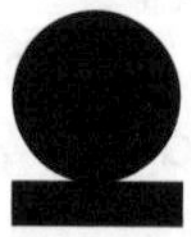

(ii) •

(b) (i) • The shadow becomes smaller.

(ii) • The shadow becomes smaller.

(c) • 

(d) • 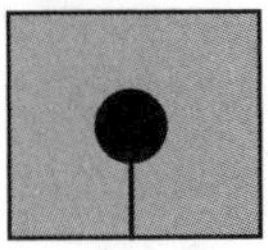

20. • Screen X: black rectangle
• Screen Y: black circle

21. • 8 am: (identical shadow but in opposite direction)

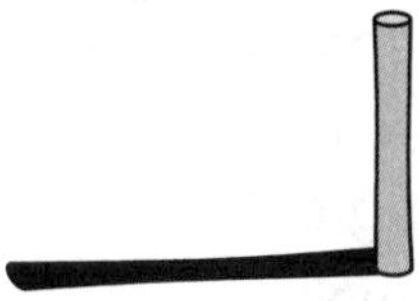

• 12 noon: (small black shadow at the base of the stick)

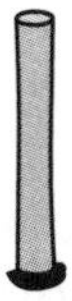

Test 10 – Energy (Pages 157–166)

Section A (15 × 2 = 30 marks)

1.	(2)	6.	(1)	11.	(3)
2.	(2)	7.	(2)	12.	(4)
3.	(2)	8.	(4)	13.	(3)
4.	(2)	9.	(1)	14.	(2)
5.	(2)	10.	(4)	15.	(2)

Section B (20 marks)

[• 1 mark per point; ○ ½ mark per point]

16. (a) • Bubbles will form when the water has reached its boiling point.
(b) (½ mark each bar; bars A and C of equal height, half the height of C and D, which are also of equal height)

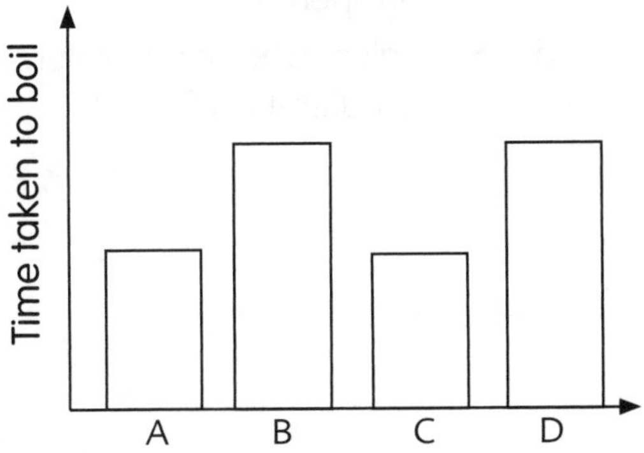

(c) • C and D

17. • Observation: The metal weight moves down a little.
• Reason: When heated, the metal wire expands
• and increases in length.

18. (a) • The ink falls first then rises.
(b) • The hot water causes the glass of the flask to expand first, causing the ink to fall.
• Then heat reaches the air in the flask,
• causing it to expand and push the ink up.

19. (1 mark for each axis label; 1 mark for line going from 120–140 °C; 1 mark for line going from 140–120 °C)

• Temperature (°C)

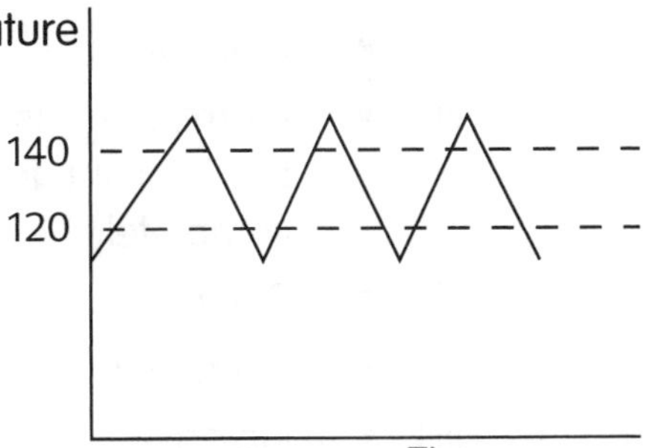

• Time

20. (a) • To allow for expansion of the rails during a hot day.
(b) • It loses heat.
(c) ○ It only needs to measure body temperature,
○ which is in the range of 35 °C to 42 °C.
(d) ○ Heat is the amount of energy in a substance.
○ Temperature is the degree of hotness or coldness of a substance.
(e) ○ It gains heat and
○ expands (increases in size).

Thematic Assessment 5 – Energy (Pages 167–186)

Section A (30 × 2 = 60 marks)

1.	(3)	11.	(4)	21.	(3)
2.	(3)	12.	(3)	22.	(1)
3.	(1)	13.	(4)	23.	(3)
4.	(2)	14.	(3)	24.	(1)
5.	(1)	15.	(4)	25.	(1)
6.	(3)	16.	(3)	26.	(2)
7.	(2)	17.	(2)	27.	(2)
8.	(2)	18.	(4)	28.	(3)
9.	(1)	19.	(2)	29.	(2)
10.	(3)	20.	(2)	30.	(1)

Section B (40 marks)

[• 1 mark per point; ○ ½ mark per point]

31. (a) (i) • Aluminium
(ii) • Aluminium is opaque. It blocks light from the torch completely.
(b) (i) • Decrease
(ii) • Decrease
(iii) • Increase

32. • Shadows A and B will become shorter and darker.
• Shadows C and D will become longer and less dark.

33. • A: 4
• B: 3
• C: 1
• D: 2

34. • In winter, the metal is cold and contracts.
• The gaps become wider, so the clicks are louder.
• In summer, the metal expands and the gaps become narrower (giving softer clicks).

35. (a) • 21 °C
(b) • (Shade from bulb to 21 °C)

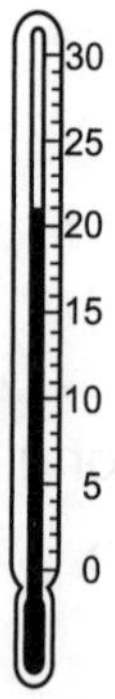

(c) • No.
• The temperature ranges of thermometers P and Q are much lower than the temperature of boiling soup. (OR Thermometers P and Q are unable to read temperatures greater than 30 °C.)

36. (a) • The wax will melt.
(b) • Cruise is correct.
(c) • Bruce is wrong because only a steel needle and no other materials were used in the experiment.
• Smith is wrong because the length of the steel needle was not measured before or after it was heated.

37. (a) • Steam OR The water bubbles/ boils in the area around the block.
(b) • Water gains heat from the hot metal.
• Some of it becomes hot enough to boil/change into the gaseous state.
(c) • Heat continues to flow from the hot metal to the water
• until both reach the same temperature.
(d) • False (The temperature will be greater than 25 °C.)

38. (a) (i)

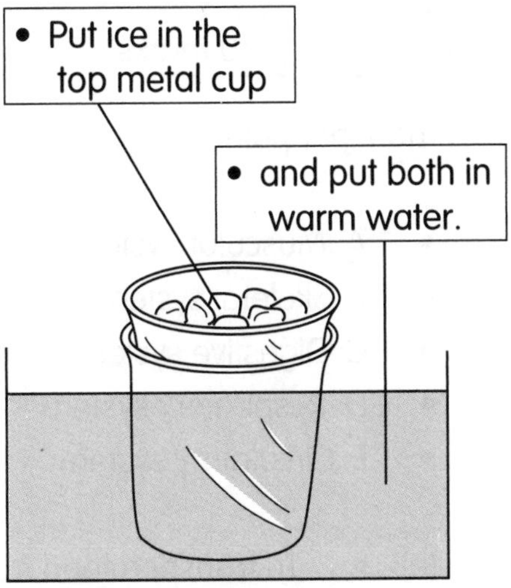
• Put ice in the top metal cup
• and put both in warm water.

(ii) • The gap between both cups will widen because

• ice will cause the cup inside to contract (by cooling it), and warm water will cause the cup outside to expand (by warming it).

(b) (i) • Flame → Frying pan → Oil → Egg

(ii) • It increases.

39. • A: Reflects light
• B: Man-made/artificial source
• C: Translucent
• D: Star / lightning / firefly
• E: Lamp / fire
• F: Clear plastic / still water

Cross-thematic Assessment 1 – Diversity, Cycles (Pages 187–201)

Section A (30 × 2 = 60 marks)

1.	(3)	11.	(2)	21.	(2)
2.	(3)	12.	(4)	22.	(3)
3.	(4)	13.	(3)	23.	(4)
4.	(3)	14.	(1)	24.	(4)
5.	(1)	15.	(3)	25.	(2)
6.	(1)	16.	(2)	26.	(3)
7.	(2)	17.	(1)	27.	(1)
8.	(2)	18.	(2)	28.	(2)
9.	(2)	19.	(4)	29.	(4)
10.	(4)	20.	(2)	30.	(2)

Section B (40 marks)

[● 1 mark per point; ○ ½ mark per point]

31. • E
• C
• D
• B
• A
• A / F
• A

32. (a) • B: Squirrel / lion / giraffe
• C: Pigeon / sparrow (most birds) / cockroach (winged insects)
• D: Prawn / crab / lobster / turtle
• E: Lizard / tortoise / kiwi / ostrich (flightless birds)

(b) • Feathers (bird) / hard outer covering (insect)

(c) (i) • C
(ii) • D
(iii) • E

(d) • Mammals

33. (a) • Sheet B
• It can support the greatest number of blocks before it breaks/ bends <u>OR</u> the greatest number of blocks is needed to cause it to break/bend.

(b) • Sheet A: Cardboard
• Sheet B: Steel
• Sheet C: Glass
• Sheet D: Plastic

34. Similarities (any 2)
• Both live in water.
• Both breathe using gills.
• Both hatch from eggs.

Tadpole	Fish
○ Looks different from the adult.	○ Young looks like the adult.
○ Does not have scales.	○ Has scales.

35. • A: Animals
• B: Plants
• C: Live on land
• D: Flowering
• E: Non-flowering
• F: Cannot fly
• G: Fish, squid, whale, dolphin
• H: Bat

36.

	Can the plunger be pushed in?	Why?
Syringe A	• No	• Cement is a solid and cannot be compressed.
Syringe B	• No	• Water is a liquid and cannot be compressed.
Syringe C	• Yes	• Carbon dioxide is a gas and can be compressed.

Cross-thematic Assessment 2 – Systems, Interactions, Energy (Pages 203–217)

Section A (30 × 2 = 60 marks)

1. (3)	11. (4)	21. (2)
2. (4)	12. (2)	22. (1)
3. (4)	13. (1)	23. (3)
4. (2)	14. (4)	24. (2)
5. (3)	15. (2)	25. (2)
6. (4)	16. (4)	26. (3)
7. (2)	17. (1)	27. (2)
8. (1)	18. (4)	28. (2)
9. (1)	19. (1)	29. (1)
10. (4)	20. (4)	30. (4)

Section B (40 marks)

[• 1 mark per point; ○ ½ mark per point]

31. • A: Muscular system
• B: Skeletal system
• C: Digestive system
• D: Respiratory system
• E: Circulatory system

32. (a) • To transport food from the mouth to the stomach.
(b) • In the mouth,
• stomach
• and small intestine.
(c) • It is cut and ground into smaller pieces by our teeth,
• moistened and partially digested by saliva.
(d) • Absorption of water.

33. (a) • Table 1: Shadow lengths at different times of the day.
• Table 2: Change in temperature with time.

(b) (i)

Barchart 1	x-axis	○ Time
	y-axis	○ Length of shadow (cm)
Barchart 2	x-axis	○ Time (min)
	y-axis	○ Temperature (°C)

(ii) Bar chart 1

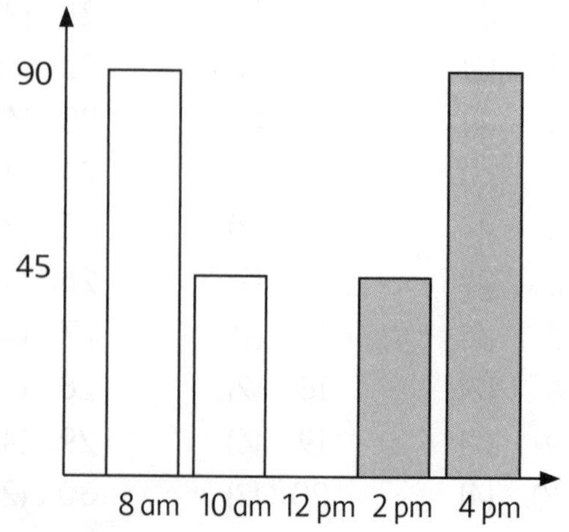

Bar chart 2

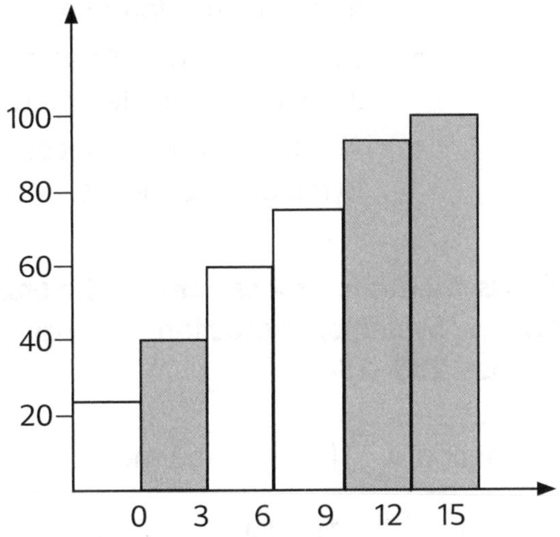

(c) (i) • Gained energy.

(ii) • The higher temperature at 15 minutes means that the water has more heat energy at 15 minutes than at 0 minutes.

(iii) • The water will change to steam (a change of state will occur) <u>OR</u> The level of water will slowly decrease as steam escapes into the atmosphere.

34. (a) (i) • Put ice in to cool down the water / decrease the temperature.

(ii) • Heat it up / increase the temperature.

(iii) • Nothing.

(b) (i) • The air is cooled and contracts (pulling the ink to the left).

(ii) • The air heats up and expands (pushing the ink to the right).

(iii) • The air does not expand nor contract.

(c) • It will be pulled to the right.

35.

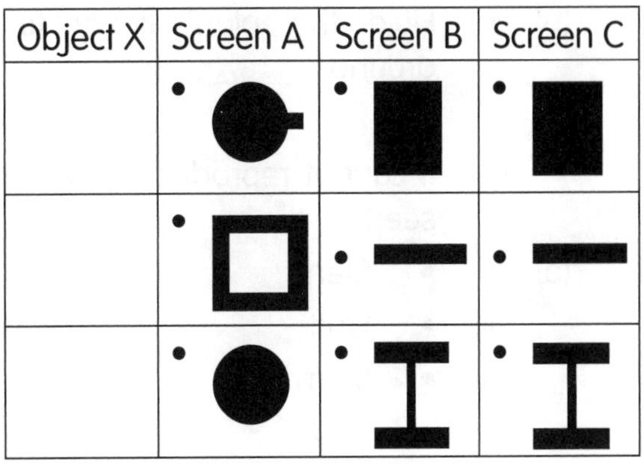

Cross-thematic Assessment 3 – Diversity, Cycles, Systems, Interactions, Energy (Pages 219–234)

Section A (30 × 2 = 60 marks)

1. (4)	11. (1)	21. (1)
2. (2)	12. (1)	22. (4)
3. (2)	13. (2)	23. (3)
4. (3)	14. (3)	24. (1)
5. (4)	15. (1)	25. (1)
6. (1)	16. (2)	26. (4)
7. (1)	17. (3)	27. (3)
8. (1)	18. (3)	28. (3)
9. (4)	19. (3)	29. (1)
10. (2)	20. (1)	30. (4)

Section B (40 marks)

[● 1 mark per point; ○ ½ mark per point]

31. (a) • A: Glass
- B: Porcelain
- C: Metal
- D: Rubber
- E: Cloth

(b) • B
- C / D / E

32. (a) • A: Roots
- B: Stem
- C: Leaves
- D: Flowers
- E: Fruit

(b) • Hold the plant firmly to the ground.

(c) • Yes.

• It cannot reproduce / form fruit/ seeds.

(d) (i) • Stem

(ii) • Fruit

(iii) • Stem

(iv) • Root

33. • P: Mammal
• Q: Bird
• N: Cannot fly
• R: Bat
• S and T: Rabbit / dog / cat / goat (any 2)
• U and V: Eagle / pigeon / sparrow (any bird that flies)
• W: Ostrich / Emu / Kiwi

34. (a) (i) • The iron filings become attracted to the iron nail.

(ii) • The electric current causes the iron nail to become an electromagnet.

• Iron filings are magnetic substances that are attracted to magnets.

(b) • More iron filings will be attracted to the iron nail

• because the iron nail will become a stronger electromagnet.

(c) • Less iron filings will be attracted to the iron nail

• because the iron nail will become a weaker electromagnet.

35. (a) • Mould

(b) • From the spores in the air that landed on the shoes.

(c) • Spoils them by feeding on the leather.

(d) • Keep the cupboard dry since mould needs water to survive.

36. (a) • (Label gullet / large intestine / anus — any 2) (2 marks)

(b) • Gullet: Transports food from the mouth to the stomach.

• Large intestine: Absorbs water from the undigested food.

• Anus: Holds in the faeces; relaxes to release the faeces.

Cross-thematic Assessment 4 – Diversity, Cycles, Systems, Interactions, Energy (Pages 235–254)

Section A (30 × 2 = 60 marks)

1. (2)	11. (3)	21. (2)
2. (3)	12. (3)	22. (2)
3. (4)	13. (4)	23. (3)
4. (1)	14. (2)	24. (1)
5. (3)	15. (1)	25. (4)
6. (4)	16. (1)	26. (3)
7. (1)	17. (4)	27. (3)
8. (1)	18. (4)	28. (3)
9. (1)	19. (2)	29. (1)
10. (2)	20. (1)	30. (4)

Section B (40 marks)

[● 1 mark per point; ○ ½ mark per point]

31. (a) • A: Flexible

• B: Fragile <u>OR</u> Poor heat conductor <u>OR</u> Non-magnetic

• C: Non-fragile <u>OR</u> Good heat conductor <u>OR</u> Magnetic

• D: Porcelain / ceramic <u>OR</u> Plastic

• E: Paper

• F: Wool / sponge / cloth / rubber

(b) • Frying pan, cooking pot, kettle (any 2) (2 marks)

32. (a) • A: Fish

• B: Plant

• C: Human / monkey / bird

• D: Frog

(b) • Yes

• Gills allow animals to extract oxygen from water.

- For example, fish and tadpoles (the young of frogs) have gills and live in water. They both (fish and frogs) also lay eggs.

33. (a)
   - A: Nose
   - B: Mouth
   - C: Wind pipe
   - D: Lungs

   (b) (i) • A and B

   (ii) • D

34. (a) (i) • Man-made

   (ii) • Transparent

   (b)

Natural	• Firefly • Sun
Man-made	• Candle flame
Transparent	• Magnifying glass • Diamond
Translucent	• Frosted window
Opaque	• Coconut palm • Earth • Cup

35. Similarities (any 2)
   - Both have a four-stage life cycle.
   - Both can fly.
   - Both reproduce by laying eggs / have six legs / have three body parts (any of the characteristics of insects)

Housefly	Mosquito
o Does not feed on blood. o Lays eggs / young lives on land.	o Feeds on blood. o Lays eggs / young lives in water.

36. (a) •

   (b) •

37.
   - Wrong direction: The shadow of the man should not point towards the Sun but should point away from the Sun (similar to the shadows of the mountains).
   - Wrong shape: The shadow of the man should not have both hands at the waist but should have one arm raised and one pointing down.

BLANK

BLANK

BLANK